GAIA·2

EMERGENCE

The New Science
of Becoming

GAIA·2
EMERGENCE
The New Science
of Becoming

edited by

WILLIAM IRWIN THOMPSON

LINDISFARNE PRESS

This volume is a publication of
the Lindisfarne Association's Program
for Biology, Cognition, and Ethics,
Cathedral Church of St. John the Divine, New York City,
and il Centro "Luigi Bazzuchi" Dipartimento di Epistemologia
e Scienze Cognitive, Perugia.

Library of Congress Cataloging-in-Publishing Data
Gaia 2 : emergence : the new science of becoming /
edited by William Irwin Thompson
p. cm.
Includes bibliographical references.
ISBN 0-940262-40-1 : $14.95
1. Gaia hypothesis — Congresses. 2. Biology — Philosophy —
Congresses. 3. Ecology — Philosophy — Congresses. 4. Geobiology —
Congresses. 5. Biosphere — Congresses. I. Thompson, William
Irwin. II. Title: Gaia two.
QH331.G2 1991 91-17431 574'.01 — dc20 CIP

10 9 8 7 6 5 4 3 2 1

Published by Lindisfarne Press
RR 4, Box 94 A-1 Hudson, NY 12534

In Memory of Evelyn Ames 1908-1990
Poet, Lindisfarne Fellow, Friend

ACKNOWLEDGEMENTS

Grateful acknowledgment is made to the Prince Trusts of Chicago for their grants to the Lindisfarne Program for Biology, Cognition, and Ethics for support of the work of Francisco Varela and Evan Thompson in their research project on color vision in Paris, and of William Irwin Thompson in Bern in the editing of this book.

To our conference hosts, President Mandrini and the provincial government of Perugia and Umbria, Professor Mauro Ceruti, Vittorina Calisi, and the staff of the Centro Luigi Bazzuchi, all the participants would like to express their gratitude for the extraordinary hospitality, aesthetic grace, and intellectual vivacity that made the conference yet another Renaissance expression of the Italian genius for combining art and philosophy.

CONTENTS

PUBLISHER'S NOTE

Gaia 2: Emergence, The New Science of Becoming is the record of an international conference held in Perugia, Italy, in May 1988. Organized by the Lindisfarne Association in collaboration with the Department of Epistemology and Cognitive Science at the University of Perugia, this conference was the second gathering of philosophers and scientists to meet to consider the wider implications of the Gaia theory. The first, held in California in 1981, considered Gaia as "a way of knowing" and examined its political implications.* The second, initially convened under the rubric *Biology as a Basis for Design,* began from the following assumption (taken from the conference program):

> Because humanity is experiencing the emergence of a new plane-
> tary culture, the *avant garde* imagination in both art and science is
> fascinated with the whole problem of "Emergence."As we witness
> the emergence of a new global electronic economy that cannot be
> modeled in the linear equations and causal explanations favored by
> the old mechanistic world picture, the way we envision "the world"
> changes and we begin to see our planet in a new way. We begin to
> notice the hitherto unseen dynamics in which little plankton in the
> sea can affect the global climate; we begin to understand how the
> origins of life affected the formation of the atmosphere; and as we
> study how the bacterial film of life affected the oceans (and thereby
> even the massive movement of the tectonic plates), we begin to
> appreciate how these invisible creatures serve as the immune sys-
> tem of the planet and help maintain conditions appropriate for life.
> As we ponder the non-linear dynamics of cognition in the immune
> system of an animal or the non-linear dynamics of the immune sys-
> tem of a planet, we have to learn to imagine what we cannot see at
> these microcosmic levels of space and time; and so the value of
> Imagination returns to challenge the arrogant reductionisms that
> have dominated our civilized mentality during the historical period

---

*Gaia, A Way of Knowing: Political Implications of the New Biology
(Lindisfarne Press, 1987)

of the mechanization of the world picture. A new mentality has historically arrived and its new view of the world is so profoundly different that it holds out, not simply new facts or a new paradigm, but a new planetary culture and a new basis for the re-design of human settlements....

On the basis of this invitation, thinkers and doers from all over the world came together in Perugia to explore the implications of the new way of knowing and to articulate the emergent properties of planetary culture "so that humanity can avoid the intense pain that is now coming from the misunderstanding of our planetary life." The conversation that spontaneously ensued, taking its own form and creating its own substance, is recorded in this volume.

WILLIAM IRWIN THOMPSON

The Imagination of a New Science and the Emergence of a Planetary Culture

What I wish to do is to sketch a horizon. One could go through the cultural history of science to gather up examples of moments in which scientists stood, not confidently, or indeed smugly in the center of things, pointing out all that they knew with scientific certainty — the very things that are, ironically, no longer central or certain for us — but at the edge of their knowledge and at the limits of their capacities. This edge is the horizon, the place where the known fades off into the unknown. It is a place of openness, of vulnerability and danger, and not of institutional security and confidence. It is the end of the world, a place haunted by dragons, monsters of the deep, and angels of the apocalypse, a place for explorers and not scribes and copiers of received knowledge. To come to this place where the relationships between imagination and perception are more clearly dark and ambiguous, the scientists of the past have often had to come to the edge of their inherited world and to the edge of their own mind.

Think of Glaser staring at the bubbles in his glass of beer and flashing with the vision of the bubble chamber for particle physics he would go on to invent. Think of Kekule slipping away from reason into mythic dreams of the serpent biting its tail as another way of solving the problem of conceptualizing the benzene ring. Think of Darwin romantically standing alone on a peak in the Andes and having a vision of life in which "We may be all netted together."[1] Or think of Alfred Russel Wallace, traveling from island to island in Indonesia in search of medicinal plants and contracting a fever in the jungle, a fever whose ravings allowed him to envision the theory of evolution. The theory of natural selection selected him, a member of the working class with the wrong accent, not a university professor or a gentleman living off a private income, to be its first humble voice for the origins of higher life from its lower forms. Sir Charles Lyell, however, could not endure the indignity and arranged for his friend Charles Darwin to share the podium of the Linnaeus Society[2] with the cockney upstart; to this day the English have not forgiven Wallace his continued fascination with horizons, for Wallace ended his life at work in the haunted realms of psychic research, whereas Darwin died more properly in the center of things, but also, in his own judgment, as a dried-up machine for grinding out facts.[3]

The cultural historian could go through history, gathering up all the examples in which dream and vision, imagination and emotion, have played as strong a part in forming science as they do in forming religion or art,[4] but I do not wish here to play the role of scribe and copier of received opinion. As a working class American-Irishman, I identify more with Wallace than Darwin, and so I am haunted by edges and horizons, and it is this edge between imagination and science that I wish to share today. Most likely it is merely my own imagination of science, the imagination of science of someone who is not himself a scientist and member of that prestigious gentleman's club. So be warned. I want to move to the edge of the world, to the place where the old maps warn: "Here be dragons."

But I do not wish to be overly Irish and fanciful, for the friendship between science and art is part of the architecture of the modern world. When we shifted out of the medieval world view, it was not the knight and the priest who held up the arch, but the merchant and the scientific artist. The movement of money was no longer considered fallen and classed as usury; it was considered to create value in moving by Cosimo di Medici and was called interest. The movement of falling bodies was also not considered to be part of the fallen and sinful world of appearances; for Galileo it was a new revelation of the scientific laws of nature. Those who worked with their hands were both artisan and artist, and those who examined nature in detail and in new ways were both the artists and scientists. In the art and architecture of perspective, or in the art of observation, the roll call of the great Italian names would be a worthy recital for this beautiful Italian Renaissance hall in which we meet. And it is interesting to note that we meet, not in a church or a palace, but in the Sala di Notari, the commercial hall of the notaries. So the fact that I, a writer, have, at your generous invitation, gathered together a group of scientific friends is very much in the spirit of the Italian Renaissance and, I hope of our time of planetary renaissance.

One of the things that makes me hope that we are entering a new period of a planetary renaissance is precisely the new friendship between art and science. In the nineteenth century there was a standoff between the mechanists and the romantics. One side of the culture sought to rule everything through reason and the mechanization of nature and culture, and the other side protested that the complexity of the organic could never be known through the simplifications of the reductionist and mechanistic methods of science. Science was seen as a threat to the life of human feeling, artistic imagination, and mystical vision. Poets such as Wordsworth protested that "We murder to dissect," and revolutionaries screamed out against the order of things, but could not make up their minds whether their protests were in favor of romantic nationalisms or scientific socialism, and to this day this split continues with the German Greens.

Although William Blake chose to speak of "single vision and Newton's sleep," Newton and Boyle were as much Hermetic mystics as Blake, and the play of a cosmic and visionary mysticism has always been present in the cultural history of science.[5] Newton had his box of Cabalistic computations on the temple in Jerusalem, and Descartes had his prophetic dreams, so even the founding fathers were more promiscuous in their affections than was recognized in their hagiographies. It was the British technologists, the French positivists, and the German academics that all came

13

together in the nineteenth century to give us the European ortho-
doxy in which one line of descent was considered legitimate and
the other, the illegitimate offspring, one did not discuss in good
company. Ironically, it was the physicists, the highest of the high
priests of matter and scientific materialism, who enabled us to
break out of the grip of the positivists, for with the indeterminacy
of Heisenberg and the relativity of Einstein, the imaginative quality of the descriptions of science began to be undeniable. As
Heisenberg said, "We do not have a science of nature, we have a
science of our descriptions of nature."[6]

Now in our contemporary passage from mimesis to autopoiesis,
the video artists, such as Gene Youngblood and Bill Viola, are as
fascinated with the work of Maturana and Varela as once the
Renaissance Italian artists were fascinated with perspective and
motion in the shift from religious faith to scientific observation.
Now there is so much going back and forth between art and science in science fiction and computer hacking, or chaos dynamics
and music video, that the new cultural landscape has become one
in which knowing is an art, and art takes science.

Fortunately for us all now, the civil war in Western civilization
between the artists and the scientists is over, for in science fiction
novels such as Gibson's *Neuromancer*, or in the work of Stanislaw
Lem, or in such epistemological satires as Italo Calvino's *Mr. Pal-
omar*, there is a new sense of the romantic attraction that artists
and scientists have for one another. Science now can admit indeterminacy, chaos, and the poiesis of its own imaginative descriptions; and art can admit that it is not simply a gush of feeling, but
a way of knowing that takes skill, intelligence, and rigor. And as
both the artist and the scientist move out to the edge of their civilization, they find themselves standing against a cosmic horizon in
which they need to use one another's imagery to try to imagine
what is out there beyond what they already know.

Picture this horizon as a painting, a work by Magritte or Escher
perhaps, in which each looks over the shoulder of the other at a
vast horizon and sees at the same time the image of the invisible
horizon at his back reflected in the eyes of the other. Let us make
one figure male and the other female, but to express the true complexity of our contemporary planetary culture, let us picture the

scientist as female, and the artist as male. Then imagine a third person, the cultural historian, who is fascinated in observing the relationship between the two observers and is entranced by the images in their eyes and the landscape in which they both are figured.

As was true in the days of the Italian Renaissance, so is it now in these days of the planetary renaissance, that one cannot bring forth this planetary horizon alone. It takes a kind of music video or mind jazz of differing intellectual domains, different ways of knowing, to bring forth the invisible meta-domain; that is "a world." Now you cannot simply be Sartre in Paris or Heidegger in the Black Forest, thinking big thoughts about being and nothingness, for no single person, no single city, and no single language or discipline is adequate to bring forth "the pattern that connects" cognitive domains in a global geometry of behavior that is the distributive lattice of the new planetary culture. And so, in the prophetic words of the Beatles, "I get by with a little help from my friends." What I hope we shall see in this week-long gathering is a pattern that will emerge in the very discussion of "Emergence," a pattern of connection between the macrocosm of the atmospheric chemistry of Lovelock, the microcosm of the bacteriology of Margulis and Guerrero, and the mesocosm of the mind in the cognitive science of Varela, Ceruti, and Oyama. As a new "nature" is brought forth in the descriptions of this subculture of scientists, a new culturing of nature is required, and the "cognitive domain" of human settlements has to be re-envisioned, as it is in the work of the Todds and Wes Jackson. My personal hope is that there is now among you in the audience an architect of a more Italian aesthetic, one who understands the implications of this work to realize that buildings are not made on a ground, but out of the pollution that is the profound description of their deepest nature. When the pollution produced by a building is made into the living membrane of that structure, we will have the architecture we need for life. At the moment, in the alternative movement in the U.S.A. we have only taken a few steps in this direction with the solar architecture of Paolo Soleri and Sim Van der Ryn, but neither one of these approaches yet envisions bacterial cultures as co-workers in the emergence of architectural domains. Neither the alternative, the post-modernist, nor the deconstructivist schools of international architecture today are seeing the Gaian interpenetration of the large in the little, of the planetary atmosphere with the biological exhausts of the building, and it is precisely this Gaia Politique that I would like to suggest to your imaginations in a sketch of our planetary horizon at this particular historical moment.

A sketch is not a fresco or a mural; it is more of a minimalist presentation of pattern, and it requires the pattern-recognition abilities of the beholder. In fact, pattern recognition is at the heart of this new cognitive science that seeks to live with complexity in the form of a new geometry of behavior. The linear equations required to describe a hurricane or the wind flow around a jet airplane begin to unravel as one tries to deal with too many variables in a many-body problem, but if one jumps up to a higher level to transpose the behavior into an image, into a hieroglyph in the structural morphogenesis of René Thom or the chaos dynamics of Ralph Abraham,[7] then the mind-boggling complexity begins to be resolved by the imagination and experienced in a very direct, human, and embodied way. "About that which we cannot speak," we can sing, or dance, or draw.

A recent article in the *New York Times*, for example, says that even when scientists are working with supercomputers, with Crays, that the best and fastest pattern-recognition device is the human eye and brain. You can take the giga-bits of information about a hurricane, transpose them into computer graphics, and when the scientist looks it over he sees an image hiding in the data and begins through the powers of the imagination to understand a behavior that is unknowable for the computer, and not obvious to the programmer in the thousands of linear equations that one could generate in the hope of controlling what cannot be known or controlled at that lower level of cognition. No computer programmer is likely to be initiate to the poetry and mysticism of W.B. Yeats to instruct his scanner to look for Yeatsian double triangles floating on the tops of hurricane clouds (the picture in the *New York Times*[8] article actually did have these double triangles in the Cray computer graphics of the hurricane). It takes a mind alive with an imagination to cross distant and isolated cognitive domains to recognize the moire pattern that emerges from their crossing, for what the mind is bringing together is precisely what the elitist culture strives to keep apart: computer science and poetry, LISP and Cabala, meteorology and hermiticism. Since no individual can be conversant with all these different cognitive domains, be they legitimate or illegitimate, discovery requires a conversation, not among specialists, but among people in differing cognitive domains. Since the university does not allow this, I quit the university and set up the Lindisfarne Association as an improvisational ensemble whose informal jam sessions could allow a mind jazz to take us over, if we are lucky, now and then. Lindisfarne is "a strange attractor" that makes new bondings and repulsions and swirls us outward in novelty, anger, and delight.

Jazz is not a product of the conservatory, and improvisation is not a product of training. Discovery, in any field, is essentially a surprise. It is the result of putting things together that, ordinarily, are kept apart. When one moves out of the corridor vision of the institution, whether one is in a college pub with Glaser, on an An-dean peak with Darwin, or in an Indonesian jungle with Wallace, one is moving into a space where that which is kept apart can be seen together. This space is what I mean by a horizon. When one perceives one's professional work against this larger horizon, then one can recognize that which one was not thinking about is a homeomorph or isomorph of that which one was thinking about in the rigors of problem-solving. Training takes rigor; it takes hanging on in one cognitive domain; but discovery takes letting go, and requires a life in, at the very least, more than one cognitive domain.

One of the reasons we are in a new creative era is precisely because our planetary culture is essentially a complex ecology of multiple cognitive domains. It is a world of diverse cultures brought into association, a world of thought in which no single imperial culture and no single civilizational elite is able to map and control; it is a world of such topological complexity that the old linear perspective of a subjective observer within an objective nature no longer orients us in our multidimensional space. The mathematical imagination of modernism, the Newtonian linear equations of motion, are no longer adequate narratives with which to describe the world we have brought forth in this planetary culture of art and science, and so we have rather instinctively and unintentionally begun to shift to the descriptive geometries of behavior in the development of mathematics from catastrophe theory to chaos dynamics.

As the cultural historian observes the artist and the scientist observing one another, she can see that there is indeed a cultural history to the geometries we use to bring forth a world. The archaic world is the world of the arithmetic mentality, of the storied lineages of Genesis and the linear stores of grain counted by the scribes in Sumer. The classical world, the world of Egyptians, Phoenicians, and Greeks, is the world of the geometrical mentality. It is a world of center and periphery, with the elite at the center and the resources at the periphery, the sound at the center and the alphabetic symbol at the periphery, the ego at the heart and the skin at the edge. It is a world of above and below, superior and inferior, a mentality in which geometry is used by the imagination to bring forth a world.

But in the very process of articulating a geometry one sets up an idea of space in which the emergent domain of cultural evolution is inconceivable. The alphabetical and geometrical imagination, with all its representations, is inconceivable to the archaic world of oral space. Here there are no graves for individuals, but the lingering presence of one's ancestors under the bed in which the children are conceived, or simply a common tomb that is the womb of the Great Mother in which all the bones of the tribe are returned together. There is no fixing of speech with the alphabet, no fixing of space with geometry, and no fixing of the ego in individualism. The archaic world is a different world, and it has its own mentality, its own mathematical imagination of the arithmetic of the problem of "the two and the one" that it expressed in its primordial icon of the phallic-necked Great Mother, icons that you can see expressed in the statuary from Cayonu, Tepe Sarab, Nea Nikomedeia, or as far back as the paleolithic in Dolne Vestonice or the Venus of Willendorf.

Similarly, the shift from the geometrical imagination of Pythagoras and Plato to the dynamical mentality of Galileo and Newton is a process of cultural evolution that is inconceivable to the guardians of the classical world in the Church. The difficulty with the articulations of a mentality is that its narratives in mathematics and literature set up constructions that the mind takes for an absolute reality. Value is in lineage for the archaic mentality, but value is the contained and the container for the classical mentality. For the dynamical mentality of modernism, however, value is in motion and change. Galileo and Newton will describe the motion in one way, the capitalist will describe the movement of money with interest in another, and the novelist such as Defoe or Dickens will describe the movement of the individual from rags to riches in yet another way. Nevertheless, the scientist, the businessman, and the artist are all within the same mathematical imagination and are setting up structures that both illuminate and delude.

Now we are at another one of those watersheds of history, or what the mathematicians would call a "catastrophe bifurcation," in which the emergent mentality is inconceivable to the high priests of the dynamical mentality, the governors of thought in the university and the nation-state. As experts these leaders must create "solutions" to treat their illusions, illusions which are their efforts to project the old mathematical narratives onto a world that, historically, no longer exists in the emergent condition of our new planetary culture. What the imagination allows us to do is to drop our "solutions" as the illusions which support them become obvious. The people who can do this we call imaginative, the people who cannot, unimaginative. When we step back to take another or a different kind of look, or when we move out of the tunnel perspective of our training to consider the geometry of behavior, we open ourselves to the visual, and this can often become visionary.

The imagination is the space that allows us to expand our horizon. If we consider Mark Johnson's recent study of imagination and reason, our human body is the field of metaphor with which we extend our perceptions to reason and infer by analogy.[9] If we extend by imagination beyond direct sight to the reading of meters and claim that the figmentary quark produced by a meter-reading for a nanosecond is "real" and "really out there," we are becoming caught by our thoughts and beginning to take the imagination literally. And that is a good definition of idolatry. The religious idolater thinks the stone statue of Baal is divinity itself; the materialistic idolater thinks that the set of sensor-response-

19

interpreted-as-quark is really matter, "the real thing." For me, as a student of cultural history, it seems ironic that human experiences known by artists and saints and yogis in different cultures over the millennia, and repeated over and over again in quite different situations, are dismissed as superstition and illusion, but an elementary particle that only exists as a nanosecond impulse on a screen seen only by a handful of high priests at CERN at a cost greater than the construction bill for the Great Pyramid is considered to be "scientifically real." Elementary particles are no more real than angels or garden dwarves; they are, in Varela's words, "brought forth." Elementary particles are brought forth by linear or ring accelerators, just as angels or bodhisattvas are brought forth by meditation. Physics, in the words of Bruce Gregory's recent book, is a language.[10] Religion is also a cultural language, and both religion and science have their systems of idolatry in which the State supports their illusions for its own political ends. In one system of thought you may wish to debate how many angels can dance on the head of a pin. (Personally, I do not regard this as a frivolous discussion, but see it as an important discussion of multidimensional topology and a koan of instruction for those whose imaginations are still stuck in Euclidian forms.) In another system of thought you may argue over whether matter is a de Broglie wave that at least can provide you with a picture or a more unsettlingly abstract Schroedinger function. If we spent as much on yoga as physics, we would witness supernatural wonders[11] that would have governments spending billions for the education of their soldiers and leaders. We invest in what we believe, and that richly endowed system of belief becomes our cultural reality.

If we step back and question that investment, or if we move entirely out of the historical condition of our cultural reality, we move from the center to the edge of the world, from the institution to the horizon. This movement can be both scientific and religious, sane and psychotic. It can be Descartes withdrawing from the world, calling all into doubt, having the initiatic vision of the mathematics behind appearances, and then going forth again to study the world with the new method of science. Notice, however, just how mythic is the structure of Descartes' *Discourse on Method;* it has what Joseph Campbell would call "the monomythic pattern" of separation, initiation, and return. It is the same structure of initiation as Moses fleeing Egypt as an outlaw, having the vision of the burning bush in the desert, discovering the hidden history of Israel, and returning to Egypt as a prophetic figure who will transform history. Moses and Descartes are culturally isomorphic, and in each case it is the exploded horizon that becomes the catastrophe bifurcation that moves the civilization from one attractor to another.

We are now at another one of those times of catastrophe bifurcation, a splitting apart between traditional civilization and the emerging planetization. And in plagues, pollution, and cultural violence, we are experiencing this bifurcation in literally catastrophic ways; but it isn't all bad news, for if we move out of the institutional definition of reality in the bureaucratic university or the political leadership of the industrial nation-state we come to a new horizon in which we see the shape of things to come. What was perceived as noise before within the institution, begins to be seen as information when one lives at large in the planetary culture. What was seen as unstable and aperiodic before, begins to take on the shape of a different and more complex geometry of behavior. What was unknowable and uncontrollable within the linear and abstract algebraic mentality of modernism now begins to become experienced and embodied in forms of behavior that dance without reason. The transition from one state to another is often experienced as a threat, and the condition is seen as a problem that requires an institutional response. So let us approach these penumbral shapes on the horizon in the normal way of considering them as problems and threats.

Consider the threat of air pollution. Consider the threat of AIDS. Consider the threat of thermonuclear war. And consider the threat of global economic collapse. Your imagination is now, no doubt, filled with the images of newspapers, magazines, and the televised news.

Now instead of imagining these phenomena as objects threatening a governing institution, let us imagine them as geometries of behavior and ask ourselves: What is the phase-portrait? What is the geometry of behavior, what is the shape of the thing I see dimly out there at the edge of my understanding on the horizon between

21

perception and imagination? What is the phase-space of the atmosphere? What is the phase-space of the Self in the immune system? What is the phase-space of the nation-state? And what is the phase-space of the global electronic economy?

I have asked Lovelock, Margulis, and Varela to join us because I think that the shape of the atmosphere in the work of Lovelock, the shape of the planetary bacterial bioplasm in the work of Margulis, the shape of the immune system in the work of Varela, and the shape of the world economy all reveal homeomorphic phase-portraits, and, I believe, this new shape of things to come is one of the emergent properties of our new mathematical and narrative imagination, of a mentality that has outgrown the Galilean world view of modernism.

In the last century the idea of "Transformation" was critical to the evolutionary narratives of Spencer and Darwin, and to the thermodynamics of Carnot. For the nineteenth century, the novels of Dickens are characteristic narratives of transformation, and the paintings of Turner were characteristic studies of the atmospheric pressure of heat and not simply the presence of light.[12] At the beginning of our twentieth century, with the emergence of the film, novel and painting were wed to give us this quintessential twentieth-century art form of transformation. Now at the end of our century, when noise is to us what heat was to Carnot, and when phase-portraits are to us what lines of descent were to Darwin, we have a new art form in music video that allows us to take the studies of the dripping faucet of Robert Shaw and wed it to the minimalist music of Philip Glass, or allows us to take the recordings of the vibrational sounds of the planets, transpose the spectroscopic analysis of starlight into sounds, and generate a music video of Kepler's dream of "the music of the spheres." These music videos do not yet exist as completed genres; they are forms of art in cooperation with science that are now emerging on the horizon, and when they are more in the center of the stage of our culture, we will no longer be in the same culture, for they are expressions not of nation-states and patriotic national languages and literatures: they are expressions of a planetary scientific culture. These are the shape-changers that are taking shape on our horizon, so let us take a closer look at the cognitive domains in which they emerge.

22

What is the shape of the atmosphere? If we consider the work of the atmospheric chemist James Lovelock, we will not simply be talking about the movement of gases, but the movement of oceans, the metabolic processes of living creatures, and the slower patterns of exchange in the tectonic plates and the magnetosphere. If we do not stop there, but go on to the Van Allen belts and the flow patterns of the solar wind, the planets, and the entire solar system, the mind will begin to boggle, and we will probably back off and return to Earth. Still, if we keep in mind the geometries of behavior, then the swirls of the magnetic core and the foam of the tectonic plates of the Earth, the spinning solar system, the galactic vortices, and the phase-portrait of the foam we stir in our small cup of Italian espresso will all be capable of being aesthetically appreciated by a delighted and unboggled mind.

Before Lovelock came along to challenge our imaginations, life was thought of as some sort of accidental stowaway on the circling hunk of rock that was the Earth. The rock was real and solid; life was soft and sloppy. A scientific description of the rock was a simple matter of Newtonian laws of motion and gravitational attraction. As a hunk of rock, the Earth had a simple location in empty space. Now the shape of the Earth has changed, and life is not to be seen as a coating of slime on a hunk of rock, but a process that is interacting with solar energy, weathering rocks, producing atmospheres and oceans, and from the sheer weight of the liquid mass of the oceans, affecting the volcanoes and the slower fluid motion of the tectonic plates. Lovelock calls this imaginative perception of planetary dynamics "Gaia," and what Gaia is, is certainly not simply an object, a mere chunk of rock in the void of black Newtonian space; Gaia is the phase-space of our planet, and a phase-portrait of the geometry of its behavior would not produce the familiar billiard ball, but a complex topology of permeable membranes between the solar wind and the Van Allen belts. In the words of Lewis Thomas, what the Earth would look like in this new imagination would be a living cell.

Gaia is essentially a new vision of the little and the large, of how the plankton in the sea can affect the sulfur cycle of the clouds, the albedo, and the autoregulating cycle of the temperature of the planet as a whole. The theory developed as a response to the

NASA project for the search for life on Mars and became instead, in the subtitle of Lovelock's book, "a new look at life on Earth." Out of the NASA project of exobiology developed the collaboration between Lovelock and Margulis in which they both sought to understand how the presence of even bacterial life on a planet would make itself known in the atmosphere as a whole. What Margulis came to understand from her work with Lovelock was that just as we were looking at the earth in the wrong way — when we saw it as a discrete hunk of rock in empty, containing space — we were also looking at a bacterium in the wrong way when we saw it as a discrete entity simply located in a Petri dish. Along with other microbiologists such as Panisset and Sonea in Montreal, Margulis began to recognize in the symbiotic architecture of the cell that bacteria were not discrete entities in simple locations. They were collective entities whose membranes were not walls but vehicles of transport and communication. Bacteria were social creatures who could exchange genes promiscuously and with such a rapid rate of mutation that they were better understood as a "superorganism" of planetary dimensions, in other words, a planetary bioplasm.

Now when you imagine a planetary bioplasm, what do you see? What begins to take shape in your mind? Not a cell, certainly, but something more like a planetary atmosphere or an ocean. A bacterium is not an object; as a temporal flow in a bioplasm, it is a phase-space that interacts with the oceans and atmosphere, and indeed has through its metabolic processes produced the beautiful blue sky as we know it today. So this bioplasm has to be envisioned as interpenetrating the geophysical processes studied by Lovelock. The hard edges between animal, vegetable, and mineral dissolve as we envision this bacterial bioplasm extruding iron ore deposits in the Gunflint sediments of Ontario, or producing oxygen in the Archaean epoch. The more one tries to envision these little creatures acting in concert, the more they begin to seem as if they were the antibodies of the planet maintaining a stable identity through time. Gaia, in essence, is the immune system of our planet; since it serves to maintain an identity, a "self," it deserves a name, and James Lovelock and the novelist William Golding did well to name it Gaia.

24

And this, of course, brings us face to face with the work of Varela on the immune system. Well, what is this immune system? Clearly it is not an object located in the thymus gland or the bone marrow; it is a process of movement, a cognitive system of re-cognitions that form a conversation, a language of identification and identity. The "Self" is the phase-space of the immune and nervous systems. When you envision this self of the immune system, what shape does it take in your imagination? I see clouds, those nebular forms that play at the edges of solid continents, liquid oceans, and the gaseous stratosphere. The immune system too plays with the solids of the bones, the liquids of the blood, and the gases of metabolic respiration. Were I a video artist or a topologist and not merely a writer with modest means, I would delight to work out the computer graphics to have these phase-portraits of the atmosphere, the bacterial bioplasm, and the immune system all dance before your eyes in a video wed to contemporary music. I am, however, in the frustrating position of being only able to imagine artistically what I am not permitted to know scientifically or perform, more expensively, with the electronic arts that are reserved for rock stars. Yet I have faith that what I am seeing in my mind's eye are, in fact, the science and the art forms that are on our cultural horizon, and that soon these images will become part of our "natural" environment.

Lovelock will show us in his simple parable of "Daisyworld" how daisies can maintain the temperature of a planet. Margulis will show us in her entrancing films of spirochetes how "the individual" is engulfed in relationships in all directions. In a unified theory of the assemblies of evolution that is as visionary and imaginative as Wallace's, she will suggest that the mitotic spindle, the dendritic neuron, and the motile flagellum of spermatozoa owe their "connectionist" architecture to the promiscuous attachments of spirochetes over time. Varela will talk about the process of learning in the immune system, of how an army of singly dumb units in the patterning of their responses through time can begin to show emergent properties. He will go on from there to consider the patterns of connection in the nervous and immune systems, to show how "the Self" emerges as the infinitely related-in-all-directions actions of these patterns of connections. And if we wonder

25

why so modern a scientist as Varela could be interested in a philosophy so ancient as Buddhism, we will not have long to wonder when we gaze at the films of Margulis, for her footage says as much as volumes of Tibetan Buddhist sutras. In Margulis's footage of the spirochete attached to the protist, *Mixotrycha paradoxa*, we shall see how "the individual" is awash in a sea of relationships, and that the membrane is not the wall containing an identity, but, like the skin of a resounding drum, an instrument of communication. The spirochete is attached to the protist and serves both as an oar to move it and a hand to pass the food on down to its point of entry, and the cellulose the protist digests becomes an excreted acetate that is the food for the termite, in whose hindgut this protist dwells. The spirochete is in the protist, the protist is in the hindgut, the termite is in the colony, the colony is in the stump, the stump is in the forest, the forest is in the atmosphere, and it keeps on going till the mind takes to Buddhist meditations on "dependent co-origination" (*pratityasamutpada*) to unboggle itself.

But with a Buddhistically unboggled mind let us not stop with the "connectionist" patterns of the spirochetes of Margulis or the lymphocytes of Varela, let us consider the idea of "an army of dumb units" producing an emergent state to consider the global electronic economy. What is the ground of value for this new electronic world economy? We can see very quickly that value is not based on land, as it was in feudalism, or on precious metals, as it was in mercantilism, or on paper currencies, as it was in early capitalism. The currency is indeed a current, a flow of differences which, in Gregory Bateson's definition of information, is "the difference that makes a difference." The differing value of the dollar in time and space between London, New York, Tokyo, Zurich, and Frankfurt, can make someone a fortune through nothing more than the flow of bits across the time difference between one currency and another in Tokyo and Frankfurt. Without the membrane of differentiation of national currencies there could be no global conversation, no process that generates value or wealth. So difference drives the system, much as a membrane drives a chemical conversation among bacteria. In this new economy, value is created in transaction; it is not based on anything. In Francisco and Evan's words, this is "a world without ground."[13]

26

Because value is created in transaction, the belief systems of late, cybernetic capitalism are even more critical than they were in the days of early, print capitalism. Now capital formation depends on confidence, not simply in corporations, but in nation-state "futures." If investors are confident that a nation-state has a great capacity for scientific innovation, has, in effect, the ability to make the shift from an industrial to a scientific economy, then the currency and the Treasury Bonds of that nation-state are bought and exchanged as a kind of scientific commodities future, very much in the way one would buy up stock in Westinghouse in expectation of a future rise, buy up unfarmed grain crops, or unmined minerals. One trades on the future according to a system of belief and expectation. It is still the same, but now the context has changed as the marketplace has expanded to become the entire planet and the time of transaction has contracted to become a matter of seconds. The crossing of these two inverse logarithms of expanding space and contracting time generates an unpredictable singularity, a crossing of the large and the little that generates a "Gaian Attractor" in which the nation-state or the multinational corporation becomes analogous to a tropical rain forest or a coral reef within the planetary biosphere.

Clearly, in the light of the cognitive science of Varela, no one is commanding this new world economy. It is an autonomous system with emergent properties that are not yet understood by "the army of dumb units," that we might wish to designate as the businessmen, economists, and politicians at work in the system. If one begins to look at the world economy in this metaphoric and completely unprofessional way — as indeed only a non-economist such as I could do — then the world news should be read in a different way. The perestroika of the Soviet Union should be seen as an effort on the part of a new generation to gain entry into this new cognitive domain of the global electronic economy, the world game. And the indebtedness of the Latin American nations should be read as another mode of entry into the world economic game, a way of purchasing loans as "junk bonds" on nation-state futures; it may even represent a form of "leveraged buy-out" in which a hitherto small nation is able to enter the global game and have an entangling effect on multinational banks far beyond the actual "value" of the ground-base of its resources.

27

When one considers the conscious world economy of business-as-usual and the unconscious polities of shadow-economies, then it becomes obvious that the geometry of behavior of an economy is not described by economists with their econometrics of GNPs. When one steps back to look at the whole condition of our time one can discern shapes out there at the very edge where perception and imagination meet on the horizon. What is the shape of Gaia, of the planetary microbial bioplasm, of the global electronic economy, of the self in the immune system? These penumbral shapes have not yet resolved into distinct form, for they are still there at the edge of the visible but at the threshold of the imaginable, and this is always an exciting place and time in the life of art and science. Once we understand these new phase-portraits of the geometry of behavior of emergent domains, we will no longer be thinking within the mathematical imagination of the dynamics of Newton and Galileo, or the Neo-Darwinism of industrial capitalism. We will be re-imagining the phase-spaces of nature, self, and society to see that they are no longer described in the mathematical and literary narratives of representation and adaptation to be experienced as "objects in containers" or organisms constrained to fit into their niches by the containing pressure of their environment. We will see the organisms extruding their environments in a fluid process of natural drift in which "the niche" is as Buddhistically "empty" and unlocated as the blue of the sky. With this new imagination, we will have crossed over in the transition of our contemporary renaissance to a new mentality in which the narratives of morphodynamics will describe the interpenetration of the large in the little, and the little in the large. Our sense of value will change as we begin to treasure the little as well as the large in a new planetary culture in which wealth is not counted in arithmetic quantities but in phase-spaces, and in this cultural geometry of behavior, the phase-spaces of the unrecognized artist and the unfamous scientist may be as extensive as those of the powerful billionaire and the famous politician.

So it is with a Renaissance sense of excitement of being in this beautiful Sala di Notari in Perugia, thinking of the past and imagining the future, that I wish to express our gratitude to the Provincial government of Perugia and Umbria for inviting Lindisfarne to express here the planetary culture to which it is dedicated.

Notes

1. "The Notebooks of Charles Darwin" in *Darwin: A Norton Critical Edition*, ed. Philip Appleman (New York: Norton, 1970), 78.

2. Arnold C. Brackman, *A Delicate Arrangement: The Strange Case of Charles Darwin and Alfred Russel Wallace.* (New York: Times Books/Quadrangle, 1980), 58.

3. See Darwin's letter of 1868 as quoted in Donald Fleming, "Charles Darwin, The Anesthetic Man," in *Darwin* op. cit.

4. See Paul Feyerabend, *Against Method* (London: Version, 1978).

5. See Frances A. Yates, *The Rosicrucian Enlightenment* (London: Routledge and Kegan Paul, 1972).

6. Werner Heisenberg, "The Representation of Nature in Contemporary Physics," in *Symbolism in Religion and Literature*, ed. Rollo May (New York: Harper & Row, 1960), 209.

7. See René Thom, *Structural Stability and Morphogenesis* (Reading, MA: Cummings Publishers, 1975). Also Ralph Abraham and Christopher D. Shaw, "Global Behavior," Part 3 in *The Geometry of Behavior* (Santa Cruz, CA: Aerial Press, 1984).

8. The *New York Times*, Sunday, October 30, 1988, 1.

9. Mark Johnson, *The Body in the Mind: The Bodily Basis of Meaning, Imagination, and Reason.* (Chicago: University of Chicago Press, 1987).

10. Bruce Gregory, *Inventing Reality: Physics as Language* (New York: John Wiley & Sons, 1988).

11. For an extensive bibliography of paranormal functioning, see *The Physical and Psychological Effects of Meditation: A Review of Contemporary Meditation Research with a Comprehensive Bibliography 1931 - 1988*, eds. Michael Murphy and Steven Donovan (San Rafael, CA: Esalen Institute, 1988).

12. See Gillian Beer, *Darwin's Plots* (London: Routledge and Kegan Paul, 1984); and Michel Serres, "Turner Traduit Carnot" in *La Traduction* (Paris: Editions de Minuit, 1974).

13. See Francisco Varela and Evan Thompson, *Worlds Without Ground: Cognitive Science and Human Experience.* (Forthcoming).

1

JAMES E. LOVELOCK

Gaia

A Planetary Emergent Phenomenon

The Gaia hypothesis was first introduced in 1972 in a letter to the journal *Atmospheric Environment,* and in two papers in 1973 with Lynn Margulis as coauthor. We postulated that the climate and chemical composition of the Earth's surface environment is, and has been, actively regulated at a state tolerable for the biota by the biota. The wording of this statement, as well as the language of these early papers, and especially that of a book on Gaia (1979), was sometimes poetic rather than scientific. This led to the belief that we had in mind a purposeful or sentient regulation of the environment by the biota. Nothing could have been further from the truth, but the misunderstanding has persisted. The Gaia hypothesis has matured over the past fifteen years and can now be more clearly stated as a theory that views the evolution of the biota and of their material environment as a single tight-coupled process, with the self-regulation of climate and chemistry as an emergent property. It is a theory that is rich in "risky" predictions, for example that oxygen is and has been regulated during the existence of land plants, within 5 ± percent of its present level. It is therefore, in the Popperian sense, falsifiable.

First, I shall give a brief account of the development of Gaia theory and then move on to illustrate, by means of numerical models, the potential for stable self-regulation that exists within tight-coupled systems comprising organisms and their environments. I shall try to distinguish the real Gaia from a taxa of parasites and inquilines such as coevolutionary, optimizing, and purposeful Gaia, all of which have recently been entertainingly categorized in a paper by J. W. Kirchner at a Chapman Conference of the American Geophysical Union in 1988.

Before the nineteenth century, scientists were comfortable with the notion of a living Earth. One of them was James Hutton, who has often been called the father of geology. In 1785 he lectured before the Royal Society of Edinburgh and said "I consider the Earth to be a super-organism and that its proper study should be by physiology." He belonged to the Circulation Society, a scientific society inspired by the discoveries of physiology, like the circulation of the blood and the connection between oxygen and life. He applied these ideas to his view of the hydrological cycle and the movements of the nutritious elements of the Earth.

James Hutton's wholesome view of the Earth was discarded early in the last century. I think that this may have been a consequence of a growing interest in origins and in evolutionary theories of the Earth and the life upon it. For biologists there was Darwin's great vision of the evolution of the species of organisms by natural selection. For the geologists there was the other part of Hutton's world view, uniformitarianism, that saw the Earth as a steady-state system, in which the rocks recycled continuously and kept the status quo. We should remember that both of these theories were radical and appeared in a cultural environment where the scriptural description of an act of creation was still widely held to be true.

The Earth and life sciences in the nineteenth century were for a time held together by the shared rejection of creationism. But it was not long before they went their separate ways. Not only was there a rapid growth in the supply of information about the Earth as exploration and exploitation increased, but the techniques for looking at organisms were very different from those for looking at the ocean, the air, and the rocks. It must have been an exciting period of science. Few were inclined to stand back and take a broader view or try to keep alive Hutton's super-organism. What is remarkable is not that the sciences divided, but that two distinct

31

and very different theories of evolution, the biological and the geological, should have coexisted, even until today.

The reason for the endurance of the division is, I think, a mutual acceptance by Earth and life scientists of the anesthetic notion of adaptation. Biologists have assumed that the physical and chemical world evolves according to rules laid down in the geology or the biochemistry department of their university and that the details of this material evolution, although interesting, need not concern them in their quest to understand the evolution of the organisms. Biologists are comfortable with the notion that whatever happens to the environment, the organisms will adapt.

In a similar way, Earth scientists were happy to accept without question their biological colleagues' idea of adaptation because it freed them from any need to constrain their Earth models on account of the needs of organisms. After all, there are organisms living in hot springs at 100 degrees Celsius and others at the freezing point. A wide enough range for climatologists.

Adaptation is a dubious notion, for in the real world the environment to which the organisms are adapting is determined by their neighbors' activities, rather than by the blind forces of chemistry and physics alone. In such a world, changing the environment is part of the survival game, and it would be absurd to suppose that organisms would refrain from changing their material environment if by so doing they left more progeny. In his time, of course, Darwin did not know, as we do now, that the air we breathe, the oceans, and the rocks are all either the direct products of living organisms or else have been greatly modified by their presence. In no way do organisms just "adapt" to a dead world determined by physics and chemistry alone. They live with a world that is the breath and bones of their ancestors and that they are now sustaining.

It was not until the present century that a minority led by the Russian scientist Vernadsky saw that the separation of the earth and life sciences had become too extreme. Vernadsky was the father of the modern science of biogeochemistry. He and his successors, like Hutchinson and Redfield, recognized that life and the physical and chemical environment interact, that gases like oxygen and methane are biological products. Where they differ from

32

Gaia is that they still accepted, without question, the dogma of mainstream biology, which is that organisms simply adapt to changes in their material environment, without then going on to think of the consequences of such an adaptation in an environment modified by the organisms themselves. Vernadsky's world view has been developed and expanded in coevolutionary theory and in biogeochemical models. Coevolution, or as some, not I, call it "the weak Gaia hypothesis," is rather like a platonic friendship. The biologist and the geologist remain friends but never move on to an intimate, close-coupled relationship. Coevolutionary theory includes no active regulation of the chemical composition and climate of the Earth by the system comprising the biota and their material environment; most importantly, it does not see the Earth as alive in any sense, nor even as a physiological system.

What Is Gaia?

Like coevolution, Gaia rejects the apartheid of Victorian biology and geology, but it goes much further. Gaia theory is about the evolution of a tightly coupled system whose constituents are the biota and their material environment, which comprises the atmosphere, the oceans, and the surface rocks. The evolutionary process leads to the emergence of a domain. The self-regulation of important properties, such as climate and chemical composition, are seen as an emergent consequence of this evolutionary process. Like living organisms and many closed-loop self-regulating systems, Gaia would be expected to be emergent, that is, the whole will be more than the sum of the parts. This kind of system is notoriously difficult if not impossible to explain by cause and effect logic, as practicing inventors know to their cost.

The testing of theories about living systems is possible but rarely easy. Consider for example the problem faced by someone unfamiliar with Earth-based life of designing a test to show that a Lombardy Poplar tree, in the winter, was alive. These trees are all males and hence can be propagated only by cuttings, 90 percent or more of a fully grown tree is dead wood and dead bark with just a thin skin of living tissue around the circumference of the wood.

Then there is the question "What does the word alive mean?" Biologists studiously avoid trying to answer it.

In many ways the Lombardy Poplar tree, alive, yet unable ever to reproduce, is like Gaia. Both are made mainly of dead matter that has been profoundly changed by living organisms, and both have just a thin skin of living tissue around their circumferences.

When biochemists examine a live animal they know that many of its reactions and processes can be adequately described by simple deterministic physics and chemistry. But they also accept the legitimacy of physiology. They know that, for an intact animal, homeostasis, the automatic regulation of temperature and chemical composition, although it involves chemistry, is an emergent property. Such properties require physiology for their explanation and understanding. I think that the same can be said of the Earth. If it is a superorganism then its explanation requires physiology as well as chemistry and physics.

Evidence for and Against Gaia

This is not the place to discuss in detail the evidence gathered over the years for and against Gaia. But I can say that intimations of Gaia arose directly from the NASA planetary exploration program. When I was asked to suggest a life detection experiment for Mars it seemed to me that the analysis of the atmospheric composition of Mars was the best way to do it. Together with Dian Hitchcock I showed that such an analysis could provide prima facie evidence for the existence of life on the planet. Briefly, a dead planet would have an atmosphere characteristic of the abiological steady state and not far from chemical equilibrium. By contrast a planet with life would be obliged to use its atmosphere as a transfer medium for waste products and raw materials. Such a use of the atmosphere would introduce disequilibria among the chemical components and this might reveal the presence of life. When the terrestrial planets are compared, Mars and Venus are found to have atmospheres dominated by carbon dioxide and close to the abiological steady state. Earth by contrast has an atmosphere where profoundly incompatible gases such as methane and oxygen

34

coexist. This disequilibrium reveals the presence of life. The persistence of the disequilibrium, at a steady state, for periods much longer than the residence times of the gases suggests the presence of an emergent system able to regulate atmospheric composition.

A more direct indication that the atmosphere is in active dynamic equilibrium, like a bicycle rider, is already coming from the unregulated injection of methane gas from the excesses of agriculture. According to Gaia theory, the atmospheric abundance of methane is a controlling variable and its arbitrary change could be destabilizing. The appearance of a hole in the ozone layer over Antarctica, due in part to the methane increase, tends to confirm this prediction.

A more practical approach is to make models of Gaia and then see how well they can be mapped onto the observed systems. But the feedback loops linking life with its environment are so numerous and so intricate that there seems little chance of quantifying or of understanding them. It occurred to me late in 1981 to reduce the environment to a single variable, temperature, and the biota to a single species, daisies.

Imagine a planet like the Earth; it travels at the Earth's orbit around a star of the same mass and composition as our Sun. This planet spins like the Earth but its atmosphere has few clouds and a constant low concentration of greenhouse gases. In these circumstances the mean surface temperature is given by the Stefan Boltzmann expression of the balance between the radiation received from the star and the heat lost by radiation from the planet to space; the albedo of the planet determines its temperature. Assume that this planet is well seeded with daisies whose growth rate is a simple parabolic function of temperature, and that it is well watered and that nutrients are not limited. In these circumstances it is easy to predict the area of the planet covered by daisies from a knowledge of the mean surface temperature and equations taken from population biology. Fig. 1A illustrates the evolution of this simple system when two different-colored daisy species are present, one dark and one light, according to conventional wisdom.

The upper panel of the figure shows the response of daisies to temperature; daisies do not grow below 5 degrees or above

40 degrees, and grow best at 22.5 degrees Celsius. The lower panel illustrates the evolution of the mean surface temperature as the star increases in luminosity, a smooth monotonic temperature increase.

In Fig. 1B the same system is modeled as a close-coupled physiology. When the surface temperature reaches 5 degrees, daisy seeds germinate. During the first season dark colored daisies will be at an advantage, since they will be warmer than the planetary surface. Light colored daisies will be at a disadvantage since by reflecting sunlight they will be cooler than the surface. At the end of the season many more dark daisy seeds will remain in the soil. When the next season begins dark daisies will be flourishing and soon will be warming, not just themselves, but their locality and, as they spread, the region and eventually the whole planet. The figure illustrates an explosive growth of both temperature and dark daisy population. The spread of dark daisies will eventually be limited by their decline in growth rate at temperatures above 22.5 degrees Celsius and by competition from light-colored daisies. As the star evolves the dark and light daisy populations adjust according to the simple population biology equations of Carter and Prince (1981). The planetary temperature moves from just above the optimum for daisy growth at low solar luminosity to just below the optimum at high solar luminosity. Eventually the output of heat from the star is too great for regulation and the plants die.

This simple model is a graphic illustration of a geophysiological process. The only criticism so far received has been the suggestion by biologists that in a real world there would be daisy species that "cheated," that is, took advantage by saving the energy needed to make the dark or light pigment and so took over the planet and returned the system to the model illustrated in Fig. 1A. Fig. 2 is a model where daisies having a neutral color, that of the bare planetary surface, are included. In this experiment, even when the neutral-colored daisies were given a 5 percent increase in growth rate, there is no indication of a planetary takeover and a failure of regulation. At low temperatures only dark daisies are fit to grow, at high temperatures only light daisies are fit. Neutral daisies grow only when there is little need for regulation. An important point here illustrated is that Gaia theory and coevolution are not always mutually exclusive. Organisms do not strive ostentatiously to regulate their environment when regulation is not needed.

Fig. 3 illustrates a model that included ten different-colored daisy species, their albedos ranging in evenly spaced steps from dark to light. The regulation of the mean surface temperature, lower panel, is more accurate than in the two- and three-species models. The middle panel shows the populations of the different-colored daisies and the upper panel the diversity index of the ecosystem as the model evolved.

The stable coexistence of three or more species in a population-biology model is contrary to the experience of modelers in that field of science. Models of the competition of three or more species, like the three-body problem of astrophysics, tend to be unstable and chaotic. The stability of Daisyworld is even more remarkable since no attempt was made to linearize the equations used in the model. Not only is the model naturally stable but it will resist severe perturbations, such as the sudden death of half or more of all daisies, and then recover homeostasis when the perturbation is removed. The models can include herbivores to graze the daisies and carnivores to cull the grazers, without significant loss of stability.

Another scientist who was like James Hutton was Alfred Lotka, the father of theoretical ecology. Like Hutton he saw the science he founded develop in a way he never expected or intended. One of the great puzzles about the history of theoretical ecology is why it has for sixty years ignored Alfred Lotka's wise advice. On page 16 of his book *Physical Biology* written in 1925, he said:

This fact deserves emphasis. It is customary to discuss the "evolution of a species of organisms." As we proceed we shall see many reasons why we should constantly take in view the evolution, as a whole, of the system [organism plus environment]. It may appear at first sight as if it should prove a more complicated problem than the consideration of a part only of the system. But it will become apparent, as we proceed, that the physical laws governing evolution in all probability take on a simpler form when referred to the system as a whole than to any portion thereof. It is not so much the organism or the species that evolves, but the entire system, species plus environment. The two are inseparable.

Daisyworld as I have described it is just an invention, a demonstration model to illustrate how I thought Gaia worked and why foresight and planning need not be invoked to explain automatic regulation. But, as we shall see, when the details are fleshed out it becomes a generality and a theoretical basis for Gaia. I would like to think of it as the kind of model Alfred Lotka had in mind but could not develop, because in his day there were no computers to carry out the immense task that the hand calculation of even a simple daisy model requires.

Andrew Watson and I (1983) described the mathematical basis of Daisyworld in *Tellus*. But at the time neither of us realized its unusual properties nor the extent to which it is an expression of the general theory of Gaia. The paper explains the essential mechanism by which homeostasis is maintained. The Daisyworld thermostat has no set point, instead the domain always moves to a stable state where the relationship between daisy population and planetary temperature and that between temperature and daisy growth converge. The emergent system seeks the most comfortable state rather like a cat as it runs and moves before settling.

Inventions often work well but are difficult to explain. Engineers and physiologists have long known that feedback is much more subtle than is commonly realized. Homeostasis is only possible when feedback is applied at the right amplitude and phase, and when the system time constants are appropriate. These professionals also know that both positive and negative feedback can lead to stability or instability according to the timing of their application.

Population biology models are notorious for their intractable mathematics, for the way they become distracted by the fairyland world of mathematical demons, the strange attractors. This would not surprise an engineer, who would see them in his words as "open loop systems," where feedback was applied — or happened by chance — in an arbitrary manner. By contrast geophysiological models, which are emergent and describe domains, have feedback, both negative and positive, included coherently. They are as a consequence robust and stable and will happily accommodate any number of nonlinear equations and still prefer to relate with stable attractors.

Fig. 4 compares the unstable and chaotic behavior (lower panel) of a model of an ecosystem of daisies, rabbits, and foxes according to population biology, with the calm stability of the same ecosystem (upper panel) when feedback from the environment is included as in a Daisy world.

But what of biogeochemical box models? Are these any more stable? Ann Henderson-Sellers drew my attention to the paper by Williamowski and Rossler (1980) suggesting that biogeochemical models were also prone to chaotic behavior, or to an unusual sensitivity to the choice of initial conditions. Geophysiology seems to be a way to avoid these distractions. The concluding model is of the period at the end of the Archaean when oxygen first began to dominate the chemistry of the atmosphere. During the long period of the Archaean, the biosphere was run by bacteria; the primary producers were cyanobacteria and the oxygen they made was almost entirely used up to oxidize reducing compounds such as ferrous iron and sulfides present in and continuously released to the environment. The organic matter of the cyanobacteria was most probably digested by methanogens. In the Archaean cyanobacteria would be like the white daisies of Daisyworld, tending to cool by removing carbon dioxide and the methanogens; like dark daisies, tending to warm by adding methane to the atmosphere. A geophysiological model constructed this way settles down to a constant climate and bacterial population and sustains an atmosphere where methane is the dominant redox gas and where traces only of oxygen are present. The continuous leak of carbon to the sediments and perhaps also hydrogen to space would have slowly driven the system oxidizing, until quite suddenly oxygen became the dominant atmospheric gas.

In this model, as in Daisyworld, a key factor is the function that sets the bounds of the environment for the biota. The same parabolic relationship between growth and temperature is used as in the daisy models, but in addition a similar function is introduced for oxygen. Fig. 5 shows how the growth of an ecosystem might increase as oxygen rises from zero. Oxygen increases the rate of rock weathering, and hence the supply of nutrients, and also increases the rate of carbon cycling through oxidative metabolism. Too much oxygen is, however, toxic. The bounds for oxygen in the figure are set by two simple exponential relationships describing nutrition and toxicity.

Other bounds, such as those set by the limitations of pH, ionic strength, and the supply of nutrients could have been included. Hutchinson saw the niche as a hypervolume negotiated among the species. In a similar way, I see the physical and chemical bounds to growth form a hypervolume whose surface intersects that of the hypervolume expressing the environmental effects of the species.

The model includes geochemical data on the carbon dioxide cycle taken from Holland's book (1984). The rate of weathering is assumed to be a function of the biomass as well as of the abundance of oxygen and carbon dioxide. Fig. 6 illustrates, in the lower window, the regulation of the temperature, constant during the Archaean but falling to a lower steady state in the Proterozoic after the appearance of oxygen as a dominant gas. The fall in temperature is due to the removal of most of the methane greenhouse effect. The middle window shows the abundances of the three gases — methane, carbon dioxide, and oxygen, during the evolution of the model. The upper panel shows the populations of the three main ecosystems — cyanobacteria, methanogens, and consumers.

Like Daisyworld, this model is just an invention and is not intended to describe the real world of those remote times. What it does illustrate is the remarkable mathematical stability of geophysiological models. Climate, three ecosystems, and three gases are regulated simultaneously, and while the model is being continuously perturbed by an increasing solar luminosity. The stable homeostasis of the system is independent of a wide range of initial conditions and other perturbations. Perhaps most usefully, the values of the environmental quantities, temperature, and gas abundances it predicts are always realistic for the organisms. My purpose in making the model was to illustrate how I think Gaia works.

I do not disagree with those who propose that some, or even a large proportion, of the total regulation of any chosen Earth property can be explained by deterministic chemistry and physics.

Living systems use chemistry economically; they do not strive ostentatiously to do better than blind chemistry or physics, there is no need. The point about Gaia is that it offers a new way of looking at the Earth and makes predictions that can be tested experimentally. Had it not been for the curiosity stimulated by thoughts on the mechanisms of Gaia, none of the important trace gases dimethyl sulfide, carbon disulfide, methyliodide, and chloride would have been sought and found when they were.

To conclude, here are three things that Gaia theory provokes us to think about:

1. Life is a planetary-scale domain that emerges after life has originated. There cannot be sparse life on a planet. It would be as unstable as half of an animal. Living organisms have to evolve with their planet to the stage of emergence when they are able to regulate their planet, otherwise the ineluctable forces of physical and chemical evolution would render it uninhabitable.

2. Gaia theory adds to Darwin's great vision. There is no longer any need to consider the evolution of the species separately from the evolution of their environment. The two processes are tight coupled as a single indivisible domain. It is not enough merely to say that the organism that leaves the most progeny succeeds. Success also depends upon coherent coupling between the evolution of the organism and the evolution of its material environment.

3. Lastly it may turn out that the gift of Gaia to science is the reduction of Alfred Lotka's insight to practice a way to look at the Earth mathematically that joyfully accepts that Nature is nonlinear without becoming overwhelmed by chaos.

REFERENCES

Carter, R. N., and S. D. Prince. 1981. Epidemic models used to explain biographical distribution limits. *Nature* 213: 644-55.

Holland, H.D. 1984. *The chemical evolution of the atmosphere and the oceans.* (Princeton, N.J.: Princeton University Press), 539.

Hutchinson, G.E. 1954. Biochemistry of the terrestrial atmosphere. *The Solar System*, ed. Kuiper. (Chicago: University of Chicago Press), Ch. 8.

Hutton, James. 1788. Theory of the Earth; or, an investigation of the laws observable in the composition, dissolution, and restoration of land upon the globe. *Roy. Soc. Edinburgh*, Tr. 1: 209-304.

Lovelock, J. E. 1972. Gaia as seen through the atmosphere. *Atmospheric Environment*, 6: 579-80.

Lovelock, J. E., R. J. Maggs, and R. A. Rasmussen. 1972. Atmospheric dimethyl sulfide and the natural sulfur cycle. *Nature* 237: 452-53.

Margulis, L., and J. E. Lovelock. 1974. Biological modulation of the Earth's atmosphere. *Icarus* 21: 471-89.

Redfield, A. C. 1958. The biological control of chemical factors in the environment. *Amer. Sci.* 46: 205-21.

Vernadsky, V. 1945. The biosphere and the noosphere. *Amer. Sci.* 33: 1-12.

Watson, A. J., and J. E. Lovelock. 1983. Biological homeostasis of the global environment: The parable of Daisyworld. *Tellus* 35B: 284-89.

Williamowski, K. D., and O. E. Rossler. 1980. Irregular oscillations in a realistic abstract quadratic mass action system. *Z. Natur. Forsch.* 35A: 317-18.

JAMES E. LOVELOCK

FIGURE LEGENDS

FIGURE 1. Models of the evolution of Daisyworld according to conventional wisdom (A) and to geophysiology (B). The upper panel illustrates daisy populations in arbitrary units; the lower panel, temperatures in degrees Celsius. Going from left to right along the horizontal axis, the star's luminosity increases from 60 to 140 percent of that of our own sun. (A) illustrates how the physicists and the biologists in complete isolation calculate their view of the evolution of the planet. According to this conventional wisdom, the daisies can only respond or adapt to changes in temperature. When it becomes too hot for comfort, they will die. But in the Gaian Daisyworld (B), the ecosystem can respond by the competitive growth of the dark and light daisies, and regulates the temperature over a wide range of solar luminosity. The dashed line in the lower panel in (B) shows how the temperature would rise on a lifeless Daisyworld.

FIGURE 2. The evolution of the climate on a three-species Daisyworld with dark, gray, and light daisies present. By comparison, the dashed line in the lower panel represents the temperature evolution in the absence of life.

FIGURE 3. The evolution of the climate on a ten-species Daisyworld. The lower panel illustrates planetary temperature, the dashed curve for no life present, and the solid line with daisies. The middle panel shows the populations of the twenty different colored daisies, with the darkest appearing first (left) and the lightest last (right). The upper panel illustrates diversity, seen to be maximum when the system temperature is closest to optimum.

FIGURE 4. Comparison of the stability of a "Daisyworld" that includes rabbits to eat the daisies and foxes to cull the rabbits, upper panel, with the instability of a population-biology model of daisies, rabbits, and foxes, lower panel. The model in the upper diagram includes environmental feedback, that in the lower diagram does not.

FIGURE 5. The effect of oxygen on the growth of organisms, solid line, and the effect of the presence of organisms on the abundance of oxygen, dashed line. Where the two curves intersect is the level of oxygen at which the system regulates.

FIGURE 6. Model of the transition from the Archaean to the Proterozoic. Lower panel shows climate with a lifeless world, dashed line, compared with a live world, solid line. Note the sudden fall of temperature when oxygen appears. The middle panel shows the abundance of atmospheric gases, carbon dioxide (dashed line), oxygen and methane (solid lines). The upper panel illustrates the changes in population of the ecosystems as the transition is entered and passed. Note how both photosynthesizers and methanogens increase when oxygen first appears and how methanogens fall back to a steady level when the oxygen-breathing consumers (dashed line), become established.

43

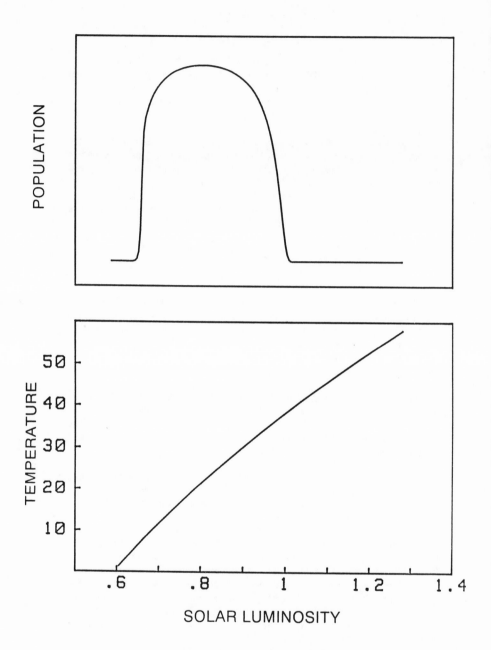

Figure 1A

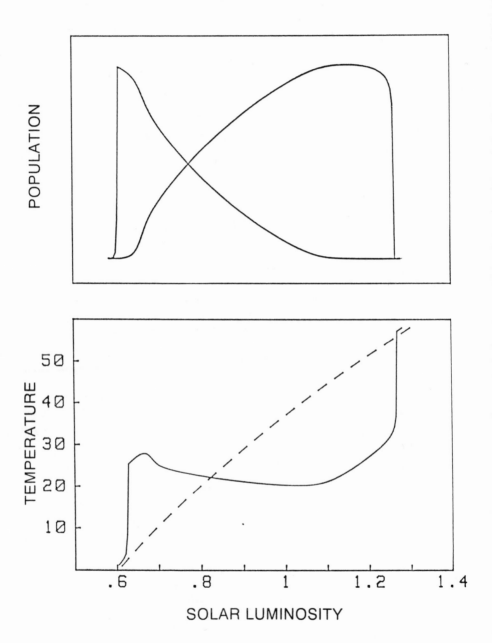

Figure 1B

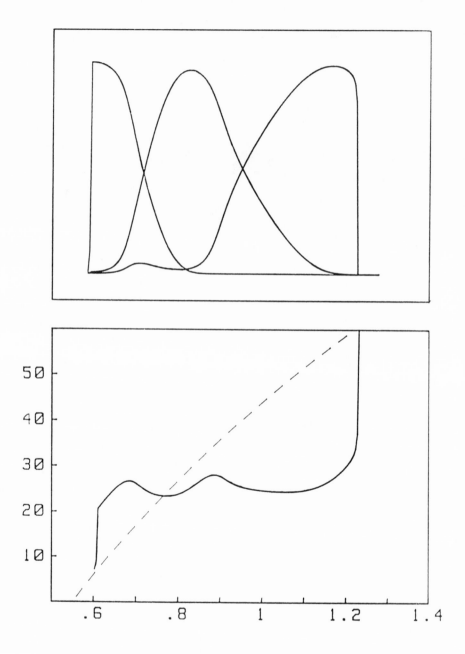

Figure 2

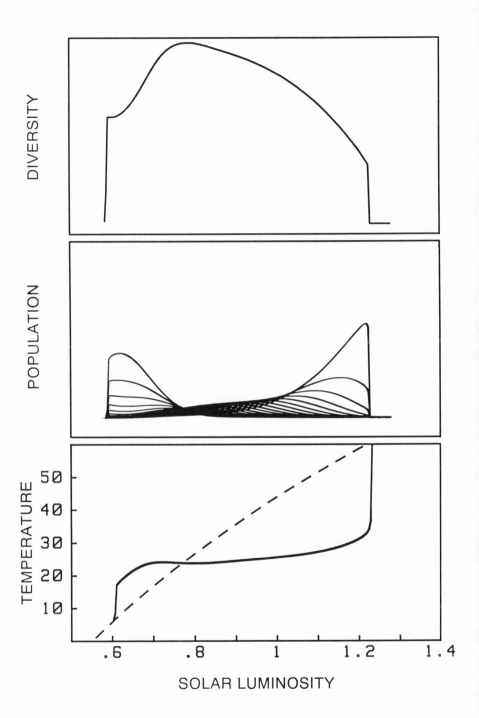

Figure 3

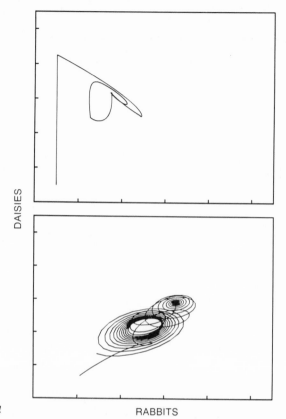

DAISIES

Figure 4   RABBITS

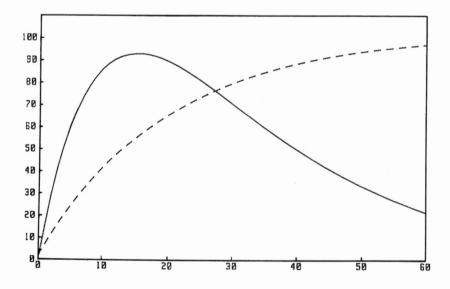

Figure 5

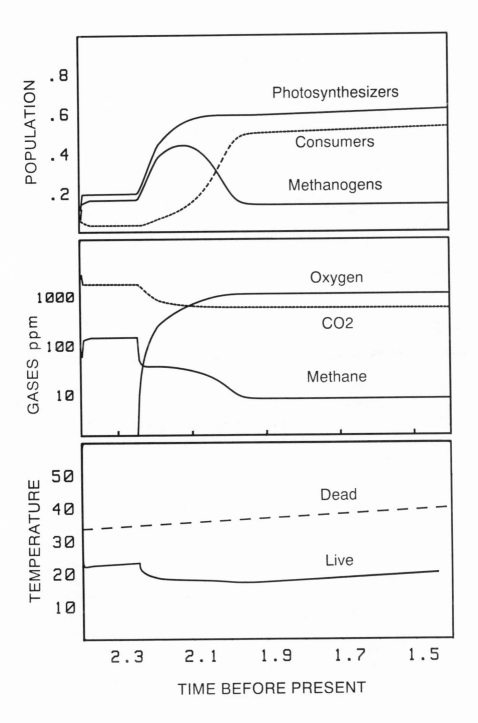

Figure 6

2

LYNN MARGULIS
RICARDO GUERRERO

Two Plus Three Equal One

Individuals Emerge from
Bacterial Communities

The arithmetic of life is not the arithmetic we learn at school. *Mixotricha paradoxa*, a protist that dwells in the hindgut of the devastating Australian drywood termite *Mastotermes darwiniensis*, is one example of the shifting values of the One and the Many. It is one cell but, as can be seen in the inset, many spirochetes and other bacteria compose it (Fig. 1). One, the living individual, is composed of five: one nucleated cell, two spirochete bacteria and other rod bacterium on the surface, and still another endosymbiotic bacterium inside — five autopoietic entities in total equal to one.

Identity is not an object; it is a process with addresses for all the different directions and dimensions in which it moves, and so it cannot so easily be fixed with a single number. We know this in our own lives, for identity card, passport, birth certificate, social security number, driver's license, home address, bank account number, telephone listing, postal code, insurance policy number, national credit rating, all assign us identity. The family dog might recognize us by pheromone, allelochemical, or other trace odorant. We always reinforce our own identity by washing, dressing, exercising, speaking, and interacting with others. In innumerable small ways we remind ourselves daily of who we are and to what we belong.

Minimal communication requires a sender, a signal, and a receiver. In the process of individualization (in which we all always participate), each of us is a sender and a receiver. The list of numbers and actions above are examples of the myriads of signals or integration that unite our component parts into a skin-bounded body and then unite each of us as individuals to our nation and our community. With so many activities, numbers, and relationships, no individual is singular and unchanging. Rather, each individual animal is itself a whole community of organisms and their relationships. That a termite or the protist *Mixotricha paradoxa* is comprised of a community of distinct organisms is clear. But because the members of the community are bounded, it is just as clear that the termite (bounded by exo-skeleton) and *Mixotricha* (bounded by spirochete-studded membrane) are also easily identified as individuals.

In the arithmetic of life, One is always Many. Many often make one, and one, when looked at more closely, can be seen to be composed of many. Conventional arithmetic leads us astray making us think that there are eternal numbers identifying real "things" — things that we tend to think in science are only known when they are numbered. But in life "things" have a different way of adding up. To appreciate the paradoxical value of "one," let us take a closer look at this paradoxical *Mixotricha*.

Spirochetes are, by definition, helically motile bacteria. They must be continuously moving. Motility is absolutely intrinsic to their nature. Some have no connections to others and freely swim about on their own; when single, all spirochetes tend to stay with their food source. But other spirochetes have the ability to attach tightly to larger cells. When they do so, they become the oars that allow the larger cell, a protist, to swim away. Without its undulating spirochetes, the naked protists would just stay put, but, with the spirochetes attached and undulating, the protists become motile and swim away in search of food for the entire complex.

Now, let us take a closer look at Fig. 2, a drawing of the spirochete-host community in the termite, and Figure 1, the drawing of

51

Mixotricha. Static preparations of *Mixotricha* observed through the light microscope and thin sections of *Mixotricha* studied on the video screen of the electron microscope permit us to reconstruct the final organism. *Mixotricha* is actually made up of five different live components, each present in a range of population numbers. The largest of these is the *Mixotricha* nucleocytoplasm (1). The others are two surface spirochetes, one a *Treponema* (2) and the other unidentified (3), an anchor rod bacterium (4), and an internal bacterium (5). So *Mixotricha* is an example of symbiosis in which organisms of completely different species, once separated, have come together and formed a completely new entity, a new entity with markedly different properties from the organisms that compose it. The scientific name of the new entity is *Mixotricha paradoxa*, which means "paradoxically mixed-up hairs."

This new entity, this swimming protist, is a good example of an "emergent domain." The first "emergent property" is motility of the complex, and a subsequent property is the ability to digest wood.

Mixotricha can break down wood, which is composed of the long polymeric carbon compounds cellulose and lignin. The protist probably converts wood chips to a two-carbon compound, acetate, first by breaking down cellulose to sugars and lignin to phenols, then to acetate. Acetate, probably the product of protist digestion, is a soluble chemical product that is taken up across the gut membrane of the termite host, *Mastotermes darwiniensis*, to be digested later. The five types of symbiotic organisms that together make up *Mixotricha* are required in concert to generate acetate from wood chips; *Mixotricha*, the emergent domain, displays a new property. The sugars and even smaller organic compounds like acetate are substances that for the host termite, resemble cash in the streets; they are taken up immediately. They would never have entered the animal's intestinal cells prior to the establishment of these symbiotic associations.

Another termite, *Pterotermes occidentis*, always has billions of organisms living inside each "individual" insect. These termites (Fig. 3) live in an ecosystem of the Sonoran Desert of northern Mexico, southeastern California, and southern Arizona; the only place they are ever found. The termites with the brown heads are the soldiers, the white animals are insects. Another variety of termite, *Kalotermes schwartzii.*, from southern Florida, is shown in Fig. 4. The first drop from the hindgut of either of these termites is always fluid excrement. In these kinds of drywood-eating termites (there are about 323 species of them), every one of the healthy "individuals" harbors at all times an internal microbial community. Although the details can vary, an enormous microbial community is absolutely necessary — termites by themselves are totally incapable of digesting wood until the wood chips are broken down to sugars and acetate by these subvisible microorganisms.

The spirochetes that inhabit termite guts, like all spirochetes, are helically motile bacteria with a distinctive ultrastructure; for example, they all have periplasmic flagella (Fig. 5). Incredible differences in detail can be seen in each of these different kinds of spirochetes, but only at the ultrastructural level, i.e., with an electron microscope. Note that the spirochetes can't tell their head-end from their back-end; they go equally happily forward and backward (Fig. 6). This trait, however, changes with attachment, so the process of attachment itself produces each emergent property. In the background of Fig. 7 are many other kinds of small bacteria, including small spirochetes. The thin spirochetes may be a hundred times as skinny as the fat ones; some differ in width and length by a factor of 100. All kinds of spirochetes are found in ponds, muds, the mouths of people, and other habitats. The large ones are particularly amenable to study, but the small ones have generated far more interest because some of them have been identified as the "causative agent" in syphilis. Traditionally, only the tiny ones — the treponemes — have been studied.

If the diet or the ambient temperature of the host termites is changed, the microbial community structure also changes. For example, if the temperature is elevated to about 30 degrees Celsius, "bloom" occurs; that is, over a few hours the growth of some members of the community increases at the expense of others. These spirochetes can reach prodigious numbers in a few days, yet all the population explosions occur inside a drop of hindgut fluid within the termite. The gut may become completely packed with spirochetes.

Spirochetes tend to attach; they tend to attach and stay at the surface, feeding at the surface, but they always continue to move. They move, they attach, and the fact that they attach and move has led to many different varieties of emergent phenomena. When spirochetes attach to other organisms such as termite protists, the emergent properties are those of association, of the spirochete plus the other organism to which it has attached. Neither the host nor the spirochete had these properties before. For example, after contact specific "attachment sites" develop and the protist-spirochete complex together begins to move.

Bundles of spirochetes attached to each other can be formed. The bundles induce the entire population of spirochetes to go together in one direction. Therefore, group movement here is an emergent property of this domain, the domain of merger of two different kinds of organisms: the protist plus a set of spirochetes. The host, previously sessile and passive, now literally becomes "animated."

Many individual spirochetes move, but the emergent property is a massive wavelike motion. We know this wave is composed of many different individual spirochetes because if we simply add water they all move every which way, so their synchronized movement is the result of a packing problem; it occurs because they are all packed together.

When the spirochetes move together in a very close space, the emergent wavelike motion is likely to increase the probability of interactions of host protists with wood particles. The wood-digesting host protist then takes advantage of the incessant spirochete movement. The protists have other "moving hairs" which are not spirochetes, but undulipodia. The moving hairs here are just like the tails in the ultrastructure of sperm cells in that they both have the [9 (2) + 2] arrangement of microtubules (Fig. 5).

Let us direct our attention for a moment to the tails of sperm cells. By themselves they have intrinsic motility, a helical motility. We believe sperm tails have their origin from spirochetes. Although to be complete they require the rest of the cell, the tails can temporarily move (for about an hour) without the rest of the cell. The sperm tails when seen with the electron microscope have the [9 (2) + 2] structure of small tubules, and each of the microtubules is made of the same protein we have in our nerve cells. In fact, this microtubule protein (called tubulin) is one of the dominant proteins of the nervous system of all animals. This is not surprising because the same microtubule structures seen in sperm tails are also found in all axons and dendrites of nerve cells. In nerve cells these microtubules are called neurotubules. When microtubules are packed in a [9 (2) + 2] array, they are called undulipodia (Fig. 5). We suspect that spirochetes became undulipodia about 1.2 billion years ago in warm, wet, crowded scenes such as that in Fig. 8.

Let us look again at the surface of the wood-eating protists in the termite hindgut. In addition to the undulipodia, if you look carefully you can see double rows of surface symbiotic bacteria of a different kind. Externally they are similar to the surface bacteria in *Mixotricha* (Fig. 1). Here, with yet a different protist, we see what looks like an individual with about 200,000 undulipodia. Electron microscopy shows that each undulipodium is composed of the same [9 (2) + 2] structure of the sperm tail. Wood enters the protist via its rear end, rather like a garbage truck. The protists swim forward in one direction and the moving, attached spirochetes aid in the delivery of wood chips into the back of its body.

In conclusion, let us return to *Mixotricha*. *Mixotricha*, which appears to be a single organism, as we saw is composed of five different kinds acting together: the emergent domain in *Mixotricha* itself. *Mixotricha* bears half a million surface spirochetes of the *Treponema* type. But the surface also bears large and casually associated spirochetes; there are probably about two hundred of them on each *Mixotricha*. In addition, there are half a million associated small *Treponema* spirochetes and its own undulipodia, four of them: three forward and one trailing. So *Mixotricha*, with its four types of regularly associated bacteria, has surface spin, yet another emergent property.

Discussion

Evan Thompson   Actually, it seems to me that there are so many layers of emergence going on here that the domains overlap. Perhaps the "domain," as opposed to the "properties" of motility and digestion, should be defined as the set of relationships of *Mixotricha* within the ecology of the hindgut, since the acetate excreted by the protists from cellulose and lignin is what is digested by the termite.

Lynn Margulis   But *Mixotricha* is an individual — its components are bound to each other. Thus we give one name to the emergent organism composed of five. Humans are 10 percent dry-weight microbes, but we don't name ourselves after these microbes; we think of our identity as a separate domain. So *Mixotricha*, rather than the whole hindgut, seems to me to be the emergent phenomenon. "Cow" is the name we give to an extraordinary complex which ingests grass, yet even though the cellular digestion is entirely microbial, we still can call the "individual" a cow just as in the case here we say two (spirochetes) plus three (other types of cells) equals one, *Mixotricha*.

Thompson   Yes, but that's my point. You have several overlapping layers of emergent domains here, so it's difficult, especially for someone who is ignorant of microbiology, to keep track of them all. Small rod bacteria, attached surface spirochetes, loosely associated spirochetes, what seems to be emergent is not merely *Mixotricha* considered as an entity, but the entity plus all these interactions within the larger niche that make the symbiotic associations possible. Perhaps, though, that is a higher level of emergence here.

Margulis   Lacking *Mixotricha*, the termite itself dies, whereas *Mixotricha* doesn't function without the termite. We have here a typical biological example of layer upon layer, of what Dr. Gail Fleischaker would call "nestedness."

Francisco Varela   Lynn, what you have shown here is so clear and breathtakingly elegant that I think there's very little that can be added. But, for the sake of precision, I would like to say that "the domain," if the word is worth anything, is multicellularity, and that within that domain you can also speak of different cells coming together. So now there is a possibility of talking about, not just separate cells coming together, but multiple cells coming together to form a higher entity; that is "the domain" that I would describe as multicellularity of multigenomicity, if you wish.

Now, within that domain there are all sorts of individual cases, but notice that within the cases, as Evan was saying, you can have multiple levels of entanglement. But I don't think that would be worth the name of "domain," other than the emergent phenomenon of multicellularity that gives rise to the emergent properties you have shown: motility, digestion, whatever.

All of this is actually what Humberto Maturana and I talked about when we discussed second order autopoiesis. It's the same thing; it probably gives rise to a domain of phenomena that otherwise is not possible. What I do disagree with is the way in which you describe it. To say that *Mixotricha* is a domain is not, I think, properly capturing the idea that a domain is a possibility which can be realized in multiple ways. What you have shown is one case of the domain of ulticellularity, that of *Mixotricha*, one that is beautiful.

Margulis   I want to show you something else about emergent properties. A free-swimming spirochete lacks attachment sites. But in the spirochete which has spent some time firmly attached, there are fancy attachment sites on the host, and equally fancy attachment sites on the spirochete. These two different sets of attachment sites are emergent properties of the association; without regular association they never occur. They never occur in the host alone, and they never occur in the spirochete alone. The attachment sites then are not a domain, but emergent properties.

"Attachment-site-fanciness" is an emergent property. Do you agree?

Varela   Yes.

Ricardo Guerrero   I think it's relevant here to explain something about individuality. This morning I spoke to Jim Lovelock about the problem of instrumentation. Our brains can detect and measure some things. If we are using a gas chromatograph, we can measure concentrations of molecules moving through a gas, but we cannot

TWO PLUS THREE EQUAL ONE

measure radiation. Even though radiation is another expression of molecules, or in this case protons, we can't measure that explosion or any kind of radiation with a gas chromatograph. To measure radiation a specific measuring apparatus is required. With different instruments, different aspects of reality are measured. We see clearly in the example of *Mixotricha* the nature of individuality. You would probably think, looking at *Mixotricha paradoxa*, and at the termite intestinal bacteria, that the bacteria and *Mixotricha* are very similar—they are both microorganisms—but, no, for we humans composed of animal cells are not very different from *Mixotricha*. The genetic distance between *Mixotricha* and our animal cells is far less than that between *Mixotricha* and the spirochete, or the other bacteria in the termite. In genetic organization, our cells are all complexes like *Mixotricha*, in that our eukaryotic cells are similar symbiotic composites.

Margulis Animals are all comprised of complex cells with components having separate origins, like *Mixotricha*. We are absolutely not like prokaryotic bacteria.

Guerrero Internal movement, transportation activities inside the cell, appears first in the protists. Bacteria don't have it. So individuality, paradoxically a product of complexity and compositeness, also appears first in protists. *Mixotricha* is on the early line to individuality; we are on this same line. Bacteria do not belong to species in the sense that we usually give to this concept. Bacteria commonly interchange genetic material. Bacteria are transitorily bounded by a so-called cell membrane, but cell membranes of bacteria are quite different from those of eukaryotes. As Antonio Lazcano has said, DNA has different forms such as insertion sequences, transposition, plasmids, etc. In bacteria, that is, in prokaryotic cells in general, the unit is the community, the genetic community. These organisms interchange any kind of information if they are present at the same time and the same place. They are not individuals in the way that animals are; their parts are scattered.

Bacteria are completely different from these complex communities we recognize as protists. We, as animals, are individuals like the well-integrated *Mixotricha*. Individuality is a derived characteristic, it is not an essential characteristic of life. Life occurred in its bacterial form as a community exchanging genetic information as far back as 3.5 billion years ago. Yet only 1.2 billion years ago did some community of component bacteria merge and remain integrated up to the present.

This complex created individuality, a different reality, and we, animals, and plant cells—all eukaryotes—are the consequence of this.

Let us consider another example, a community of bacteria in a small red lake in Spain. The cause of the redness is a bloom of chromatium, a purple sulfur bacterium that, like the spirochetes, is also motile. In the overall community of the lake, this bacterium is absolutely necessary, but it is the population, not the individual, that is necessary. Any individual is entirely dispensable. The population of bacteria in the lake has certain characteristics exactly analogous to those of any animal, for instance, a cow. A cow does not reproduce using all its cells. The reproducing part of a cow is limited to eggs in the ovaries. Only very few cells can reproduce and thus maintain the species through time. The cow has a shape, just as the lake has a shape. The cow's shape is somewhat more fixed; in the case of the phototrophic bacteria, the shape of the population is the shape of the lake. The lake is like a "liquid animal" in shape. The bacterial community has layers, and each of them is a population. One part of this community is composed of cells which divide very actively and therefore produce more cells. The chromatium cells fall towards the bottom of the lake; their remains feed other bacteria. All of this activity maintains the "liquid organism's" physiology, its cycling. So bacteria are not acting as individuals but intrinsically as a community of interacting members, which are different populations. Some of the cells reproduce single bacteria, but the entity of interest that makes sense is the community. An "individual" is intrinsically complex and intrinsically divisible. It sounds paradoxical, but in the prokaryotic world (i.e., all life until a mere 1.2 billion years ago) nothing smaller than a community can be an individual. The integrating mechanisms of the members of the community make the individual. Bacteria, prokaryotes in general, can practically interchange genes or other materials among themselves. "Individuals"

59

emerge when this interchange is restricted; the membrane toughens, the genes become packaged into a membrane bounded nucleus, and our world of sex and death emerges.

Margulis   I'd like to clarify Ricardo's comments for people who are not familiar with bacteria. Imagine if John Todd went out for coffee and drank some genes, drank up someone else's genes so when he comes back John Todd, who was blond when he went out, now has Nancy Todd's brunette hair. I mean, he simply changes his genetic makeup by eating; this is what bacteria do all the time.

We have trouble imagining the promiscuity, the genetic laxity of bacteria that consume genes as if they were food. Genes for bacteria are replicating food. Bacteria exchange genetic material in a way that is completely different from our experience. "Individuals" like *Mixotricha paradoxa* form when a temporary end is put to bacterial promiscuity, and this kind of gene exchange is restricted. Most paradoxical of all is that an "individual" is exactly not that—it is intrinsically a complex, a community. The "individuality" of an organism derives from the tightness of the integrating mechanisms that bind the members of the community. Ricardo's lake is a liquid organism, and we are all skin-bounded microbial communities. Two types of spirochetes, two types of omnibacteria (one cortical and one internal), and one nucleocytoplasm do not make five microbes. Biologists can't add: two plus two plus one do not make five; they make one paradoxical *Mixotricha*. And in our ineluctable tendency to discriminate, identify, name, and make entities into signals with meanings, we create "the individual" in Fig. 1, Señor *Mixotricha*. Two spirochetes plus three other microbes make one Mixotricha with its emergent properties: it can sense, it moves forward, it can take in wood through its hind end, and it can produce the acetate which the termite finds delicious. Two lack these properties, the other three also lack these properties, but since five together have them, five is equal to one!

The bacteria taken together on Earth are probably one Gaian sort of entity. They form one network entity. When we deal with bacteria we are dealing with the population, not with the "individual." "Pure cultures" of bacteria, that is, cultures in Petri-dish concentration camps, are just bacteria whose social and community behavior has been reduced to the level that we investigators can manage. But we miss the point. The point of the bacteria is that they are enormous computers and that all the terminals are connected to one another. This idea of the new bacteriology has been beautifully explained in the writings of Sorin Sonea.[1] So, as you see, it all adds up.

Notes

1. Sorin Sonea and Maurice Panisset, 1983, *A New Bacteriology*, (Boston: Jones & Bartlett).

FIGURE LEGENDS

FIGURE 1. The "large microbe" *Mixotricha paradoxa* is comprised of two types of spirochetes [one large unidentified one (s) and smaller treponemes (t)], surface rod bacteria, (b), and spherical endosymbionts (e) associated with its endoplasmic reticulum (er). The "individual" organism with its nucleus (n), undulipodia (u), and axostyle (a), has formed from at least five and perhaps as many as seven different types of "individual" bacteria. The periphery, or cortex (c) of *Mixotricha paradoxa* with its surface associates is seen at higher manifestation in the inset. (Drawing by Christie Lyons)

FIGURE 2. Microbial community (mc) that digests wood in the Sonoran desert termite *Pterotermes occidentis.* Fragments of four termite intestinal cells bounded by chitin are seen on top (T); below protists and bacteria busily transform indigestible cellulose to acetate and other products easily assimilated by the animal. (Drawing by Christie Lyons)

FIGURE 3. Complex community of phototrophic bacteria and their protist and other associates in a thin, densely populated layer at the surface in Lake Ciso. (Drawing by Christie Lyons)

FIGURE 4. Spirochetes showing periplasmic flagella (A) and (B); undulipodia showing microtubules in the [9 (2) + 2] array. (Drawing by Christie Lyons)

FIGURE 5. Spirochete that cannot tell its head from its tail. (Drawing by J.S. Alexander)

FIGURE 6. Spirochetes (s) in the midst of udulipodia (u). Scene similar to that drawn in Figure 2, the magnification is 75,000 times in this electron micrograph of the hindgut of the dry wood-eating termite *Reticulitermes hesperus*, from California. (Photograph by David G. Chase)

FIGURE 7. Certain symbiotic spirochetes became so firmly attached to the surface of other organisms that some of them, we think, even evolved into udulipodia. This concept of "spirochetes becoming udulipodia" is drawn by Christie Lyons.

FIGURE 8. Although the anterior and posterior ends of free-swimming spirochetes are indistinguishable (see Figure 5) after attachment to hosts are regularized the attached end (a) of spirochete cells become flattened and modified as seen in this negatively stained preparation (A). The flagella (f) of the spirochete (s) and a bit of the protist (p), part of the attachment can be seen in this spirochete that has pulled off its "docking site" during preparation. By transmission electron microscopy the protist host (p) the attachment structure itself (a) and the spirochete are seen (B). In some cases two spirochetes on a single protist (here a pyrosonymphid) share a single attachment or "docking site (C). Electron micrographs of the hindgut of the same kind of termite shown in Figure 6 were taken by David G. Chase. Magnification in (A) and (B) is 75,000; in (C) it is 112,000.

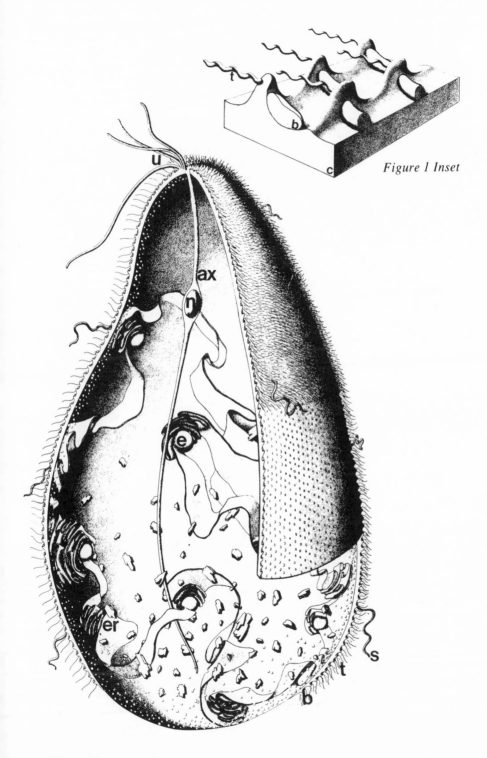

Figure 1 Inset

Figure 1

Figure 2

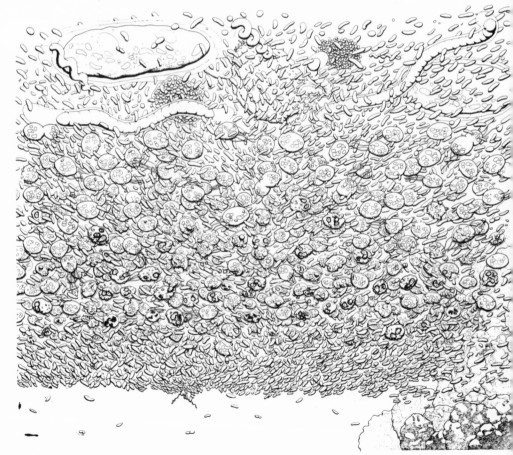

Figure 3

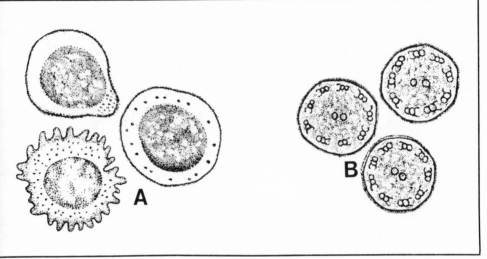

Figure 4 A   *Figure 4 B*

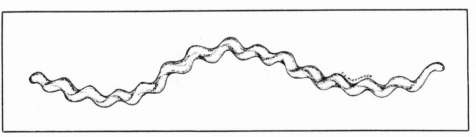

Figure 5

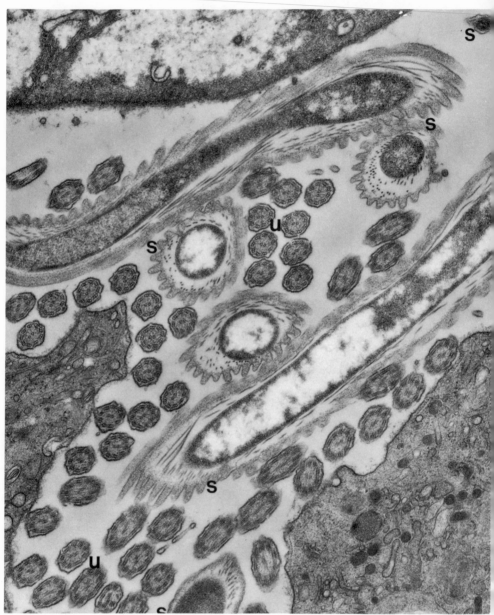

Figure 6

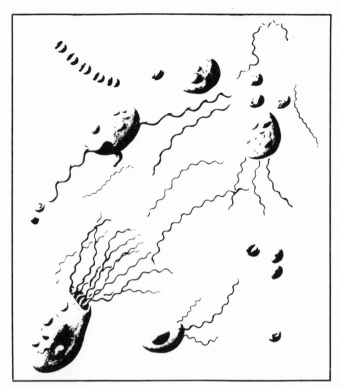

Figure 7

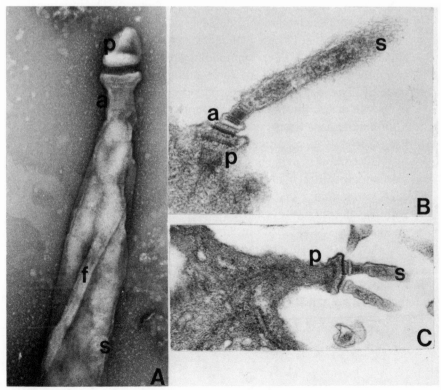

Figure 8

3

FRANCISCO J. VARELA
MARK ANSPACH

Immu-knowledge

The Process of Somatic Individuation

I. A Change of Metaphors

The standard role attributed to immunity is to protect the "self" from the assault of foreign infections. The immune system is supposed to produce defenses against invaders, and surveillance cells that kill the pathogens and keep the self from foreignness or non-self. Every immunology text will start by defining immunology as the study of such immune responses. A recent issue of *Time* magazine carried a cover story on immunity complete with diagrams of platoons of troops ready for battle.

Immunological discourse is centered around military metaphors just as strongly as cognitive science was once centered around the (digital) computer metaphor. Our purpose here is to introduce a substantially different metaphor and conceptual framework for the study of immunity, one that puts the emphasis on the "cognitive" abilities of immune events. Although the term cognitive will undoubtedly sound too strong to many people, it seems useful to introduce here, if for nothing else than as a sharp contrast to the military framework of immunity as defense. For the time being let us agree to use the word cognitive in the same (vague) sense that can be applied to other biological processes such as brains and ecosystems, and not exclusively to mental and linguistic human processes.

The alternative view we are suggesting can be likened to the notion of Gaia claims that the atmosphere and earth crust cannot be explained in their current configurations (gas composition, sea chemistry, mountain shapes, and so on) without their direct partnership with life on Earth. We all are used to thinking that the biosphere is constrained by and adapted to its terrestrial environment. But the Gaia hypothesis proposes that there is a circularity here: this terrestrial environment is itself the result of what the biosphere did to it. As Lovelock puts it metaphorically: we live in the breath and bones of our ancestors. As a result the entire biosphere/Earth "Gaia" has an identity as a whole, an adaptable and plastic unity, acquired through time in this dynamic partnership between life and its terrestrial environment.

We are not concerned here with the scientific merits of this idea, which Jim discusses elsewhere in this volume. Let us transpose the metaphor to immunobiology, and suggest that the body is like Earth, a textured environment for diverse and highly interactive populations of individuals. The individuals in this case are the white blood cells or lymphocytes which constitute the immune system. The lymphocytes are a diverse collection of species, each differentiated by the peculiar molecular markers or antibodies its members advertise on their membrane surfaces. Like the living species of the biosphere, these lymphocyte populations stimulate or inhibit each other's growth. Like species in an ecosystem, they are also enormous generators of diversity: the antibodies and other molecules produced by lymphocytes are by far (a millionfold) the most varied collection of molecules produced in the body, and there are exquisite mechanisms to assure the constant change and diversity of those present at all times.

The lymphocytes' network exists in harmony with their natural ecology, the somatic environment of the body, which shapes which lymphocyte species exist. But as in Gaia, the existing lymphocytes alter in a radical way every molecular profile in the body. Thus, as adults, our molecular identity is none other than the immune/body partnership shaped throughout life, in a unique configuration. Like a microcosmic version of Gaia.

Let us now try and give substance to this alternative view of immune events, by shifting from a metaphorical mode into an analysis of the way in which military metaphors became dominant in immunology and the problems that such a view raised.

II. The Inescapable Cognitive Side of Immune Phenomena

In fact, even to fulfill a defensive role the immune system must exhibit properties which are typically cognitive. To start with, there must be some form of "recognition" of molecular profiles: the shapes of the intruding agents, or antigens in the jargon of immunology, the "foreignness" capable of endangering the bodily integrity of the subject. Next, it must have a learning to recognize and defend itself against the new antigens. Then there must be a memory in order to retain this new form once encountered.

Recognition, learning, and memory are the kinds of processes and mechanisms discussed in current connectionism or network approaches to cognitive mechanisms. Such models are normally linked to the brain as their biological counterpart. We argue that the immune system is a cognitive network, not only because of properties which it shares with the brain, but also, more interestingly, because in both cases we have similar (or at least comparable) global properties of biological networks giving rise to cognitive behavior as emergent properties. This makes the immune system a significant voice in the current investigations of basic cognitive mechanisms.

This discussion would not be possible without new results and trends in experimental immunobiology which emphasize the network side of things. This view entails important shifts in immunological practice and applications. We can illustrate this by the well-established observation of the "Promethean" character of the immune system: it can respond to antigens it has never seen, including those which are man-made and hence not even explainable by some form of evolutionary adaptation. If one were to think of the immune system merely as a genetically programmed repertoire of responses disconnected one from the other, it would be necessary to find a specific response to unpredictable events.

70

Briefly, the immune system would be the kind of general problem solver which artificial intelligence has concluded after years of frustrating trials to be an impossibility. Instead, immunology points to very specific processes through which this network operates. We want to show that this network view naturally leads to the notion of an autonomous "cognitive" self at the molecular level as the proper view of immune events.

III. The Emergence of the Immunological Double Bind

The first immunological theories confronted these cognitive issues by ignoring them. The basic assumption was that all foreign molecules or antigens would act as instructions to form the corresponding antibodies against them. Instructionist theories viewed the immune system as entirely directed from the outside — a heteronomous process, since antibodies would operate like molecular playdough. The idea was strongly motivated by the apparent completeness of the immune responses, including those to artificial substances, as demonstrated in 1912 by Landsteiner. These observations made it literally inconceivable that the system could have all of that inside; it would be too wasteful. Things must by necessity have to be guided from the antigenic side directly.

In these theories "the antibody molecule was considered like universal glue, able to interact with any antigenic form, to take its complementary form, to remove the antigen, and to keep the memory of the 'learned' configuration" (Urbain 1986). The quotation marks around the word learning are significant here. Since the cognitive nature of the process is inevitable one must refer to some sort of learning, but, at the same time, the process involved is evidently far from cognitive. Otherwise the paper on which one's signature appears could be said to have learned. Furthermore the lack of cognitive capacities is more evident in that a reference to an individuality for which the discrimination and learning happens is completely absent. "These theories contained their own death since such a universal dough cannot discriminate between self and non-self antigens" (Urbain 1986, 58).

This touches the key issue. It is by now classical in immunology to talk about the self/non-self discrimination. This arises

71

inevitably since the immune system acts in its discriminative capacities inside a body. This simple fact has deep consequences. Until recently, as we will discuss below, immunology has followed the same tendency as other areas of cognitive science, considering any form of cognitive capacity some form of information processing. Information is supposed to come in, and the system is supposed to act adequately on it so as to produce an appropriate response. Such input/output relations, usually conceived in terms of internal programs for their "information" processing, are the core of heteronomous approaches — i.e., viewing a system as outer-directed (Varela 1979).

This heteronomous scheme has been faithfully followed by immunologists. There is an antigen that comes in, and the appropriate response is the production of an antibody, with the resulting removal of the antigen. But what is going to determine how the antibody is formed? Unlike in the nervous system, there are no spatially located sensorial organs in the immune system. Antibodies circulate freely inside the organism, and they have as much chance of meeting molecules which belong to the organism tissues (self) as of meeting antigens (non-self). Briefly stated, antibody recognition makes it inevitable that there must be a way to recognize what has to be recognized.

If the reader thinks things are getting a little too complicated, we agree: they are. But it is important to see well that the inevitable need to postulate some form of knowing what needs to be known makes a simple heteronomous operation for immunity, that is, an automatic response to something coming from outside, very unsatisfactory. Without anticipating too much what we will develop later, we shall see that recent immunology (1950- 1970) has tried, with little success, to circumvent this difficulty while still keeping the heteronomous viewpoint, and that a more satisfying solution demands a more radical revision towards understanding the immune system as an autonomous network. But let's go step-by-step and examine a little more precisely what "recognition" could mean in this context.

To say that an antibody "recognizes" an antigen means that it binds chemically to it, and by so doing neutralizes it. Admirable economy when the molecules in question are foreign molecules, and not ones which are essential components of the organism. This simple logic has been the reason why immunologists have excluded a priori the possibility that antibodies could attach to self molecules without triggering consequences typical of autoimmune diseases. Outside of these pathological conditions the organism normally does not manifest deleterious immune reactions against its own tissues. This is the phenomenon of tolerance identified in 1900 by Ehrlich as horror autotoxicus.

One important idea established gradually was that the recognition of unknown antigens can be to some important extent based on the imprecision of the mechanism itself, that is, on the fact that an antibody can bind with varying degrees of affinity to a large spectrum of molecular shapes. Thus a repertoire of 10^5 kinds of antibodies is sufficient to make the tadpole live, while man possesses a repertoire of more than 10^9 varieties and is also viable. In other words there are various ways of being complete for the task performed by the immune system. This makes the self/non-self issue much more complex.

Double discrimination, double recognition: it is necessary to know who is a non-self antigen before knowing which one it is; logically to recognize non-self entails knowing what self is. The difficulty is that, as we have said, recognition entails destruction, a diabolical predicament that can be summarized thus: "The classical theories demand on the one hand the comparison that differentiates between self and non-self structures, while, on the other hand, it imposes the ignorance of the existence of self or the threat of immunological self-destruction" (Coutinho et al. 1984, 152). We would like to call this predicament the immunological double bind: one cannot defend without recognizing, one cannot recognize without destroying. Like the U.S. policy in Vietnam of "destroying to save," one is faced with two incompatible constraints linked in an inextricable fashion, as in a malicious traffic signal that asserts: IGNORE THIS SIGN.

IV. The Establishment of Current Doctrine (Clonal Selection)

We are now in a position to examine the next important step in

73

immunological thinking to confront the knot evoked above, while still holding tightly to a heteronomous view of the immune system. Clonal Selection Theory was the result of the contributions of Niels Jerne and MacFarland Burnet during the 1950s, and has dominated immunology until recently, much like the symbolic/computational view of cognition has dominated cognitive sciences since that time. It took quite a while for immunology to let go of the grip of instructionist theories, and it did so reluctantly.

The first main idea, due to Jerne, was that of an antibody repertoire that remains in the body permanently. In contrast to instructionist theories, he proposed that antibody production precedes and in a certain sense anticipates the coming of the antigen. At the time, as we have said, this was quite inconceivable. Today we know that there are about 10^{20} antibodies with a high degree of diversity and degeneracy of binding, and the notion of an internal repertoire is no longer in doubt.

It remained to be explained how a collection of antibodies, initially random relative to a given world of antigens, could be shaped by that world. One knows that antigenic encounters leave a trace in the system: the antibodies that bind to it augment in substantial amounts the key aspect of an immune response. In fact it is these sorts of phenomena that eventually will force us to come to grips with cognitive properties, but we aren't there yet. Jerne made the most remarkable suggestion to circumvent this difficulty: he invoked Darwin and natural selection. Even if the antigen does not operate as the blueprint or instruction for the antibody to be formed, it can nevertheless select from those antibodies which were there already and bind to one of them sufficiently, and cause it to increase in numbers. It was then left for M. Burnet to propose a specific mechanism whereby this selective process could be embodied in terms of mere lymphocyte traffic. The basic idea was that every lymphocyte only carries (and can produce) one type of antibody, so that a subclass of lymphocyte families, clones, would link up to each antigen. The contact between antigen and clone leads to the proliferation of the cells of that clone, which then leads to an increased production of antibodies of that particular type, thus neutralizing the incoming antigen (Burnet 1959). In this fashion, the lymphocyte and antibody population evolve under the selective pressure of the antigen. It is not a genetic but an antigenic determination; the name "antigenic determinant" is still in use.

Clonal selection theory, that is, the ensemble of ideas we have evoked, was a brilliant answer to the thorny question of how the immune system operates when faced with unbounded novelty. The cognitive issues here appear under the garb of an evolutionary play. Transposition of one temporal scale to another; transposition also from the outside environment to an organismic inside. Still, the question of self-tolerance has not been answered.

The answer of clonal selection theory to this perennial problem was simple. It postulates that the initial antibody repertoire is not, in fact, complete: it is missing precisely those clones which can recognize self molecules. But this simple solution shifted the initial problem to a new one, since self-recognition could not be explained a priori through genetic mechanisms, as we have already discussed. Thus one could invoke neither genetic process nor selective process in the adult to accomplish this necessary pruning. The only viable solution was to leave this intermediate step to the embryo, where clonal selection theory proposed that anti-self clones had to be deleted. This idea is usually expressed by saying that the organism learns the self/non-self discrimination during ontogeny.

Thus, the old cognitive issues reappear through the window after being chased through the door. The selectionist model is not sufficient by itself; one is still forced to introduce a process of learning to delimit a self, albeit relegated to embryonic life. By which specific mechanisms would this be accomplished? As Burnet says, anti-self clones can be avoided "by assuming that at this stage of embryonic life the antigenic contact leads to cell death" (Burnet 1959, 58). Curious twist of the previous logic: the mechanism that assures the discrimination between self and antigens becomes precisely the opposite of that which later allows discrimination between different antigens. In the second case antigen contact leads to antigen removal. In the first case antigen contact leads to cell removal. The theoretical move here consists of separating the two poles of the immunological double bind, leaving one side of the discrimination to the adult and the other to the embryo. Moreover, the clones to be eliminated in embryonic life are themselves

self-components, and thus self-destruction is implicit in a framework developed to avoid it. Clearly the clumsy fit between these
two contradictory processes is a matter of logical consistency.

Clonal selection provided a rich source of guidance for experimental work. It led Burnet to postulate the possibility of fooling
the immune system by introducing cells into an embryo to render
it tolerant against molecules not normally present. This proved to
be experimentally correct, and it was established clearly that tolerance was learned. However, it was later found that such tolerance is not the exclusive domain of the embryo. The adult also can
be made tolerant, and hence the learning cannot be boxed into a
particular period of time. This already poses difficult questions to
clonal selection theory.

Furthermore, the notion of a complete repertoire except for self-
determinants, is already problematic. This "except for," so inno-
cent, is demonic, if one keeps in mind what we said about the
broad range of molecular profiles to which an antibody binds, and
which is at the base of the notion of completeness in the first place.
The simple notion of anti-self clonal deletion is only simple under
the assumption of antibody specificity, dear at the medical origins
of immunology, and strengthened by vaccination procedures in the
few instances when these work by inducing a narrow class of antibodies against a pathogen. But a rule of the form "one antibody,
one antigen" is certainly wrong. If we were to remove sufficient
clones to have no response to self molecules, this would amount to
depriving the animal of a response to such a huge number of
potential antigens that its completeness would be compromised.
The protective immunity shield would be perforated like a perco-
lator. We thus see that the formula of a complete repertoire "except
for," conceived to solve the dilemma of the two contradictory
forms of recognition necessary for self/non-self discrimination,
ends up in another form of contradiction demanding a precision in
recognition towards self that is incompatible with the assumption
of completeness.

As often happens, over a few decades of dominance the weak-
nesses of the clonal selection theory have become sharper and
sharper. We shall not elaborate this evidence further. But it was the
combination of the theoretical unsatisfactoriness (not always a

concern for immunologists) evoked above, and a few key empirical observations, that opened up in the mid-seventies a new perspective, to which we now turn.

V. *Towards an Autonomous Immune Network*

The dilemmas evoked above remain untouched unless one is willing to give up the original notion of horror autotoxicus. It is clear
today that there are normal circulating antibodies that bind to
many (all?) self molecules, both in embryos and adults. These are
not antibodies that can be conceived as being against self molecules. In fact, these same antibody types when in larger concentration may cause autoimmune diseases, but not in their normal
circulating level.

But there is something even more important that needs to be re-
evaluated. One cannot forget that antibodies that circulate and that
are supposed to carry on the self/non-self discrimination are themselves part of the self. This entails the existence of antibodies
which bind to other antibodies, or anti-idiotypic antibodies in technical jargon. There is now ample evidence that this is indeed so,
and hence that the circulating elements of free-floating-serum
antibodies and the antibodies advertised on cell surfaces are not
separate individual elements or clones, but are tightly meshed with
each other, in what is properly a network organization, an idea
(again!) due for the first time to Jerne in 1974 (Jerne 1974; 1984).
Thus for the first time it was necessary to see that the system could
operate by its own internal dynamics in what Jerne called an
"eigenbehavior" (self-determined behavior) in a dynamical equi-
libria. With these ideas the notion of an heteronomous immune
system was deeply questioned. But it is still necessary to change a
few other theoretical assumptions before we can arrive, in our opinion, at its full consequences. Let us take this one step at a time.

Imagine a foreign antigen entering the organism. A part of the
antigen, its antigenic determinant, will be recognized by certain
antibodies. Let us call this molecular profile E (for epitope in
technical jargon). In the old framework these would be the anti-
E antibodies, ready to eliminate the E-carrying antigen. Recognition happens only between the two of them, and the antigen

keeps its selective role. In the network perspective this private dialogue is no longer valid, first, because this is not a dual but a multiple binding between E and several anti-E antibodies; second, and more significant, now we have to take into account the antibodies which bind to the idiotypes of the anti-E's. These, in turn, will have antibodies which bind to their idiotypes, and so on.... The end result is that we will always run into antibody classes that will at least partially resemble the incoming epitype E. Stated more simply, the antigen will be able to enter the network to the extent that there is already circulating an antibody with a molecular profile sufficiently similar to it, an "internal image." The antigen ceases to be a "determinant," and becomes a small perturbation in an ongoing network. This means that, as with any perturbation in a rich network, the effects of an incoming antigen will be varied and dependent on the entire context of the network, as is now known to be the case.

We see how the heteronomous view of the system is weakened by merely examining the network logic with which it is constructed. Evidently, when the immunologist injects large amounts of an antigen, the immune response seems like a heteronomous response of the system. But the network view brings into focus that this is a highly contrived laboratory situation. Normally we do not receive large amounts of an antigen. We have small amounts of various self molecules that change during life, and a certain amount of molecules we are exposed to through feeding and breathing. In other words, the system is basically an autonomous unit, open to all sorts of modulations which act to slightly change its internal levels, but it is certainly not a machine to produce immune responses. Thus, for example, animals that are not exposed to antigens at all from birth (antigen-free animals) develop an immune system which is quite normal, in blatant contradiction to clonal selection theory, which would have predicted an atrophied immune system.

The next important step to take, then, is to drop the notion of the immune system as a defensive device built to address external events, and to conceive it in terms of self-assertion, establishing a molecular identity by the maintenance of circulation levels of molecules through the entire distributed network. It is here where the

78

immune system acquires its full dignity, and joins in full the current research on biological networks. Like all rich interconnected networks, the immune system generates internal levels through distributed processes. More precisely, a dynamic level of antibody/cell encounters regulates cell numbers and circulating levels of molecular profiles. This idea is strictly parallel to the species network giving an ecosystem an identity within its environment. The interesting consequence, of course, is that such an ecology of lymphocytes exists within the body which it affects and changes, and is affected and changed by.

The mutual dance between immune system and body is the key to the alternative view proposed here, since it is this mutual dance that allows the body to have a changing and plastic identity throughout its life and its multiple encounters. Now the establishment of the system's identity is a positive task, and not a reaction against antigens. The task of specifying the identity is seen here as both logically and biologically primary; the ontogenic antigenic history modulates that process.

This requires that the immune network — like an ecosystem — have a specific learning mechanism. And this mechanism is precisely based on the constant changing of the components of the network by recruitment of new lymphocytes from a resting pool in an active process that reaches up to 20 percent of all lymphocytes in a mouse, for example. It is this ongoing replacement that provides the mechanism for learning and memory, instead of the better-known learning algorithms for neural networks. In fact, from the theoretical standpoint, the flexibility of the immune system resembles the flexibility sought by current research in artificial intelligence known as genetic algorithms or classifier systems (Varela et al. 1988a, b).

Now, the reader is surely aware that this presentation of the immune system is sketchy and simplified. It leaves aside enormously important issues such as the different cell classes that cooperate inside the system (in technical jargon, there are a host of distinctions to be made among lymphocytes: e.g., T-helper, T-suppressor, small and large B, etc.), the incredible complexity of its molecular mechanisms and genetic controls (again, in immune jargon: MHC restriction markers, somatic hypermutations, etc.). But our purpose here is to trace some fundamental conceptual outlines and logical backbones. In this sense it is important to understand properly what is meant today by a network perspective in immunology. The reality of anti-idiotypic antibodies is unquestioned. What is less clear is their importance and significance. In the eyes of most immunologists, immune network means a chain of successive anti-idiotypes. The richness of the network processes and their emergent properties so pervasive elsewhere in the study of complex systems and cognitive science is, however, not well understood. The number of experimental papers which, properly speaking, study immune network problems can be counted with the fingers of one hand, and the theoretical explorations are just beginning (Varela and Coutinho 1991). This depends crucially on the willingness to leave behind the view of immunity as defense even when mediated through idiotype network processes, and, instead, to learn how to see the immune system as establishing a molecular identity, that is, as an autonomous immune system. The accent here is on autonomous — self-production — instead of heteronomous — outer directed.

Let us now turn to see how this autonomous network viewpoint deals with the immunological double bind and the eternal self/ non-self discrimination issue. In fact the answer is quite simple. This approach does what the resolution of any paradox entails: jumping outside of the domain where it is valid. In the case at hand this means that the immune system fundamentally does not (cannot) discriminate between self and non-self. As we have been discussing the ongoing network can only be perturbed or modulated by incoming antigens, thus responding only to that resembling what is already there. So any antigen that perturbs the immune network is by definition an "antigen on the interior," and therefore will only modulate the ongoing network dynamics. Something that cannot do so is simply nonsensical, and may well trigger a "reflexive" immune response, that is, one produced by quasi-automatic processes which are only peripheral to the network itself. The old self/non-self discrimination becomes, in this light, a self/ nonsense distinction.

Normally, antigens come in through food or air intake, and will be regulated by the multiple loops impinging on them; thus low

80

levels of both the antigens and the binding antibodies will be created. This is precisely what happens with self components. All during development, self molecules interact with the immune components in such a way that their levels are kept within bounds because there is an ongoing immune activity incorporating them. Thus, for example, the level of renin, a normally existing hormone, can be shown to be under the regulation of the multiple antibodies normally present in the individual's immune system. Notice that these ongoing phenomena need not be (and most generally are not) a matter of stability; there is too much variety and replacement of components to be so. It is rather a matter of viability, a process that moves along some constantly changing trajectory but that, nevertheless, never goes over certain limits (such as explosive amounts of one antibody type for example). In this sense the immune system, unlike the nervous system, is more a matter of constrained patterns of change, like the weather, than of a few stable nodes acquired through experience, as is typical of neural-network models. This is what we mean by a positive assertion of a molecular identity: what we are in the molecular domain and what our immune system is relative to each other as two co-evolving processes. Again, we are squarely here in what seems like a re-enactment of Gaia inside the body.

The reader used to thinking of immunity as defense may be getting impatient. Surely, he says, you must be joking. For instance, if we have a weakened immunity as in AIDS, we are immediately ravaged by pathogens. To be sure, the system is also able to mount an immune response against infection. This will happen when the antigen enters too quickly, or in too large an amount, and triggers specific mechanisms to mount an immune response, including inflammation at the wound site. But these mechanisms are, interestingly, mostly independent of the network processes just described, and it is almost exclusively this "reflex" immune reactivity that has been the concern of classical immunology.

The point is not to deny that defense is possible, but to see it as a limiting case of something more fundamental: individual molecular identity. In fact, multicellular life is possible without immune defense, as in invertebrates. Defensive responses, the center of attention in medical immunology, are secondary acquisitions, much like defensive/avoidance reactions in neural behavior are necessary later variants of the more fundamental task of motion/ relationship in multicellular life. Or in the Gaian metaphor, certainly the stability and plasticity of the eco/biosphere has been remarkably successful in coping with, say, large meteoric impacts. But such events were rare, and it seems odd to say that ecosystems evolved because of those events. To say that immunity is fundamentally defense is as distorted as to say that the brain is fundamentally about defense avoidance. Certainly we do defend and escape attack, but this hardly does justice to what cognition must be about, i.e., being alive with flexibility.

VI. Remarks on the Future

The implications of this alternative view are multifarious, but for the sake of brevity let us emphasize three of special significance in our own current work:

1. RESEARCH QUESTIONS: This viewpoint suggests new questions about the dynamics of immune events, e.g., population dynamics, network nonlinearities and emergent properties, connectivity issues, and mechanisms of learning. The number of published papers addressing directly such network questions can (literally) be counted with the fingers of one hand. See Lundqvist et al. (1989) for an example.

2. CLINICAL QUESTIONS: This viewpoint suggests some alternative ways to address old problems in medicine such as autoimmunity. In fact, if this Gaian viewpoint is correct, every molecular profile in the body is under immune regulation and could be manipulated in principle. For more on this see Huetz et al. (1988).

3. MACHINE LEARNING: This viewpoint suggests specific mechanisms through which a complex network is capable of adaptive learning in a changing environment. Such algorithms can naturally be lifted and embodied in artificial devices, thus providing artificial intelligence with another biological source of metaphors beyond neural networks. See Varela et al. (1988b) for more on this.

VII. Coda

We have been following the conceptual movement of immunological thinking, from its instructionist inception, through clonal
selection, into a modern network perspective. This research logic
is inseparable from cognitive issues. It is in fact fascinating that,
in this light, the immune network takes a place beside neural networks as a source of both mechanisms and explanations for basic
cognitive phenomena such as recognition, learning, memory, and
adaptability. If one accepts that connectionism and artificial networks are a valid research alternative in cognitive science then, for
the very same reasons, immune activities are cognitive phenomena. We are fully aware however that many would prefer to keep
the word cognitive exclusively for phenomena that involve language and reasoning in humans or machines. We fully acknowledge that this use of cognitive is a defensible one, but it seems
equally defensible to see these "higher" processes in continuity
with "simpler" ones such as those studied by connectionists and
exhibited by immune networks. We are not interested in the trivial
semantic issue, but in the underlying conceptual issues raised by
immune events.

Immunology is about to emerge from a long dominance resulting from its original sin of having been born from the medicine of
infectious diseases, and thus having vaccinations as its main paradigm, an heteronomous view par excellence. This is happening
just at the time that the cognitive sciences are waking up from the
dominance of having the digital computer as their main metaphor.
If we are willing to follow the central importance of the autonomy
of process in both these biological networks, neural and immune,
they can teach us how we think with our entire body.

A NOTE ON FURTHER READING

The ideas presented here have been discussed in more detail elsewhere. For the biological-conceptual motivation see Vaz and Varela
(1978), Coutinho et al, (1984), Varela and Coutinho (1991). For the

cognitive-modelling side see Varela, (1979), Varela et al., (1988, a, b.). In particular, this article is partly adapted from a document originally drafted by Mark Anspach, whom we heartily thank for his diligent clarifications. A presentation to The Learning Conference IV (Big Sur, CA) on October 1 and 2, 1988, and to The Reality Club (New York City) on October 5, 1988 raised a number of interesting points which helped to clarify this draft. Special thanks to Paul Ryan for his detailed comments. A similar version of these ideas has been published in J. Brockman (ed.), *The Reality Club*, vol.2, Phoenix Press, New York, 1989.

ACKNOWLEDGMENTS

None of this work would have been possible without the fruitful collaboration with my friend Antonio Coutinho, head of the Unité d'Immunbiologie at the Pasteur Institute. Any credit for inspiration to be found here should be shared by him in full.

Financial support for this work was provided by the Fondation de France (Chaire Scientifique to FV) and a grant from the Prince Trust Fund.

REFERENCES

Burnet, M. 1959. *The Clonal Selection Theory of Acquired Immunity.* Nashville: Vanderbilt University Press.

Coutinho, A., and F. Varela. Immune networks: A review of current work, *Immunol. Today.* (in press).

Coutinho, A., L. Forni, D. Holmberg, F. Ivars, and N. Vaz. 1984. From an antigen-centered, clonal perspective on immune responses to an organism-centered network perspective of autonomous activity in a self-referential immune system. *Immunol. Revs.* 79L: 151-169.

Huetz, F., F. Jacquemart, C. Pena-Rossi, F. Varela, and A. Coutinho. Auto-immunity: The moving boundaries between physiology and pathology. *J. Autoimmunity.* (in press).

Jerne, N. 1974. Towards a network theory of the immune system, *Ann. Immun. Inst. Pasteur* 125C: 373-89. Jerne, N. 1984. Idiotypic networks and other preconceived ideas. *Immunol. Revs.* 79: 5-24.

Lundqvist, I., A. Coutinho, F. Varela, and D. Holmberg. 1989. Evidence for the functional interactions among natural antibodies. *Proc. Natl. Acad. Sci* (USA).

Urbain, J. 1986. Idiotypic networks: A noisy background or a breakthrough in immunological thinking? *Ann. Inst. Pasteur/Immologie.* 137C: 57-64.

Varela, F. 1979. *Principles of Biological Autonomy.* New York: North-Holland.

Varela, F., A. Coutinho, B. Dupire, and N. Vaz. 1988a. Cognitive networks: Immune, neural and otherwise. In *Theoretical Immunology.* Ed. A. Perelson. Vol. 2. (SFI Series on Complexity). New Jersey: Addison Wesley.

Varela, F., V. Sanchez, and A. Coutinho. 1988b. Viable strategies gleaned from immune systems dynamics. In *Epigenetic and Evolutionary Order in Complex Systems: A Waddington Memorial Symposium.* Eds. P. Sauders and B. Goodwin Edinburgh: Edinburgh University Press.

Vaz, N., and F. Varela. 1978. Self and nonsense: An organism- centered approach to immunology. *Medical Hypothesis.*

4

EVAN THOMPSON

Perception and the
Emergence Of Color

C olor is the "place where our brain and the universe meet."
So Merleau-Ponty wrote shortly before his death, attribut-
ing the statement to Cezanne.[1] We usually think of a meeting-
place as a space that is prepared in advance for those who will
gather there, such as this lecture room or a concert hall. But Merleau-Ponty's invocation of Cezanne's metaphor has a different
sense. Here the "place" cannot be specified prior to the meeting; it
is brought forth in the very meeting itself. Thus Cezanne's metaphor asks that we think of color as a domain, or in Merleau-Ponty's words, a "dimension," that emerges from the mutual
encounter of the (visual) brain and the universe.

Merleau-Ponty offered this idea in a reflection on color and
painting. I will explore a similar idea by taking color vision and
the philosophy of perception as my theme. Whereas Merleau-
Ponty spoke of color as a dimension of "the visible" (*la visible*)
that emerges from the meeting of brain and universe, I wish to consider color as a visual domain that emerges from the mutual
encounter of the perceiving animal and its environment. Thus the
theme of my presentation will be that color constitutes an ecologically emergent visual domain.

The sense that I intend to give to the term "emergence" will
become clear later. For the moment, let me simply say that rather

86

than speaking of emergent properties, I will speak of an emergent domain of phenomena. Color provides a fascinating example of such an emergent domain, for as we will see, there can be different types of "color domains" depending on the structure and ecological context of the perceiver.

Let me begin by reviewing the classical or "received" account of color, which owes its origin to Isaac Newton's theory of light and color and to John Locke's epistemology.[2] (I refer to this conception of color as the "received account" because it continues to determine how people think and write about color, especially in introductory texts and popular science books, despite the fact that vision research has long since departed from this account.) According to this received view, color is not found among the fundamental properties of things: things as they are in themselves do not have colors; they have colors only by virtue of how they appear to us. Thus color provides a paradigm of what Locke called a secondary quality. Locke argued that whereas primary qualities like size, shape, number, and motion correspond to real, physical properties of an object, secondary qualities like colors, tastes, smells, etc., consist only in the dispositions of the primary qualities to cause sensory experiences in a perceiver. In the Lockean terminology (which has since become standard in empiricist philosophy), then, color corresponds simply to the disposition that something has to look colored.

There are contemporary philosophers who hold that this conception of color — indeed, this conception of so-called secondary qualities in general — represents an a priori, philosophical discovery, rather than an empirical scientific one.[3] I disagree. This conception of color is intimately tied to early modern science and natural philosophy, especially to Newton's theory of light and color. Consider, for example, this famous passage from Newton's *Opticks*:

> The homogeneal Light and Rays which appear red, or rather make Objects appear so, I call Rubrifick or Red-making; those which make Objects appear yellow, green, blue, and violet, I call Yellow-making, Green-making, Blue-making, Violet-making, and so of the rest. And if at any time I speak of Light

and rays as colored or enbued with Colors, I would be understood to speak not philosophically and properly, but grossly, and accordingly to such Conceptions as vulgar People in seeing all these Experiments would be apt to frame. For the Rays to speak properly are not colored. In them there is nothing else than a certain Power and Disposition to stir up a Sensation of this or that Color. For as Sound in a Bell or musical String, or other sounding Body, is nothing but a trembling Motion, and in the Air no thing but that Motion propagated from the Object, and in the Sensorium 'tis a Sense of that Motion under the Form of Sound; so Colors in the Object are nothing but a Disposition to reflect this or that sort of Rays more copiously than the rest; in the Rays they are nothing but their Dispositions to propagate this or that Motion into the Sensorium, and in the sensorium they are Sensations of those Motions under the Forms of Colors.[4]

In this paragraph, Newton does not offer an a priori argument; instead, he makes several empirical assertions, and then draws a conclusion that is both empirical and philosophical. The first empirical claim is that the cause of color perception is light. The second is that the color an object is perceived to have corresponds to the light that is reflected from that object. On the basis of these two ideas, Newton then asserts that the so-called color of an object actually corresponds to the character of the light that is reflected by the surface of the object. Therefore, to the extent that we speak of an object or surface as colored, its color will correspond simply to its disposition to reflect light of a given character. Furthermore, light is not itself colored, for the labels "red-making," "yellow-making," etc., can be correlated with physical properties of light that are mathematically specified (degree of "refrangibility" or refraction). Newton therefore concludes that colors are not real qualities of things: things do not look colored because they really are colored; they are colored only because they reflect light which causes them to look colored.

As we shall presently see, contemporary vision research clearly shows that the empirical foundation of this account gives way in virtually every respect. The point I wish to emphasize now, however, is that although the received account of color is usually considered to be a form of subjectivism (because of its claim that things are colored only because they look to be so), this account actually generates the modern debate between objectivism and subjectivism about color. This debate over whether colors are objective, physical properties or subjective sensations defines what I will call the "problem-space" of the received account. Despite the demonstrable inadequacy of the received account as an empirical theory of color, the problem-space of the received view persists in much of contemporary philosophical and scientific discussion of color.[5]

To generate this problem-space we need only consider the relation between being colored and looking colored implicit in Newton's and Locke's treatment of color: On the one hand, whether something is colored is ontologically more fundamental than whether it looks colored. On the other hand, whether something *looks* colored is conceptually and epistemologically more fundamental than whether it *is* colored. It is the tension between these two sides of the Newtonian and Lockean treatment that generates the problem-space of objectivism versus subjectivism. Let me explain.

First, remember that being colored consists, according to Newton and Locke, in having the disposition to look colored. Now something can possess this disposition without actually looking colored: for example , things do not look colored in the dark, but they still have the disposition to look colored (they would look colored if we placed them in the light). Similarly, if there were no perceivers in the world, things would not look colored, but they would still possess the disposition to look colored; there would simply be no circumstance in which this disposition could be manifested. It is in this sense that being colored (having the disposition to look colored) is ontologically prior to, or more fundamental than, looking colored.

Second, remember that for Newton and Locke things do not look colored because they really are colored; they are colored only because they have the disposition to look to be so. This disposition is not itself color; it indicates only that something would look colored in certain circumstances to certain kinds of perceivers. We

89

cannot, then, specify what color is without referring to the way things look or would look to perceivers. Therefore, we must invoke the concept of looking colored to explicate the concept of being colored. Furthermore, we cannot know whether something is colored without knowing whether it looks or would look colored to a perceiver. It is in this sense that looking colored is conceptually and epistemologically prior to, or more fundamental than, being colored.

Given this tension between "being colored" and "looking colored" within the received account, it is not surprising that philosophers with objectivist inclinations emphasize the ontological priority of the first, "dispositional" component, whereas subjectivists insist upon the conceptual priority of the latter, "subjective" component. In general, the effect of the Newtonian and Lockean heritage upon philosophy has been a tangle of issues in metaphysics and epistemology, especially those branches concerned with the mind and perception. In the case of color perception, philosophers have continued to be unsure over whether to treat color as a complex physical property or as a projection of subjective experience. Furthermore, given this uncertainty, it is hardly surprising that the general trend among those aware of the fundamental empirical inadequacies of the received account is to abandon this view in favor of even more extreme versions of either objectivism or subjectivism.[6]

In the remainder of this presentation, I will try to persuade you that neither objectivism nor subjectivism provides a satisfactory account of color. Contrary to objectivism, a satisfactory account of color must be experientialist, but contrary to subjectivism it must also be ecological. According to this "ecological experientialism," color is neither objectively present in an unexperienced world, nor is it a mere subjective projection. Instead, color provides a paradigm of an experiential domain that emerges from the codetermination of perceiving animals and their environments. In other words, color is a property of the ecological and experiential world of perceiving and cognizing animals. Thus by avoiding both objectivist and subjectivist extremes, this "ecological experientialism" represents a genuine departure from the problem-space of the received view.

90

Let me first outline the fundamental problems with the received account. These problems become apparent in the face of two general phenomena: (1) the structure of color appearance — for example, that yellow is brighter and less saturated than blue, that orange is a combination of red and yellow, etc. — is not determined by the structure of light; and (2) the color that an area is perceived to have is not determined by the light reflected locally by that area. I will consider each of these in turn.

There are two important features of the structure of color appearance. First, all of the colors that we see can be described as some combination of six basic colors: red, green, yellow, blue, black, and white. Second, the appearances of these colors vary along three dimensions, those of hue, saturation, and brightness. Hue refers to the degree of redness, greenness, yellowness, or blueness of a given color. Red, green, yellow, and blue are the four fundamental or psychologically "unique" hues, which combine to form complex or psychologically "binary" hues. For example, red and yellow combine to form binary hues of reddish-yellow and yellowish-red (oranges), whereas blue and red combine to form binary hues of bluish-red and reddish-blue (purples). For each of the unique hues, there is another unique hue with which it cannot co-exist to form a binary hue. Thus red cannot co-exist with green, and yellow cannot co-exist with blue. Red and green, and yellow and blue, are therefore known as opponent or antagonistic hues. Not every color, however, need be of a certain hue. White and black, as well as the intermediate shades of gray, are colors, but they have no hue. These colors are therefore known as the achromatic colors, i.e., colors that possess zero hue content, whereas colors with non-zero hue content are referred to as chromatic colors. The chromatic colors can also differ in the strength or saturation of their hue. Saturated colors have a greater degree of hue, whereas desaturated colors are closer to gray. Brightness is the final dimension of color appearance. Along this dimension, appearances vary from dazzling colors at one end to dim or barely visible colors at the other end.

These three dimensions of hue, saturation, and brightness, and their interrelations provide the skeleton for the structure of color appearance. They also specify the phenomenon of color at what could be called its own proper level of generalization. In other words, these dimensions describe the structure of color appearance, but leave open the nature of the processes responsible for the generation of this structure. Thus by referring to these dimensions we can make informative statements about color, but we do not commit ourselves to any specific assertions about how the phenomenon of color comes to be. Nonetheless, since the structure of color appearance specifies what color is, this structure constrains theories of color: to be acceptable, a theory of color must provide the resources to explain the six basic colors and their interrelations in terms of hue, saturation, and brightness.

Let us now apply this constraint to the received account. We have seen that according to this account, being colored is identified with a dispositional property. Thus light has the disposition to cause sensations of color. This point, however, though true, is relatively uninteresting, for although light does act as the proximal stimulus for color vision, it is not responsible for the structure that color exemplifies. In other words, light does not determine that color varies along the three dimensions of hue, saturation, and brightness; nor does light determine, for example, that yellow is a desaturated, unique hue and that purple is a saturated, binary hue. Furthermore, the received account generally treats perceived color as simple or internally unstructured: each type of color that we perceive (red, green, yellow, blue, etc.) is treated merely as a sensation that happens to result from stimulation by light. Such simple and externally related sensations, however, cannot be pieced together to form the internal relations that compose the structure of color appearance.[7]

We can now turn to the second shortcoming of the received account. Since we perceive colors to be spatially located, we might assume — as does the received account — that the color we perceive an area to have is correlated with the light reflected locally from that area. Suppose, for example, that we perceive the area to be green. Areas that look green typically reflect a high percentage of middle-wave light, and a low percentage of long-wave and short-wave light. We might suppose, then, that the area looks green because it reflects more middle-wave light to the eye. This supposition would be true if the area were viewed in isolation, i.e., if we excluded everything else from the field of view. But when this area is viewed as part of a complex scene, it will continue to look green even if it reflects more long-wave and short-wave light than middle-wave light. In other words, when the area is viewed as part of a complex scene, the light that it locally reflects is not sufficient to predict its perceived color. Thus contrary to the received account, there simply is no one-to-one correspondence between perceived color and locally reflected light.

This relative independence of perceived color from locally reflected light has been known for quite some time by vision scientists and has been extensively documented for human color vision.[8] It has also begun to be studied in other species.[9] The independence is manifested in two complementary phenomena. In the first, the perceived colors of things remain relatively constant despite large changes in the illumination. This phenomenon is known as approximate color constancy. In the second, two areas that reflect light of the same spectral composition can be perceived to have different colors depending on the surround in which they are placed. This phenomenon is known as simultaneous color contrast or chromatic induction.[10]

These two phenomena suffice to reveal both of the inadequacies in the received account of color. First, color constancy and color contrast both indicate that color vision is not concerned with detecting locally reflected light. Instead, color vision is concerned with the light reflected from an area in relation to other areas in the field of view. Second, color contrast exemplifies the salience of the structure of color appearance. For example, a green surround tends to induce a reddish hue, whereas a blue surround tends to induce a yellowish hue. Therefore, a yellow patch on a green background appears more reddish than on a gray background. On a blue background, the yellow appears more saturated, whereas on a yellow background it appears desaturated. Thus these contrast phenomena exemplify a central feature of the structure of color appearance: the hue opponency or antagonism between red and green, and yellow and blue.

We now have two basic constraints that any theory of color must satisfy. A theory of color must (1) explain the structure of color appearance; and (2) explain the approximate constancy of

93

perceived color. Let me now briefly indicate how contemporary models of color vision attempt to explain these two phenomena.

The model of color vision that takes as its point of departure the structure of color appearance is known as the opponent-process theory of color vision. This theory owes its origin to the research of the nineteenth century physiologist, Ewald Hering.[11] Hering proposed that there are four fundamental, neural chromatic processes, but they are organized into two antagonistic or opponent pairs: red-green and yellow-blue. Hering also argued that there is an achromatic pair formed by white and black. Increases in any one member of a pair are always gained at the expense of the other member. Thus an increase in red leads to a decrease in green, and vice-versa. Red and green can therefore never occur together, nor can yellow and blue. But red can be combined with either yellow or blue, as can green. For example, the activation of red combined with the activation of blue generates purple, and so purple is appropriately described as a binary combination of red and blue. Unique yellow occurs, however, when the yellow process is activated and the red-green process is neutral or balanced. Thus our experience of yellow as qualitatively different from red and green is thought to reflect a certain neural organization, and appealing to this organization explains why we never describe anything as a mixture of red and green (or yellow and blue).

Until the past fifty years or so, this opponent-process theory was in direct competition with the trichromatic theory of Thomas Young and Herman von Helmholtz. According to this theory, color vision results from the differential stimulation of three kinds of photoreceptors in the human eye. In 1957, however, Leo Hurvich and Dorothea Jameson combined this trichromatic theory with Hering's theory into one comprehensive opponent-process model.[12] In this model, the signals generated by the three photo- receptors are both added and subtracted at post-receptoral stages: the addition of the signals generates the achromatic (brightness) process; the subtractive comparison of the signals generates two opponent chromatic processes (red-green, yellow-blue). The trichromacy of human color vision therefore depends not just on three types of photoreceptors, but also on the cross-connections of these receptors to three post-receptoral systems (one achromatic + two chromatic).

94

This opponent-process model explains the structure of color appearance by showing how it results from the differential responses of the achromatic and chromatic processes. Unique hue perceptions result from a signal from one chromatic process while the other chromatic process is neutral or balanced. For example, a unique hue perception of green would result if the red-green process signals "green" and the yellow-blue process is neutral or balanced so that it signals neither "yellow" nor "blue." Binary hue perceptions result from the interplay of the two chromatic processes with each other. Furthermore, some binary hues may be balanced: a balanced orange, for example, is one that contains an equal amount of red and of yellow. According to this model, such binary hue perceptions result when the strengths of the signals from each chromatic process are equal. When they are unequal, the binary hues are said to be unbalanced.

This opponent-process model of color vision is now relatively well established on both psychophysical and physiological grounds. It is universally agreed among vision researchers that opponent-processing plays a central role in color vision, though there is debate over whether there is a further non-opponent stage in the generation of color experience.[13] In contrast, models that take color constancy as their point of departure are considerably more controversial. I will present only the basic idea behind these models.

Consider first that the ambient light in a scene is the product of both illumination and surface reflectance (the percentage of light as each wavelength throughout the spectrum that a given surface reflects). Therefore, as the illumination varies, so too does the ambient light and the light that reaches the eye. But the percentage of the incident light that a surface reflects, which depends on the physical structure of the surface, does not change. These two variables of illumination and surface reflectance, however, are confounded in the light that is actually reflected to the eye. Nevertheless, within certain limits, the colors that we perceive objects to have can be correlated with the reflectances of their surfaces. The explanation of color constancy would therefore seem to require that we solve the following problem: How is it possible to evaluate and then to discount the illumination, and so recover chromatic values that correspond to reflectance? Virtually all of the current models of color constancy proceed by attempting to solve this problem.

It would take us too far afield to examine these models and criticisms of this formulation of the so-called "problem" of color constancy.[14] The point I wish to emphasize here is simply that the physical correlates of color within these models are not light wavelength and intensity, but rather properties like "average relative reflectance," i.e., the surface reflectance of an area relative to the average reflectance of its surround.[15] This property is actually a complex of properties that includes an area's surface reflectance, its immediate surroundings, and its global context. Thus models of color constancy typically appeal to high-level, macroscopic, and global properties of the physical environment.

Now at this point I would like you to notice the temptation that we feel to slip into the problem-space of the received view. This temptation becomes paramount when we ask: "Where is color?" If we take color constancy as our reference point, we might be tempted to say that color corresponds to the macroscopic physical property of surface reflectance, and so is "out there" independent of our perception. On the other hand, if we take the structure of color appearance as our reference point, we might be tempted to say that color corresponds to a kind of subjective sensation, and so is really just "in the perceiver."

Neither of these two views, however, provides a satisfactory account of color. First, we have seen that color owes its structure to the three dimensions of hue, saturation, and brightness. Indeed, these dimensions specify what color is. The physical property of surface reflectance, however, does not display this structure. Thus we cannot generate a model of the structure of color simply by referring to this physical property. For example, unlike hues, surface reflectances are neither unique nor binary, balanced nor unbalanced. Second, although color is experiential, it does not follow that subjectivism provides the proper explication of color experience. Indeed, within the problem-space of the received view, experiential is typically conflated with subjective. Thus the possibility of a non-subjectivist account of color experience is simply ignored. As we will now see, however, although color is experiential, it is not subjective; it is, rather, ecological.

Since our world of color is so familiar, it is tempting to assume that our color vision should provide the norm for understanding color. This assumption might be justifiable if human beings — or our primate relatives — were unique in possessing color vision. In fact, color vision is not only widespread throughout the animal world, but varies significantly from species to species.[16]

The most general approach to these variations is through a comparison of the number of dimensions needed to represent the color vision of a given animal. For example, we saw in the previous section that our color vision is trichromatic. Therefore, three dimensions are needed to represent our color vision, i.e., to represent the kinds of color distinctions that we can make. Trichromacy is certainly not unique to humans; indeed, it would appear that virtually every animal class contains some species with trichromatic vision. More interesting, however, is that some animals are dichromats, others are tetrachromats, and some may even be pentachromats. (Dichromats include squirrels, rabbits, tree shrews, some fishes, possibly cats, and some New World monkeys; tetrachromats include fishes that live close to the surface of the water and diurnal birds; diurnal birds may even be pentachromats.[17]) While two dimensions are needed to represent dichromatic vision, four dimensions are needed for tetrachromatic vision, and five for pentachromatic vision. What might these differences in dimensionality imply?

Many people when they hear of the evidence for, say, tetrachromacy in certain fishes and diurnal birds respond by asking: "Well, what are the extra colors that these tetrachromats see?" This question is understandable, but naive: it supposes that a tetrachromat is simply better at seeing the colors that we see. But to see in four dimensions, as it were, is not a better way of seeing in three dimensions; it is simply different. Strictly speaking, the colors that trichromats and tetrachromats see are incommensurable, for there is no way to make the kinds of distinctions available in three dimensions without remainder. Thus a tetrachromat should not be thought of as a perceiver that simply makes finer hue-saturation-brightness discriminations among, say, blue and green, or red and yellow, i.e., as a perceiver who simply sees finer shades of our colors than we do. Such an ability would not amount to an increase in the dimensionality of color vision; it would consist only in a relative increase in hue-saturation-brightness sensitivity within the dimensions of our color domain. As we just saw, however, to be a tetrachromat is not to be more sensitive within the dimensions available to a trichromat; it is, rather, to possess an additional dimension of sensitivity in relation to trichromats. Therefore, if we wish to appreciate what tetrachromatic experience might be like, we must ask what the possession of an additional dimension in which to make color distinctions could mean in experiential terms.

At this point, we can offer only imaginative speculation, for we have no access to the color domains of tetrachromatic creatures like the goldfish or the pigeon. Nevertheless, by returning to consider our color domain, and by asking how this domain would be transformed by the addition of a new dimension, we can perhaps achieve an indirect appreciation of what a tetrachromatic domain might be like. Recall, then, that our color domain contains four unique hues (red, green, yellow, and blue), as well as their binary combinations (purple, greenish-blue, orange, etc.). Recall also that according to the opponent-process theory, this structure is generated by the interplay of two chromatically opponent systems: the red-green and yellow-blue processes. (The third process is achromatic.) Now a tetrachromat presumably has an additional opponent system. We might speculate, then, that the three chromatically opponent systems of a tetrachromat (the fourth would be achromatic) would enable a tetrachromat to experience six unique hues, binary combinations of these hues, as well as ternary combinations of these hues. Thus the color domain of a tetrachromat might reflect a structure composed not only of two new unique hues, which would combine to form new binaries, but also an entirely new kind of hue not found in the structure of our color domain, namely, ternary hues.[18] These ternary hues would correspond to the additional kind of color distinction that is available to a tetrachromat, but not to us. Since a color domain that contains ternary hues obviously cannot be mapped into a color domain that contains only unique and binary hues, the structure that color exemplifies for a tetrachromat would be incommensurable with the structure that color exemplifies for us.

In a sense, then, there are more colors than we are capable of perceiving, but these colors are inaccessible to us because they belong to a different color domain. Properly speaking, it is this domain that is inaccessible to us. In other words, the colors that tetrachromats see are not inaccessible, simple sensations, as the received account would lead us to suppose. Colors themselves are not discrete elements, which when put together constitute a visual mosaic.[19] Colors are specified by the dimensions that constitute a color domain. We see colors because we live our color domain. Since our color domain is three-dimensional, we have no direct access to the colors that would be generated in four dimensions.

Although these incommensurable color domains are relative to the perceiving animal, we should avoid the idea that they are subjective, i.e., that they can be explained entirely in terms of internal states of the perceiver. This point is best appreciated through the use of examples.

Consider first the polymorphism in the color vision of two species of New World monkeys: the squirrel monkey and the spider monkey. In these species, all males are dichromats, whereas three-quarters of the females are trichromats. Several hypotheses have been proposed to explain this polymorphism.[20] The first appeals to the spatial heterogeneity of the environment: it is possible that different phenotypes inhabit regions of the jungle that differ in the spectral composition of their ambient light. The second appeals to the concept of group selection in evolutionary theory: the animal community might benefit from having members with several forms of color vision. A third hypothesis appeals to an ecological balance between the availability of certain fruits and the number of monkeys that can detect them. Finally, the most interesting hypothesis suggests that the colors of local fruits co-evolved with the differences in color vision.

This idea of organism-environment coevolution has also been invoked to explain the color vision of bees. Forager honey bees are trichromats whose overall spectral sensitivity is shifted towards the ultraviolet region of the spectrum. It has been suggested that this distinctive form of trichromacy coevolved with the colors of flowers, which often have contrasting patterns in ultraviolet light.[21]

It should be noted that the causation involved in this hypothesis of coevolution is two-way and circular: the hypothesis entails not only that bee color vision is sensitive to ultraviolet because flowers have ultraviolet reflectance patterns, it also entails that flowers have these patterns because bees are sensitive to ultraviolet light. Such coevolution therefore provides an excellent example of how the environment is not simply relative to the perceiving animal, but also constructed, or in Francisco Varela's terms "enacted," by the perceptually guided activity of the animal.

My final example is closer to home, for it is drawn from the human realm. In the 1960s, the linguists Brent Berlin and Paul Kay established that human languages contain a limited number of "basic" color terms.[22] For any language, there are only eleven basic terms (in English: black, white, red, yellow, green, blue, brown, purple, pink, orange, and gray), though not all languages contain all eleven. Berlin and Kay found that although there was considerable variation among speakers over color boundaries, speakers virtually always agreed on best examples of a color. Furthermore, they found that when several languages contained a common basic term, e.g., a basic term for blue, speakers virtually always agreed on the best example of a color no matter which language they spoke. On the basis of these examples, Berlin and Kay argued that basic color terms name basic color categories, and that these basic categories constitute "pan-human perceptual universals."

Since these categories are universal for the human species, we might suppose that they can be explained entirely in terms of our neurophysiological structure. But although a neurophysiological account seems adequate for the primary hues (red, green, yellow, and blue), it is difficult to explain the categories of brown and pink in entirely neural terms. Other phenomena that seem intractable at a purely neural level are the variations in the boundaries of color categories and how such variations change, evolve, or develop. Indeed, some languages appear to have generated color categories whose development cannot — at least at present — be explained in neurophysiological terms.[23] In a recent discussion of these findings, the linguist George Lakoff concludes that "color categories are more than merely a consequence of the nature of the world plus choice of which basic color categories there are."[24]

These three examples all highlight the distinctly ecological

100

dimensions of color. Thus to explain the polymorphism in certain kinds of monkey color vision, and the resulting differences in color experience, we must appeal not simply to the internal constitution of these animals, but also to the evolutionary history of their environmental interactions. Similarly, to understand not only why bee color vision is shifted towards the ultraviolet, but also why flowers exhibit contrasting patterns in ultraviolet light, we must refer to the co-evolution of neural structures and plant features. It is not merely the neural structure of the bee, but this co-evolution that explains why the color domain of the bee is shifted towards the ultraviolet. Finally, to explain human color experience we must understand not only how our color domain is neurophysiologically embodied, but also how experientially significant variations within our color domain emerge from cognitive development and cultural change.

We can now appreciate that color is both experiential and ecological: color is a form of experience that emerges from the coupling between perceiving animals and their environments. Thus the structure of a given, emergent color domain depends on the relevant animal-environment coupling. Apart from this coupling color cannot be found: color belongs neither to an animal-independent physical world, nor to an inner, private world of sensation. Instead, color belongs to the "extradermal" ecological world that is constituted or enacted by animal activity.

What do these ecological and experiential dimensions of color imply for our understanding of perception? This question brings us to the final topic of my presentation.

The most prevalent view within perception research today holds that perception is a process of representation. According to this idea, visual perception consists in the "recovery" of an independent, "distal" environment from "proximal" retinal images. This approach to vision is often called "inverse optics," for the task is to show how properties of the world can be recovered from images.[25]

Although this view places considerable emphasis upon internal processes of inference and reconstruction, it nonetheless makes a supposedly independent, distal environment the ultimate reference point for understanding perception. For example, the function of color vision is considered to be the recovery of the surface spectral reflectances in a scene. Given this idea, it is natural to suppose that types of color vision can be ordered according to how well they recover surface reflectance. Thus it is supposed that tetrachromats recover more of the reflectance profiles of surfaces, and so simply have better color vision than we do.

This representationist view is inadequate, for it neglects the ecological embodiment of the perceiver. Natural color vision is always relative to a given photic environment.[26] In an aquatic setting, for example, there is a continuous range of luminous environments. The chromatic abilities of fish are always embodied in these various types of niches. Deep water fishes tend to be monochromats and dichromats; fishes that live close to the surface tend to be trichromats and tetrachromats.[27] We cannot, then, simply say that tetrachromatic vision is better than dichromatic vision. A tetrachromat would be just as out of place in a dark environment as a dichromat in a richly luminous environment.

Although this kind of relativity between color vision and ecological niche can be encompassed by the representationist approach, there are deeper problems that cannot. First, not all natural color vision is concerned with discriminating surfaces. Second, the visual segmentation of the world into regions that correspond to distinct surfaces is itself relative to the structure and ecological context of the animal. I will take each of these points in turn.

The representationist approach typically plays color favoritism by downplaying non-surface modes of color appearance and by assuming that the only function of color vision is object discrimination. Natural color vision, however, appears to be as concerned with providing information about properties that change, such as ambient lighting conditions, weather, and the time of day, as with providing information about properties that remain constant, such as surface reflectance.[28]

This non-surface dimension of color is particularly fascinating when seen in a comparative ecological context. For example, I have already mentioned that the trichromatic, ultraviolet-sensitive vision of bees enables them to detect the contrasting ultraviolet reflectance patterns of flowers. After visiting these flowers,

102

however, the bee takes a straight path back to its hive using not only landmarks, but also features of the sky for its orientation. Among these features is the pattern of linearly polarized light in the sky. Information about light polarization appears to be color-coded for the bee by means of interactions between photoreceptors that have different spectral and polarization sensitivities.

To take one more example, the tetrachromatic — perhaps even pentachromatic — vision of pigeons includes excellent short-wave and ultraviolet discrimination. As a recent article notes, it is possible that:

> The excellent spectral discrimination within this range... represents an adaptation to the coloration of an unclouded sky. This property enables the pigeon to evaluate shortwave color gradients in the sky, ranging from white at the sun's locus to highly saturated (ultra) violet at angles of 90 degrees to the axis between observer and sun.

Furthermore, since pigeon navigation is based on orientation with respect to the sun's azimuth, "the perception of color gradients in the sky may control navigation indirectly when the sun is hidden by clouds."[29]

One other aspect of color vision deserves mention. Color vision yields a set of experiential categories that have "signal significance" for perceiving animals in a variety of interactions. For example, the category red can guide behavior in various ways depending on the things to which it is applied: in the case of fruits it indicates ripeness, and so guides feeding, whereas in the case of animal coloration it may guide certain kinds of social interaction. Although the discrimination of objects is obviously important for these forms of behavior, the "signal significance" of color may have an affective or emotional dimension that cannot be explained simply as a function of object discrimination.

Let me now turn to the second point about surfaces. It is typically assumed that surface spectral reflectance can be specified without taking into consideration the ecological embodiment of the perceiver. This assumption rests on the supposition that since surface reflectance is a physical property, it can be measured and

103

specified in entirely physical terms. But although the reflectance at any point in a scene can be specified in physical terms, what counts as a surface may in fact involve tacit reference to a type of perceiver. I believe that this point is not evident to us for two reasons. First, many theories of perception typically focus on perceptual tasks in an already well-specified or segmented context. Thus computational theories of color vision constrain the problem of recovering surface reflectance by appealing to the limited degrees of freedom in which reflectance can vary for "pre-specified" objects, i.e., for objects that have been picked out prior to the actual task of vision. Second, virtually all theories of perception focus on our familiar human environment, not on the considerably different environments of, say, birds, fishes, or insects. Thus the pre-specified objects to be perceived are typically middle-sized, frontally viewed, "human" objects, such as bricks, grass, buildings, Munsell color chips, etc. They are not, for example, silhouettes against the background sky as viewed both frontally and laterally by a bird, ultraviolet reflectance patterns of flowers as seen by both birds and bees, aquatic objects which contrast with the downwelling light or background space light as viewed by fish, etc. Because of this attention to pre-specified human objects, the issue of how the world comes to be segmented into a given collection of surfaces is hardly ever raised. It is therefore important to remember that color vision is intimately involved in this process of visual segmentation. To quote the eloquent formulation of P. Gouras and E. Zrenner: "It is impossible to separate the object sensed from its color because it is the color contrast itself that forms the object."[30] Since color vision contributes to the visual specification of a surface, and since color vision varies considerably in the natural world, we should expect the kinds of surfaces that populate the world as visually experienced by animals to vary as well. Therefore, the specification of surfaces — at least for the purpose of visual perception — is likely to depend upon the perceptually guided and ecologically embodied activity of the animal.

Perception, then, is poorly described as the recovery or representation of an independent, distal world. The world that we perceive is not "out there," given and ready-made; it is, rather, "brought forth" or "enacted" in our perceptually guided and ecologically embodied activity. If we take this view seriously, then our research endeavor should no longer be to search for internal representations of an independent, external environment. We should instead attempt to determine the common principles or lawful linkages between perceptual and motor processes that enable animal activity to be perceptually guided in a continually changing, animal-dependent environment.[31] Thus in the study of color vision, our task will no longer be to determine how the visual system manages to achieve a representation of surface reflectance. Rather, it will be to understand how color domains emerge from animal-environment coupling.

It should be noted that this refusal to separate the environment from the perceptually guided activity of the animal does not entail a subjectivist stance towards perception. Subjectivism too takes representation as its central notion; it simply holds that the perceived world is "projected" rather than "recovered." The approach that I have outlined here, however, sidesteps both objectivism and subjectivism. On the one hand, to hold that the perceived world is ecologically emergent counters the objectivist view that the world is simply "out-there" to be recovered. On the other hand, to hold that the perceived world is ecologically embodied counters the subjectivist view that the world is simply "in-here" to be projected.

To consider perception in an ecological context suggests that we also relinquish the idea that at the source of the perceived world is to be found an individual ego, whether this be the transcendental ego of Kant and Husserl, or the empirical ego of modern cognitive psychology. This idea construes the perceiving subject as a detached spectator who either recovers or projects a distal world. To consider perception in an ecological context, however, reminds us that perception and action have evolved together — that in fact perception is always perceptually guided action. Thus the world that we see and hear, taste, touch, and smell, owes its origin neither to recovery nor to projection, but to a shared history of ecological activity.

An experiential echo of this idea can be found in some remarks made by Merleau-Ponty, for he too attempted to consider the perceived world as both emergent and embodied, yet not traceable to

105

an individual ego. Thus in a discussion of color in his *Phenomenology of Perception*, he wrote:

> It is my gaze which subtends color... or rather my gaze pairs off with color... and in this transaction between the subject of sensation and the sensible it cannot be held that one acts while the other suffers the action, or that one confers significance on the other.... I cannot say that I see the blue of the sky in the sense in which I understand a book.... My perception, even when seen from the inside expresses a given situation: I can see blue because I am sensitive to colors.... So, if I wanted to render precisely the perceptual experience, I ought to say that one perceives in me, and not that I perceive.[32]

The blue of the sky provides a wonderful example of what Merleau-Ponty meant by "the visible" (*la visible*). The blue of the sky is not the property of a surface, and yet is located in visual space, supported by the edges of the horizon. It rests in itself, and yet cannot be found apart from our vision and its sensibility. It is that part of the Gaian atmosphere that emerges in perception, and yet we also live within it and are sustained by it. "It is as though our vision were formed in the heart of the visible, or as though there were between it and us an intimacy as close as that between the sea and the strand."[33]

The logic of emergence ultimately requires, then, that we appreciate this reciprocal circularity between self and world, mind and nature, inner and outer. We are made of the world, of Gaia. Our very existence presupposes this Gaian world which forms us, and yet extends beyond us in all domains. But it is from our embodiment — as well as those of other visual creatures — that the visible emerges in Gaia. Thus the visible is neither in the mind, nor in the world; it is where our mind and the universe meet.

Notes

1. Maurice Merleau-Ponty, "Eye and Mind," *The Primacy of Perception and Other Essays*, ed. James M. Edie (Evanston, IL: Northwestern University Press, 1964), 180.

EVAN THOMPSON

2. See Isaac Newton, "A New Theory of Light and Colors," reprinted in *Newton's Philosophy of Nature*, ed. H.S. Thayer (New York and London: Hafner Publishing Company, 1953); Isaac Newton, *Opticks* (New York: Dover Publications, 1953); John Locke, *An Essay Concerning Human Understanding* (Oxford University Press, 1975), Book II, Chapter VIII.

3. For example, Thomas Nagel, *The View from Nowhere* (New York: Oxford University Press, 1986), 75.

4. Newton, *Opticks*, 124-25.

5. Consider, for example, these two statements from two prominent scientists, one who works in the field of computational vision and the other who studies the neurophysiology of color vision: (1) "... what we call color corresponds to an objective property of physical surfaces. Depending on the light and surfaces in a scene, we succeed or fail in estimating these properties." L.T. Maloney, "Computational Approaches to Color Constancy," Stanford University, Applied Psychological Laboratory, Technical Report, 1985, 1: 119. (2) "....the nervous system, rather than analyze colors, takes what information there is in the external environment... and transforms that information to construct colors, using its own algorithms to do so. In other words, it constructs something which is a property of the brain, not the world outside." [Italics in original.] S. Zeki, "Color Coding in the Cerebral Cortex: The Reaction of Cells in Monkey Visual Cortex to Wavelengths and Colors," *Neuroscience* 9 (1983): 741-65. These two statements clearly indicate that despite the considerable advance made in the study of color vision in recent years, the ontology of color basically remains captive to the problem-space of objectivism, which we have inherited from Newton and Locke.

6. See David R. Hilbert, *Color and Color Perception: A Study in Anthropocentric Realism* (Stanford University: Center for the Study of Language and Information, 1987); and C. L. Hardin, *Color for Philosophers: Unweaving the Rainbow* (Indianapolis/Cambridge: Hackett Publishing Company, 1988).

7. Cf. Jonathan Westphal, *Color: Some Philosophical Problems from Wittgenstein* (Oxford: Basil Blackwell), Chapter 7.

8. The most recent demonstrations are due to Edwin Land. See his "Recent Advances in Retinex Theory and Some Implications for Cortical Computations: Color Vision and the Natural Image," *Proceedings of the National Academy of Sciences* (USA) 80 (1983): 5163-69. For earlier work see H. Helson, "Fundamental Problems in Color Vision, I: The Principles Governing Changes in Hue, Saturation, and Lightness of Nonselective Samples in Chromatic Illumination, " *Journal of Experimental*

Psychology 23 (1938): 439-76; H. Helson and V. B. Jeffers, "Fundamental Problems of Color Vision, II: Hue, Lightness and Saturation of Selective Samples in Chromatic Illumination," *Journal of Experimental Psychology* 26 (1940): 1-27; and D. B. Judd, "Hue, Saturation, and Lightness of Surface Colors with Chromatic Illumination," *Journal of the Optical Society of America* 30 (1940): 2-32.

9. See C. Neumeyer, "Chromatic Adaptation in the Honey Bee: Successive Color Contrast and Color Constancy," *Journal of Comparative Physiology* 144 (1981): 543-53; D. J. Ingle, "The Goldfish as a Retinex Animal," *Science* 225 (1984): 651-53; and Vivian Budnik, et. al., "Chromatic Induction: A Comparative Study," *Perception*, forthcoming.

10. For a vivid demonstration of these two phenomena, see Phillippe Brou, et. al., "The Colors of Things, "*Scientific American* 255 (no. 3) (1986): 84-91.

11. For a historical treatment of theories of color vision, see Gerald Wasserman, *Color Vision: A Historical Introduction* (New York: John Wiley & Sons, 1978).

12. L. M. Hurvich and D. Jameson, "An Opponent-Process Theory of Color Vision," *Psychological Review* 64 (1957): 384-404. For more recent developments, see L. M. Hurvich, "Opponent Colors Theory," and D. Jameson, "Opponent Colors Theory in the Light of Physiological Findings," both in *Central and Peripheral Mechanisms of Colour Vision*, ed. D. Ottoson and S. Zeki (London: Macmillan, 1985).

13. See the papers collected in Ottoson and Zeki, ibid.

14. The most well-known model is Edwin Land's "retinex theory." See Land, op. cit. For more recent models, see L. T. Maloney, op. cit.; and R. Gershon, *The Use of Color in Computational Vision* (University of Toronto, Department of Computer Science: Technical Reports on Research in Biological and Computational Vision: RCBV-84-4, 1984). These models, as well as the formulation of the "problem" of color constancy on which they rely, have been criticized in an important recent paper by Dorothea Jameson and Leo Hurvich, "Essay Concerning Color Constancy," *Annual Review of Psychology* 40 (1989): 1-22.

15. See Edwin Land, "An Alternative Technique for the Computation of the Designator in the Retinex Theory of Color Vision," *Proceedings of the National Academy of Sciences* (USA) 83 (1986): 3078-80.

16. See G. Jacobs, *Comparative Color Vision* (New York: Academic Press, 1981); and J. F. W. Nuboer, "A Comparative Review on Colour Vision," *Netherlands Journal of Zoology* 36 (1986): 344-80.

17. See ibid. For tetrachromacy in fishes, see F. I. Harosi and Y. Hashimoto, "Ultraviolet Visual Pigment in a Vertebrate: A Tetrachromatic

Cone System in the Dace," *Science* 222 (1983): 1021-23; C. Neumeyer, "An Ultraviolet Receptor as a Fourth Receptor Type in Goldfish Color Vision," *Naturwissen-schaften* 72 (1985): 162-63; and "Wavelength Discrimination in the Goldfish," *Journal of Comparative Physiology* 158 (1958): 203-13. For birds, see S. D. Jane and J. K. Bowmaker, "Tetrachromatic Colour Vision in the Duck (*Anas platyrhynchos L.*): Microspectrophotometry of Visual Pigments and Oil Droplets," *Journal of Comparative Physiology* 162 (1988): 225-35; and D. Burkhardt, "UV Vision: A Bird's Eye View of Feathers," *Journal of Comparative Physiology* 164 (1989): 787-96.

18. Hardin, op. cit., 146, notes this possibility of ternary hues by imagining a hypothetical, tetrachromatic "visual superwoman," but does not extend his discussion to actual tetrachromacy among vertebrates, such as birds and fishes.

19. Cf. Jonathan Westphal's criticism of the "mosaic conception of color," op. cit.

20. See Nuboer, op. cit.

21. Ibid., and J. Lythgoe, *The Ecology of Vision* (Oxford: Clarendon Press, 1979), 188-93.

22. Brent Berlin and Paul Kay, *Basic Color Terms: Their Universality and Evolution* (Berkeley, CA: University of California Press, 1969).

23. See R. E. MacLaury, "Color Category Evolution and Shuswap Yellow-with-Green," *American Anthropologist* 89 (1987): 107-24.

24. George Lakoff, *Women, Fire, and Dangerous Things: What Categories Reveal About the Mind* (Chicago: University of Chicago Press, 1987), 29.

25. See T. Poggio, V. Torre, and C. Koch, "Computational Vision and Regularization Theory," *Nature* 317 (1985): 314-19; and A. Hurlbert and T. Poggio, "Making Machines (and Artificial Intelligence) See," *Daedalus* 117(no. 1) (1988): 213-39.

26. See Lythgoe, op. cit.

27. See Harosi and Hashimoto, op. cit.; and J. S. Levine and E. F. MacNichol, "Color Vision in Fishes," *Scientific American* 246 (1982): 140-49.

28. See Jameson and Hurvich, op. cit.

29. Nuboer, op. cit., 370-71.

30. P. Gouras and E. Zrenner, "Color Vision: A Review from a Neurophysiological Perspective," *Progress in Sensory Physiology* 1 (1981): 139- 79.

31. See Francisco Varela, "Vision as Action," *Models of Visual Perception: From Biological to Artificial*, ed. Michel Imbert (Oxford University

Press, 1989); and J. A. S. Kelso and B. A. Kay, "Information and Control: A Macroscopic Analysis of Perception-Action Coupling," *Perspectives on Perception and Action.*, ed. H. Heuer and A. F. Sanders (New Jersey: Lawrence Erlbaum Associates, 1987).

32. Maurice Merleau-Ponty, *Phenomenology of Perception.*, trsl. Colin Smith (London: Routledge and Kegan Paul, 1962), 214-15.

33. Maurice Merleau-Ponty, *The Visible and the Invisible*, trsl. Alphonso Lingis (Evanston, IL: Northwestern University Press, 1968), 130-31.

5

ARTHUR G. ZAJONC

Light and Cognition

In 1864 the poet Gerard Manley Hopkins, then a very young man, saw a rainbow. In writing of it Hopkins captured the problem of "emergence" in cognition, an issue central to this conference.

> It was a hard thing to undo this knot
> The rainbow shines but only in the thought
> Of him that looks. Yet not in that alone,
> For who makes rainbows by invention?
> And many standing round a waterfall
> See one bow each, yet not the same to all,
> But each a hand's breadth further than the next.
> The sun on falling waters writes the text
> Which yet is in the eye or in the thought.
> It was a hard thing to undo this knot.

At the close of the *ceri* race in Gubbio we too saw a rainbow arched triumphantly overhead in a cold, gray sky. Like Hopkins, where did we locate the rainbow: in the rain, in the sunlight, in the eye, or in the mind?

Phenomena emerge, they fill the mind with sights and sounds, yet how do they arise? What is our part in their production and what is the part played by an external world? More important to this paper and the conference theme, is the pattern of emergence immutable, myopic, single-minded; or can it, like a Proteus, assume myriad forms calling forth worlds whose emergent properties reflect connections hidden to other forms of ourselves, and are there cogent reasons for doing so?

Motives for change have arisen within many fields, from biology, ecology, atmospheric chemistry, immunology, to my own field of quantum optics. In it compelling new experiments have renewed the challenge that quantum physics made at the turn of the century regarding the strictures of classical forms of thought. By following two threads from recent developments, I hope to strengthen the challenge further and point to characteristics of the novel modes of understanding now required by the facts. Once the need is convincingly demonstrated, the project itself begins, the project of creating the requisite faculties adequate to the understanding of these newly emergent phenomena of science.

The significance of such considerations may seem slight, or to be merely so much academic epistemology, but I would argue to the contrary. Thought and, more basic still, the process of thinking are the progenitors of our civilization, and, like the ouroboros, their effects work back on themselves, rigidifying and reinforcing those modalities of thinking characteristic of an age, hindering the development of new modalities.

Our manner of thinking has shaped the planet and ourselves, and possesses the power to reshape them once more. The monuments of the past speak of traditions that have sculpted not only our exterior landscape, but an interior one as well. The textures and patterns of thought in which we now live are the outcome of hard-fought, spiritual battles that established a general mode of discourse, understanding, feeling, and action. While we may be unconscious of their history, these traditions are part of us and shape our habits of thought and understanding, our very seeing. In our own day, contemporary spiritual battles and new modes of knowledge are emerging. These will require fresh patterns of thought, unknown metaphors, and will also one day shape a future landscape.

In Perugia, Florence, Rome — indeed throughout Italy — we stand always within the aura of antiquity. Its noble institutions, its great artists and thinkers have exchanged the landscape of the wilderness — so close to us in the U.S. — for that of the garden, or better the protected hillside city, crafted into a work of art. The accomplishments of Dante, Ficino, Giotto, Leonardo, Michelangelo, Raphael and countless others have nourished and defined not only Italian culture, but that of the entire West. We are the inheritors not only of material monuments but cognitive ones as well.

Our Cognitive Inheritance

> Praise to thee, my Lord, for all thy creatures,
> Above all Brother Sun
> Who brings us the day and lends us his light,
>
> Lovely is he, radiant with great splendor,
> And speaks to us of thee,
> O Most High.
>
> Praise to thee, my Lord, for Sister Moon and the stars
> Which thou hast set in the heavens,
> Clear, precious, and fair.

When in 1225 Saint Francis composed these lines of his *Canticle to the Sun* while in the convent of Saint Damian, he was a participant in a long tradition of sacred and mythic knowledge that saw nature as alive and ensouled, that is, as a being. She was still the goddess Natura, as Bernard Silvestris or Alanus ab Insulis called her at Chartres.[1] Persephone still walked the earth. By the thirteenth century, however, the experience was so attenuated that Nature usually appeared only as a figure within Christian allegory. Her presence there, nonetheless, belies a rich and more intense ancestry, one that stretches back to Thales' declaration that "All things are full of gods," and beyond.

In the fifteenth century Marsilio Ficino, that student and interpreter of the "divine Plato," was also part of an ancient tradition, one that he saw as running back through Plato and Pythagoras to Orpheus, Hermes Trismegistus, and Zoroaster. Like St. Francis, he saw God and his multiplicity of angelic beings as manifested through light and the radiant celestial bodies of our universe.

Look at the heaven, please oh citizen of the celestial father-
land, at the heaven which was made orderly and manifest by
God for the purpose of making [clear the multiplicity of
beings]. When you look upward, the celestial entities tell you
the glory of God through the ray of the stars, like the glances
and signs of their eyes, and the firmament announces the
works of his hands. But the sun can signify to you God Himself in the greatest degree. The sun will give you the signs;
who would dare to call the sun false? So the invisible things
of God, that is, the angelic divinities, are seen and understood
particularly through the stars, and God's eternal power and
divinity through the sun.[2]

Thus is the universe a cosmos not of matter in motion, but a multiplicity of beings ordered and animated by the Godhead.

Around 1300, shortly after the life of St. Francis, a novel technical device appeared in medieval Europe, one that symbolized an
incipient change of enormous proportions. It did no work, nor did
it ease the burdens of manual labor, yet it became both in fact and
as metaphor the machine that grew to regulate the tempo of human
life. I am speaking, of course, of the mechanical clock. There had
been clocks of other sorts for centuries before — sundials, water
clocks, fire clocks, and sand clocks — but the development of the
mechanical clock marks a decisive point in the evolution of the
West.[3] I am interested, however, not in the mechanical clock as
technology, but as an instance where technology becomes image,
wherein a human invention comes to shape the imagination and to
provide a basis for understanding the natural world.

Following the discussion of Lynn White, Jr. the introduction of
the clock as part of the iconography of Christian theology occurred
shortly after the invention of the clock itself.[4] In the short span of
one hundred and fifty years, the mechanical clock became the
invariant attribute of the principal Virtue of the fifteenth century,
Temperance. Like the clock, the human body and soul require regulation by reason; and what was true for the microcosm was true
also for the macrocosm. At the end of the fourteenth century,
Nicole Oresme, in his *Duciel*, invoked the escapement feature of a
clockwork to explain how God regulated the orbital velocities of

the planets. It remained for Galileo to complete the unification of terrestrial and celestial mechanics and so provide the basis for the Deist notion of the mechanization of the entirety of God's creation.

With the gradual perfecting of the clock mechanism, life is no longer regulated by the movement of the sun during the day, or the stars at night. Civilized man is freed from nature and so may order his life, whether mercantile or monastic, by the hours of the mechanical clock. In Lynn White's words, "Human life no longer adapts the mechanism to its need; mankind is in some measure shaped by a machine which it adores."[5]

Thus, close on the heels of St. Francis, Ficino, and the Italian Renaissance, indeed almost within their embrace, were the stirrings of another nascent tradition. It found its fulfillment a century after Ficino's death when the modern world conception was born through Copernicus, Descartes, and Galileo. Like those before him, Galileo too was a student of nature who admired its extraordinary order. He heard in it, however, a different voice, one that spoke the language of mathematics and whose meaning was the principles of mechanics. While many threads connected Galileo with the past, both his contemporaries and we recognize in him the exponent of a new science. It is four hundred years since the birth of modern science. Our world has been profoundly changed by its presence. If the architects and artists of the Renaissance lifted their cities into works of art, we in turn have filled them with the technological offspring of the scientific revolution. Into Perugia's fifteenth-century "Hall of the Notary" we have brought the electronics required for simultaneous translation of English into Italian. Two traditions, two cultures are entwined in the Italian landscape, one that ended in Ficino and another that began in Galileo. I believe we in our time stand at a similar juncture, one in which the tension between these two cultures may find the resolution so urgently needed.

Our cognitive inheritance is twofold. Our aspirations to be good stewards of the earth, to dress creation with the beautiful work of our own hands, and to recognize within nature the goddess Natura, all echo the song of St. Francis. They are born of a participation in cosmos and an experience of self that reaches to a distant past, one in which the divine was everywhere immanent and open to us. The

115

strains of a different song, brilliant and strong, ring out from the technological offspring of the scientific revolution. A clockwork universe excludes human participation except as another component of its vast mechanism. It seems without inherent value or meaning. This dimension of our cognitive inheritance is more recent and more pressing. Both voices still resound, but too often the discord between them leads to misunderstandings and tragedies: at Chernobyl or Bhopal.

One of those who clearly heard both voices and the tension between them was the nineteenth-century American thinker and essayist Ralph Waldo Emerson, patriarch of the Transcendentalist movement.[6] Together with a good many others on both sides of the Atlantic, he recognized that the old order of things (Ficino's and St. Francis's) was fast crumbling about Western man. The spiritual convictions and values of earlier centuries were being challenged by a newer vision of man and nature espoused by the then flourishing savants of natural science. In a letter he wrote:

Natural science is the point of interest now, and, I think, is dimming and extinguishing a good deal that was called poetry. These sublime and all-reconciling revelations of nature will exact of poetry a correspondent height and scope, or put an end to it.[7]

As the old forms fell, Emerson held that we were freed to create an original, participatory relation to nature, not one mediated through scripture, prophets, and history but experienced directly.

Why should not we have a poetry and philosophy of insight and not of tradition, and a religion by revelation to us and not the history of theirs?... The sun shines today also. There is more wool and flax in the fields. There are new lands, new men, new thoughts.[8]

"The venerable and beautiful traditions in which we were educated are losing their hold on human belief, day by day."[9] As the old forms rattle, the new falteringly appear. The fashioning of a new tradition, a philosophy of contemporary insight — such was

116

the project that Emerson, Thoreau, Alcott, and their collaborators envisioned, but left unrealized in their lifetime. It is one that stands before us still.

The Facts of Light

Contemporary motivations for change go beyond the dissatisfactions of the nineteenth-century Romantics. At their best they are grounded in the scientific facts and powerful moral dilemmas of our modern world. The invention of the mechanical clock is a single instance in the extraordinary technological transformation that dawned with its invention. Since then we have seen both the industrial revolution and the recent advent of cybernetics. Each elaborated the clockwork image, expanding its dominion until it appeared to encompass all of existence. Yet are there objects whose nature is so radically non-mechanical that they defy all honest attempts to include them in the catalog of machines? I am convinced there are many, but none is so unambiguously non-mechanical as light.

I begin by referring to the old saw regarding the impossibility of creating a classical model of certain quantum phenomena. Recently the issue has taken on more dramatic proportions with the experimental realizations in several scientific laboratories of what had heretofore been mere thought experiments, only a gleam in the minds of Einstein and Bohr.[10] These include John Archibald Wheeler's proposal of a so-called "delayed-choice" experiment,[11] the Einstein-Podolsky-Rosen experiment, and the phenomena associated with superconductivity so much in the news. Each of these effects, and many others, requires the concept of "quantum superposition," a concept that simply defies our traditional clockwork imagination and challenges us to develop new imaginative modalities. I begin with the specific case of the delayed-choice experiment, an experiment in which I collaborated at the Max Planck Institute for Quantum Optics in Garching.[12]

The experiment dramatizes the so-called wave-particle duality of light. In order to understand its results we need to establish the criteria for the recognition of particles and waves; that is, how do

117

we know whether we have the one or the other? The standard test for a particle is indivisibility. If we can split the particle, then it may have been composed of other particles, or it could be a wave. If, however, the particle is resolutely indivisible then we can declare it unequivocally to have been a single particle. The criterion for a wave is the phenomenon of interference. That is, when two wave-trains cross, the disturbance displays very characteristic maxima and minima. Make a slit with two extended fingers and look through the slit at a source of light. You will notice alternating light and dark bands in the region between your fingers. This is evidence for the wave nature of light. With these two criteria, indivisibility and interference, we are now ready to interpret experiments that will give us the "definitive" answer to the question regarding the nature of light.

A light source has been invented which claims to produce one "particle" of light at a time. How do I test it? I do so, naturally, by attempting to divide the particle in half. The apparatus for this is very simple, merely a half-silvered mirror.[13] It possesses the property of transmitting half the light incident on it and reflecting the remaining half. Obviously if there is, in fact, only a single indivisible "particle" of light, then the mirror will be unable to split the light in two. Rather it will either transmit the light or reflect it. The apparatus is completed by placing two light detectors as shown in Fig. 1. They are of sufficient sensitivity to respond to single "particles" of light. If the "particle" is divisible then the detectors will fire simultaneously, thereby showing that part of the light was reflected and part transmitted. If, however, only one fires for each particle incident on the half-silvered mirror, then we did possess a single "particle" of light.

Several so-called, single-photon sources have been invented and the tests outlined above performed. The results of these experiments confirms that under special circumstances one can produce single, indivisible "particles" of light. It is important to stress the experimentally determined indivisibility of the "particles" as the paradox hinges on it.

We now turn to the second aspect of the experiment, namely interferometry. The principle of an interferometer is very simple. It is a device designed to divide light into two beams and then to recombine them so as to show interference effects. Remember interference is proof of the "wave" nature of light. If we succeed in dividing light into two beams and, through recombination, to create interference, then we will have demonstrated that light is a wave. An interferometer (of the Mach-Zehnder type) is shown in Fig. 2. Light of the usual sort (not the single-particle kind) enters the interferometer through a half-silvered mirror, is split into two beams, and, after reflection from two fully silvered mirrors, recombines on a second half-silvered mirror. If one looks on a placard at some distance from the final mirror, one sees light and dark bands, that is, interference, which is clear evidence for light as a wave.

Now the critical moment. Use the single-particle light source as the light source for the interferometer. What will happen? Recall that the success of the interferometer experiment requires that the light be divided at the first beam splitter. By contrast, the success of the particle experiment requires that the light remain undivided for a single-particle source. These are logical opposites. We cannot entertain both ideas at the same time without cognitive dissonance of a rather high order.

We will further heighten the stakes by the following experimental ruse. The experimentalist will at first only set up part of the experiment. The experiment begins with the final half-silvered mirror missing (see Fig. 3). The attentive reader will now recognize an ambiguity in the design. By leaving the final half-silvered mirror out I have described an apparatus suited to test for single particles of light. By inserting the final half-silvered mirror the device becomes an interferometer suited to test for the wave nature of light. Simply inserting or removing the final mirror changes the entire intention of the apparatus. Moreover, I am free to insert or remove the final mirror at any time. This is what Wheeler termed "delayed-choice."

Allow the single-particle source to emit its particles one at a time into the apparatus, and run the experiment in three modes. The first two are simply to insert and remove the final half-silvered mirror prior to running the experiment. What is found? With the mirror removed we find experimentally that half the time one detector fires and half the time the other, but the two never fire together. This is the signature for indivisible "particles of light." Now with the source unchanged, insert the final beam splitter and run the experiment. What do the detectors show? They now display the unambiguous signature of interference. But interference requires the particle to divide at the first half-silvered mirror, which we just showed never to happen with the single-photon source used! Is there some way the particle could, perhaps by "sensing" the intent of the experiment, divide in the latter instance but not in the former? This is a bizarre scenario but one that can be tested by the delayed-choice experiment.

In the third mode of running the experiment we wait to insert or remove the final half-silvered mirror until after the "particle" of light has passed the first half-silvered mirror, that is, we delay our choice of what experiment to run until the light is deep inside the interferometer. Even in these circumstances one still detects an interference pattern when the final half-silvered mirror is inserted, and no interference without it! What this implies is that light must be in an ambiguous quantum "superposition" state during the interval from entry into the apparatus until departure through the final half-silvered mirror (or at least until we choose).

For purposes of clarity I will repeat what I take to be the ultimate results of the experiment. If we think classically (by which in this instance I mean mechanically), we confront a situation that requires an indivisible particle of light to travel a single path to a single detector, and simultaneously requires it to travel two distinct paths to two detectors. This is a logical impossibility. An entity, whatever it is, cannot travel along both a single trajectory and a pair of trajectories at the same time.

The standard conclusion drawn by orthodox quantum mechanics is that one has created a non-classical, quantum (i.e., non-mechanical) state termed a superposition state. Invoking such a phrase does not, of course, constitute an explanation, any more than reference to the somniferous quality of a tablet explains the effect of a sleeping pill. Such language simply locates that which we do not understand. There does exist, however, a precise mathematical meaning to the phrase, "quantum superposition state." Still, the clarity of the mathematical formalism has not translated into a clear understanding of the physical phenomena themselves.

120

In fact, the suggestion is very often advanced that we must give up understanding in favor of computing. But this is to give up too much. There is an important lesson here, one we should not shy away from, a challenge before which we should not shrink.

Understanding appears to require an image, and the inevitable trend is toward the machine. The imagination of a mechanical universe has provided science with a powerful means of understanding a large but finite range of effects. There exist however, even within the domain of physics, phenomena such as those described above that simply cannot be thought of in mechanical terms without spectacular violations of logic, or simple "common sense." Here enters the arrogance of the tradition. What cannot be imagined mechanically cannot be imagined at all. One can compute, and predict on the bases of computation, but one must forego the old pleasures of understanding, or at least modify our traditional sense of what it means to understand.

Nor is the problem with light limited to the wave-particle question. There are other puzzling features of its apparent nature, such as the lack of a quantum-mechanically acceptable concept of position.[14] Electrons and similar elementary particles formally possess a clear position variable. This is not the case with light. To ask the simple question *Where?* is far more subtle for light than for matter. But this seems consistent with the results of the delayed-choice experiment.

Such issues are a small matter, say some. After all, consider the extremes to which you have to go to find a phenomenon that cannot be embraced within the mechanical universe. We can well afford a few borderland phenomena that fall outside of our mechanical paradigm. Yet I fear that these phenomena are multiplying, and, like the few resistant phenomena that ultimately led to the development of quantum mechanics, these too will ultimately require of us serious and responsible attention. Many of the solid-state electronic devices common today, from television to calculator, operate because the mechanical paradigm fails, and perhaps the most spectacular failure will be high-temperature superconductivity.

The single-photon, delayed-choice interferometer ran on one photon at a time. Conceptually you cannot find a cleaner experiment. Its practical consequences, however, are in proportion to the intensity of the light used. Light just never appears as a single photon in nature or in the technical world. With the discovery of superconductivity in 1911 by H. Kammerling Onnes, and now the promise of massive technological implementation of the effect, macroscopic quantum effects of a kind apparently similar to the arcane ones of light may literally drive the engines of industry. The theory of superconductivity requires a cooperative behavior of electrons over distances that, on an atomic scale, are staggeringly large. There again is no classical imagination that can capture the quantum state of a superconductor. Paradoxes and conceptual confusions of the same kind attend any attempt to force the phenomenon into a classical straitjacket.

One can be confident that the pattern will continue to evolve, like a spider weaving its web in ever expanding circles. Just how much of the world and our surroundings are we willing not to understand? Or shall we take up the challenge and begin to imagine in new ways, faltering at first but gradually learning from our mistakes and fashioning other images of nature? How can mathematics capture in its formal net something which our imagination cannot? Should we not follow the lead of our mathematics and create an imaginative faculty of comparable scope and flexibility?

Lynn White, Jr., has traced the origin of the metaphor "a clock-work universe" back to the Middle Ages and to the fabrication of that extraordinary human device, the mechanical clock, that effectively freed man's sense of time from the motions of the heavens and fixed it to the rhythms of a physical instrument. Could it be that the technical innovations of quantum mechanics will engender a similar revolution in thought? Will we come to imagine our universe and ourselves differently for the existence of a revolutionary, quantum technology?

Harbingers of Imagination

If contemporary science points to inadequacies in present-day modes of thinking, we can ask: what will be the shape of the new manner of understanding required by our future? Perhaps ironically, I believe the harbingers of our future mentality, as required by science and the imperatives of living in our precarious times, will be artists. For centuries they have struggled to create ways of seeing and knowing that often appeared to be at odds with the burgeoning science of our era. I believe that we now truly stand in need, not only as scientists but as a civilization, of their cognitive capacities. In them, when rightly developed, will the two streams of our cognitive inheritance be married.

Few artists have worked consciously with the ideas I have suggested. An exception was the German poet, playwright, author, and scientist Johann Wolfgang von Goethe. Although internationally distinguished by his literary career, Goethe's own evaluation of his life's work diverged from both that of his contemporaries and posterity. He felt that his most significant contributions were not to poetry but to science. In our treatment of Goethe's scientific work, I would have us look not at his impressive contributions to botany, osteology, color science, or meteorology, but to his distinctive method and objective.[15]

Through an exchange of letters in 1798 with his friend Friedrich Schiller, Goethe gained clarity about his methodology, which was becoming, as Schiller termed it, a "rational empiricism."[16] Of his process of investigation Goethe wrote to Schiller that one passed through three stages:

1. The empirical phenomenon, which everyone finds in nature, and which is then raised through experiments to the level of

2. The scientific phenomenon by producing it under circumstances and conditions different from those in which it was first observed, in a sequence which is more or less successful.

3. The pure phenomenon now stands before us as the result of all our observations and experiments. It can never be isolated, but it appears in a continuous sequence of events. To depict it, the human mind gives definition to the empirically variable, excludes the accidental, sets aside the impure, untangles the complicated, and even discovers the unknown.[17]

It is essential to note that each of the three stages is referred to as a phenomenon, the latter of a higher order than the former, until

123

finally one attains what Goethe variously termed the "pure" or "archetypal phenomenon." In this mode of inquiry never does one slip off into abstract, mathematical representations of the phenomenon under study, nor is it a "question of causes, but of conditions under which the phenomena appear."[18] In these two ways Goethe appears to distinguish himself radically from orthodox views of the scientific method and its goal. For Kant, as for most since, science without mathematics is not science at all. Moreover, if one is not searching for causes, then what can be the objective of scientific inquiry?

Goethe's response to the last remark would certainly be to point to the archetypal phenomenon which is for him the endpoint of scientific investigation. He recognizes that many will wish to reach beyond the phenomenon to hypothetical entities or supposed causes, but for him the archetypal phenomenon represents the point of culmination beyond which one should not go. In that moment "the human mind can come closest to things in their general state, draw them near, and, so to speak, form an amalgam with them."[19] In one of his "Maxims and Reflections" Goethe describes the process in a similar manner as follows:

> There is a delicate empiricism which makes itself utterly identical with the object, thereby becoming true theory. But this enhancement of our mental powers belongs to a highly evolved age.[20]

Thus it is that Goethe holds always to experience, to phenomena, even when reaching to the theoretical level. To understand this it is perhaps helpful to recall the original meaning of our word "theory." It is derived from the Greek *theoria* which means "to behold." Goethe was in this and other ways like the Greeks. To understand, one must see, envision, behold in the mind as well as in the external world. In fact, are not these two, inner and outer, subject and object, like cause and effect, caught up into a single unity in the phenomenon? By "making itself utterly identical with the object" one's experience becomes true theory.

> The ultimate goal would be: to grasp that everything in the realm of fact is already theory. The blue of the sky shows us

the basic law of chromatics. Let us not seek for something
behind the phenomena — they themselves are the theory.[21]

As unusual as it may at first seem, the point of all scientific
inquiry is to behold a phenomenon as theory. Nor is this goal alien
to the history of science — it stands behind every scientific discovery. When Newton perceives in the falling apple the orbit of the
Moon, he is seeing "fact as theory." He had puzzled long and tena-
ciously to win from nature his vision of the coherence we now all
can learn to see after him. Galileo in the cathedral of Pisa, in seeing
the swinging chandelier, saw the isochronous pendulum of a
clock. What is it that allows such theoretical seeing?

First of all we should realize that all of our seeing is structured
and informed by us. We do not have raw sense impressions, we see
red, green, blue; we see particular objects from wood shavings to
hand-held calculators. These already possess a conceptual character. Our observing is always, as Hanson calls it, "theory-
laden."[22]

Out of the practice of science Goethe saw the possibility for
developing new cognitive faculties, ones whose emergence would
bring with them the perception of novel and hitherto unseen coher-
ences within nature. Our manner of thinking limits and even forms
the very world we experience. Cognitive science has taught us
much concerning the hidden forces that shape our individual and
culturally shared view of the world. Goethe proposed that by stay-
ing with the phenomena, varying their conditions of appearance,
experimenting with them but holding the phenomena always in
view, cognitive capacities would arise suited to the proper understanding of them. "Every new object, clearly seen, opens up a new
organ of perception in us."[23]

With the new organs so fashioned, understanding arises in what
Goethe termed an *aperçu*, and "such a discovery is infinitely fruitful."[24] Moments such as these, whether experienced by Newton,
Goethe, or any passionately inquiring scientist, are artistic
moments. It is a kind of seeing into nature. For Emerson, the poet's
task was nothing more than this: To walk within nature not as a
spy, but as the transcendency of her own being, and so to articulate
in words what she performs for and within us.[25] Emerson realized
the kinship between artistry and the exhilarating moment of

scientific discovery when he wrote: "And never did any science originate but by a poetic perception."[26]

If we would create the capacities for understanding our future, then we must dwell precisely in the tensions, the paradoxes, the annoying anomalies of our time. Only thus will we develop the faculties suited to understand the nature of light and, I believe, see the way through our perilous times. We may think with Goethe that such "mental powers belong to a highly evolved age," but I believe that ours is the dawn of that age. The prerequisites are there: the mandate of orthodox science to develop our imaginative capacities, and the dictates of our conscience if we would avoid the technical calamities that threaten our well-being and survival. On nearly every front we are being called on to re-imagine the world we inhabit. It simply awaits an act of courage for us to begin, and patient perseverance for us to succeed in the self-conscious education now in our hands.

* * * * *

The builders of the beautiful, stained-glass windows of Chartres saw light as a Christ-like emanation from God which in passing through the colored glass they had fashioned, reenacted the mystery of Mary, of the Incarnation. The infinite became finite. God made man. This too is part of the story of light. Into the fabric of light are woven patterns at every hierarchical level, sensory and spiritual. The faculties with which we see it can impoverish it, but we are forever challenged to reshape ourselves, to stand within the full phenomenon of light and color so that organs may be formed that correspond to it at every level of its being, whether that be the quantum level of modern physics, or the spiritual level of St. Francis, Ficino, and the Chartres masters.

Notes

1. Alan of Lille, *The Plaint of Nature*, translation and commentary by James J. Sheridan (Toronto: Pontifical Institute of Mediaeval Studies,

1980), and Bernardus Silvestris, *The Cosmographia*, translated and edited by Winthrop Wetherbee (New York: Columbia University Press, 1973).

2. Paul Oskar Kristeller, *The Philosophy of Marsilio Ficino*, transl. Virginia Conant (Gloucester, MA: Peter Smith, 1964).

3. David S. Landes, *Revolutions in Time* (Cambridge, MA: Belknap Press of Harvard University, 1983).

4. Lynn White, Jr., "Tempermentia and the Virtuousness of Technology," in *Medieval Religion and Technology* (Berkeley, CA: University of California Press, 1978).

5. White, "Tempermentia," op. cit., 198.

6. See Peter A. Obuchowski, "The Relationship of Emerson's Interest in Science to his Thought," 1969, Ph.D. dissertation (Ann Arbor, MI: University Microfilms).

7. Ralph Waldo Emerson, *The Letters of Ralph Waldo Emerson*, ed. Ralph L. Rusk (New York: Columbia University Press, 1939) vol. 6, 63.

8. Ralph Waldo Emerson, "Nature," in *The Complete Works of Ralph Waldo Emerson*, ed. Edward Waldo Emerson (Boston: Riverside Press, 1903-1904). The Centenary Edition, vol.1.

9. Emerson, *Complete Works* vol. 10, 217-18.

10. For a good collection of the original materials see J.A. Wheeler and W.H. Zurek, eds., *Quantum Theory and Measurement* (Princeton: Princeton University Press, 1983).

11. John A. Wheeler, in *Mathematical Foundations of Quantum Theory*, ed. A. R. Marlow (New York: Academic Press, 1978), 9.

12. T. Hellmuth, H. Walther, A. Zajonc, and W. Schleich, "Delayed-choice Experiments in Quantum Interference," *Phys. Rev. A.* 35 (March 1987): 2532-41.

13. P. Grangier, G. Roger, and A. Aspect, "Experimental Evidence for a Photon Anti-Correlation Effect on a Beam Splitter: A New Light on Single-Photon Interferences," *Europhysics Letters* 1 (February 1986.): 173-79.

14. T. D. Newton and E. P. Wigner, "Localized States for Elementary Systems," *Reviews of Modern Physics* 21 (July 1949): 405.

15. For a fuller discussion of Goethe's scientific work see: Arthur G. Zajonc, "Facts as Theory: Aspects of Goethe's Philosophy of Science," in *Goethe and the Sciences: A Reappraisal*, ed. F. Amrine, F. Zucker, and Harvey Wheeler (Boston: Reidel Publishing Co., 1987), 219-46. This volume contains an important bibliography of writings on Goethe and the sciences.

16. Rudolf Steiner, *A Theory of Knowledge Implicit in Goethe's World*

Conception, transl. Olin Wannamaker (Spring Valley, NY: Anthroposophic Press, 1968), 119.

17. Johann W. von Goethe, "Empirical Observation and Science," (Jan. 15, 1798) in *Scientific Studies*, ed. and transl. Douglas Miller (Boston: Suhrkamp Publishers, 1988), 24-25.

18. Ibid., 25.

19. Ibid.

20. Ibid., 307.

21. Ibid., 307.

22. N. R. Hanson, *Patterns of Discovery: An Inquiry Into the Conceptual Foundations of Science* (Cambridge: Cambridge University Press, 1958).

23. Goethe, *Scientific Studies*, 39.

24. Goethe, from a letter to Soret, December 30, 1823, quoted by Rike Wankmuller in the *Hamburger Ausgabe* of *Goethes Werke*, vol 13, 616.

25. Emerson, "The Poet," in *Complete Works*, op. cit. vol. 2.

26. Emerson, *Complete Works* vol. 8, 365.

FIGURE LEGENDS

FIGURE 1. "Particle Test": A pulse of light is incident on the beam splitter (BS), which is a half-silvered mirror. If the light is a wave, then half will go towards detector x and half towards detector y. If the light is a single particle, then it will go either towards x or towards y, but not both.

FIGURE 2. "Wave Test": A pulse of light is incident on beam splitter one (BS1). If it is a wave, then as before half will go along path x and half along path y. Mirrors (M) are used to recombine the two beams onto beam splitter 2 (BS2). The resulting "interference" phenomenon is proof that the light traveled both paths.

FIGURE 3. "Delayed-choice Experiment": (1 and 2) A light pulse enters an interferometer of the type shown in Fig. 2, except that the final beam splitter is missing. By leaving the final beam splitter out, one discovers which route the quantum followed. (3B) By inserting beam splitter two (BS2), interference arises and the quantum is shown to have traveled both routes.

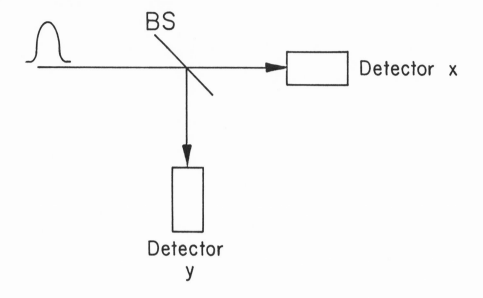

Figure 1

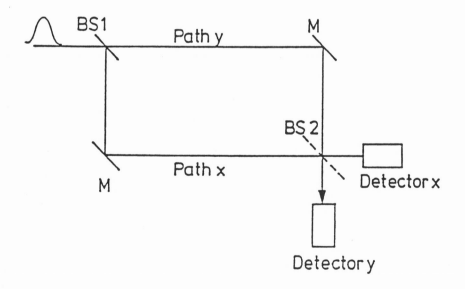

Figure 2

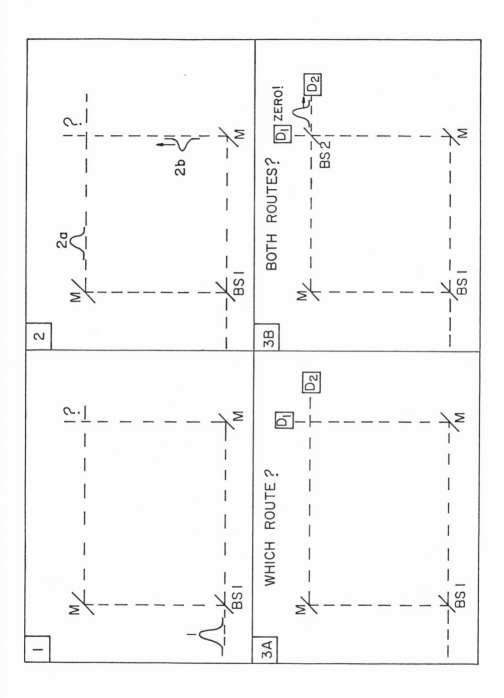

Figure 3

6

WES JACKSON

Hierarchical Levels, Emergent Qualities, Ecosystems, and the Ground for a New Agriculture

There has been a revival of interest in the nature-nurture question lately, spawned in part, I suppose, by the anxiety generated from the claims of that fast-moving field, biotechnology. A lot of the old ground is being covered again, but this time around the questioning includes knowledge gained during elucidation of the hereditary code: how genes are turned on and off. Also, this time more of us are worried that we may be going too far, too fast, and too heedlessly. Yet the corporate state and big government are investing billions in tinkering with nature.

The question is, how are we to think about what nature is or what is natural? It is not good enough to say that everything is natural if the word is to have any meaning. We need a deepening of the discussion if we are to develop the criteria for a more critical analysis. If we don't tighten up, the slugfest against nature will continue, whether the battering comes from agriculture or from industry.

Nature gives birth. That is part of the meaning of nature. It is an important concept in considering the nature-nurture question, for every child born is a unique combination, a product different from its parents, a change in the family. The logic is straightforward. Nature means birth. Birth implies change. Change is therefore inevitable. This line of thinking doesn't help us much; in fact, it creates problems for those of us who would use nature as a standard. This standard is a moving target and the prodigal have the upper hand here; since they treat nature as though it is expendable, they believe they can justify imprudent actions with the argument that "nature changes."

A nearly opposite but no more helpful tack on the nature-nurture question is taken by the group of researchers whose daily work involves the question of what nature is in ways that are quantifiable in nearly absolute terms. These are the plant and animal breeders who work with genotype-environment interactions. Their approach goes like this: Before a breeder can select a desirable trait, he must know how much the trait is influenced by heredity and how much by environment. In this narrow sense, heredity is equivalent to nature and environment is the nurturer. There is a mathematical model and also experimental designs for resolving that question. The model might be called a heritability equation, for it yields a value that breeders can rely on in working for yield improvement or insect and pathogen resistance or whatever. If you achieve a value of 0.7 from your heritability equation you have something to work with in a breeding program. If the heritable component is down around 0.3 on the other hand, one may as well forget any improvement through genetic manipulation. In its realm, this equation is pretty sound.

For the breeders, in an admittedly limited but nevertheless very practical sense, the nature-nurture question has been resolved. For them the proof is in the pudding. Corn yields averaged around 30 bushels per acre 50 years ago but are well over 100 bushels per acre now. I mention this because plant and animal breeders are likely to be impatient with any philosophical mishmash on the nature-nurture question. Their hard data, reflected in yield improvement, is indisputable. There will be little philosophical help from this quarter and probably very little sympathy for any anxiety expressed over the question "what is nature?"

There are, nevertheless, very practical reasons to think about nature and agriculture and the associated ethical considerations.

There is a third realm or line of inquiry we might consider on this question, and it springs from a major problem, the problem of germ plasm loss in our crops and livestock and the germ plasm loss due to species extinction, especially in the tropics. The leading assumption here is that biological information is being lost. We are talking about, in other words, a loss of hereditary material, meaning the chemical basis of heredity, the very language of life. Countless combinations of DNA have come into existence over the millennia through natural selection. The loss of this material is a major worry of biologists and rightly so. But even here, we have no first or final absolute to call upon.

The problem is that we have treated information as though it always has a material basis, assuming that high information equals complexity. As soon as we set out to measure information, several problems develop. We can use the Shannon information measure on organisms, for example. Here we just check the DNA code of each organism and tote up the number of three-letter words consisting of a four-letter alphabet. We get interesting results that way; some amphibians are more complex than humans, and, indeed, many invertebrates have more information than many vertebrates. As Levins and Lewontin have said:

> The problem is that complexity and information have only a metaphorical, not an exact, equivalence. While it is appealing to speak of "information" about the environment being "coded" in the structural and physiological complexity of organisms, such statements remain in the realm of poetry.[1]

Part of the problem is that the human being has the ability to name "nothingness." It is like speaking of the void: There is nothing there, but we have named it anyway. (I understand that it is at least 2 degrees Kelvin in space, but even if there were nothing there we would still call it void.) But this isn't just a human language problem. Three examples come immediately to mind, and I want to tell you about them for they represent a major consideration.

Green Revolution researchers pushing for high yield in the big three — corn, wheat, and rice — selected for "high fertilizer response" genes. In some cases at least, what Green Revolution researchers effectively accomplished was the removal of those genes that cause plants to discriminate in the uptake of nutrients. In other words, the genetic paupers they created were biological vacuum cleaners designed to suck up the fossil-fuel-sponsored fertility applied to the fields. It was the destruction of biological discrimination rather than enlargement of the genetic code. With the genes for discrimination gone, or mutated beyond expression, the "blank" or disrupted area of the code effectively became what we might call a "high fertilizer response" locus.

Another example is the corn in which breeding was carried out for resistance to the fungus responsible for southern leaf blight. Corn breeders selected for resistance to this fungus, gradually accumulating genes which would grant physiological resistance to this pest. As they were progressing toward piling up genes for physiological resistance, something happened that reversed the tack. At the other end of the spectrum for physiological resistance in corn was supersensitivity. Here sensitivity was so acute that following infection there was an immediate cellular death of corn leaf tissue around the infecting spore, so immediate and complete that the dead tissue effectively walled off the fungus. Some breeders then began to select corn genotypes so sensitive, so lacking in the genetic material responsible for fighting the fungus, that they achieved the end they were after. The corn plant was protected, in other words, because it lacked the biological information that the Shannon information method would measure.

Finally, from a recent article in *Science* about why women live longer, the work of Professor Kirby Smith of Johns Hopkins University is relevant. He has studied death rates in four generations of an Amish family. Functionally normal males in this particular family have an average life span of 82.3 years. They outlive their female counterparts who live to an average age of 77.4 years. In two nearby Amish families, the women died in their mid-70s and the men died five or six years earlier, about what you would expect in a normal population. A study of the chromosomes of the long-lived males revealed that they are missing the long arm of the Y chromosome. Professor Smith does not know what is in the arm that is missing. Only one gene has ever been identified. But in this case, what is apparently a loss of genetic information results in greater longevity.[2]

I am not offering these three examples about the loss of biological information for the purpose of encouraging a Ludwig to restart his bulldozers to resume clearing tropical forests, or of encouraging breeders to further narrow the germ plasm of our crops. I cite them for two purposes: the first is to pull ourselves away from thinking of some easily quantifiable criterion for what constitutes biological information, and the second is to recognize chaos or deficiency as an important source of information as we think of the ontogeny of information. More on this later.

The "bits" and "bytes" of the computer industry are countable, an "amount" of information that can be determined. But the computer world is not the whole world. And though there is the easily quantifiable genotype/environment interaction that the breeders calculate, we must remember the breeders are not paying attention to nucleotide bases. Rather they are looking at phenotypes, and they don't know whether there are nucleotide bases present or whether it is the absence of such bases that is responsible for the "hereditary" component they identify.

There is one other little tidbit worthy of consideration here that has come out of our detailed exploration of the genetic code. There is a gene in mice associated with a common mammary tumor. It turns out that this oncogene, which is to say cancer gene, is found to be the same gene responsible for the wingless mutant in the fruit fly.[3] It is likely that this is a developmental gene that has been conserved over evolutionary time. What is interesting, however, is that the expression of this gene is in two apparently unrelated ontogenetic parts of the two organisms involved. One would hope and expect that a gene would be a gene would be a gene, recognizable by its expression anywhere it is found, fruit fly or mouse. This further complicates our understanding of information.

What we have, then, is a subject packed with numerous uncertainties and no absolutes. I find myself repeatedly drifting back to David Ehrenfeld's essay "Conservation of Non-Resources," in which he examines and lays to rest all of the usually held arguments in favor of saving threatened life forms.

Nevertheless, examining the relationship between nature and

agriculture is of great practical importance during this era of a widespread emphasis on biotechnology. The main target of the biotechnologists at the moment seems to be agriculture, one of the most defenseless sectors in the society.

What is the basis for our objections though, if the easy philosophical base lines are absent? First of all, we can object to the speed at which biotechnology is being brought on. It is possible to approach a busy intersection at 100 miles an hour, but it would not be regarded as prudent even if it were lawful. The multibillion-dollar biotechnology industry is coming on so fast that the public has little time to assess its possible consequences to agriculture and to culture. The bottom line being offered by biotech promoters is increased production at a time of overproduction. What we need now is time for our imaginations to work, time to contemplate the intersection where biotechnology and agriculture converge. If the plant and animal breeders were the main promoters, it would be understandable. But if they are weary of the long time frames they have been forced to work in, I have seen little evidence of it. Plant life cycles usually do involve a year. Breeding programs take many years, unlike chemical manipulations in which chemists can mix up some chemicals and get a reaction immediately.

A second consideration may have more to do with the character of our civilization. It may be rooted in our technological culture that we put "high tech" at the top of the pecking order. This motivation was made apparent recently by a high USDA official in what must have been a slip of the tongue or truth's insistence on being heard. Orville Bentley is the former Dean of the College of Agriculture at the University of Illinois and is now Assistant Secretary for Science and Education in the USDA. His office is in charge of the Agricultural Research Service, the Cooperative State Research Service, and the Extension Service. Mr. Bentley told *Chemical & Engineering News* (November 22, 1982):

There is a change taking place that is more rapid than gradual. There will be a swing toward mobilizing our resources toward biotechnology, genetic manipulation. I think the driving force will be efforts to increase yields, productivity, and production as a way to keep the level of technology high.

It becomes clear why a one-percent annual yield increase in several of the major crops is unsatisfying.

The statement "to increase yields, productivity, and production as a way to keep the level of technology high" is orders of magnitude worse than "art for art's sake." The new slogan might be "high technology for the sake of high technology," even at the expense of farm families and rural communities.

If Jefferson were alive today and involved in setting up a new nation, might he insist as strongly on the separation of science and state as he did on the separation of church and state? The consequences of the church-state alliance seem small compared to the ecological and social consequences of the science-state alliance.

I have identified the problem of biotechnology altering nature as being one of speed and the desire to keep the level of technology high. Though we may have no absolutes on which to hang our argument, we do have some consequences we should take very seriously. When a human growth-hormone gene is spliced into hogs in order to make them bigger and leaner, we also make them arthritic and cross-eyed. One could go on and on with a list of such biological freaks already created, but the worst case scenario might be one in which everything that has been promised actually works. Imagine the consequences if the new crops and livestock have no natural enemies. Will they be like Johnson grass or kudzu, crowding out anything in their way? What if the bovine growth hormone does increase milk production 30 percent (and it seems certain to)? The small-family dairy farmer and his family may have to leave the farm and work in the city. When the gene for herbicide resistance is successfully spliced into the soybean, Monsanto will give neither their bean seed nor the herbicide away. Monsanto scientists are well paid. Should we not expect high costs being passed on to farmers who buy into the technologies? Input costs are half the cause of the farm crisis. Who will buy these products, anyway? The insurance companies who own farms or the major corporate farms?

I am entertaining this apparent digression on purpose because the title for our symposium is "Biology as a Basis for Design." What I suppose stands behind that title selection is the hope, if not the expectation, that we need a different understanding of nature for this last part of the twentieth century: an expansion of the definition, perhaps. I agree, but I don't believe this expansion is likely to occur by discovering more ways in which nature strikes back when we do something stupid or by being shown more ways in which nature bats last. That's only expanding the inventory of the kinds of things we are all familiar with. This is the "ain't the consequences of the Aswan Dam awful" syndrome.

Where then do we begin? We are all interested in healing the Earth and redeeming ecosystems. We are all interested in diversity. Whether our field is economics or ecology, we are all interested in avoiding the overshoots that lead to wild oscillations before settling down to a dynamic equilibrium at a much lower level.

I think one beginning point is to acknowledge that we do not know what the Earth is, let alone what the Earth is about. In this respect, the concept of Gaia, as it is popularly conceived, which is not necessarily as Jim Lovelock and Lynn Margulis conceived it, may be doing humanity a disservice. Ask anyone who has heard of the Gaia concept to explain what it means to him or her. One of the first statements is that the "Earth is an organism." That is the notion I want to examine more closely.

In his paper on the ecosystem as a conceptual tool in managing natural resources, Arnold Schultz explains why ecosystems should be studied as a separate science. He thinks the study of ecosystems should be a separate field because it is not like studying botany, zoology, not even ecology. Schultz argues that such a science would provide a framework for analyzing any organization integrated immediately above the level of the individual organism.[4]

The ecologist A. G. Tansley, who coined the term ecosystem in 1935, described it as "the whole system, including not only the organism complex, but also the whole complex of physical factors forming what we call the environment."[5] It would be more accurate to say "forming what we normally have been calling the environment of the organisms." Defining ecosystem more succinctly than Tansley, R. L. Lindeman described it as "a system composed of physical-chemical-biological processes active within a space-time unit of any magnitude."[6]

Good descriptions are difficult. Both of these could, I suppose, include the Earth, sun, and moon, and so they are limited. Rather than worry for now how large an ecosystem can be before it is no longer an ecosystem, let us consider where it stands in relation to everything else downward in the universe. J.S. Rowe says the ecosystem is part of an integrated hierarchy of things from atoms to molecules to cells to tissues to organs to organisms.[7] The ecosystem stands immediately above the organism. That the ecosystem should stand at this particular place is not immediately obvious because beyond organisms we are used to thinking about plant communities, biotic communities, vegetation, populations, species, and world fauna and flora. Schultz asked this question and finally agreed with Rowe that what an ecosystem has that these categories do not have is "thinghood." Rowe's argument is that nature has "chunks of space-time or 'events' which have both qualitative and quantitative properties. Events which endure are known as objects." For something to have "thinghood" — that is, to be an object — it must have volume because volume is the basic component of perception. These other categories, species, populations, and so on, lack volume because they do not include their surroundings.

But volume alone won't do because, as Schultz says (leaning on Rowe),

> For objects to have a high degree of "thinghood" they must exist in both space and time. Form and function must be constant or have rhythmic stability. Organized entities have strongly marked structure and function. When organized entities have strongly marked structural and functional characteristics, they are perceived as autonomous and stand out as natural objects of study.

The integrative levels of atom, molecule, cellular organelles, cell, tissue, organ, organ systems, and organisms are all natural objects of study. They are "slabs of space-time," as Rowe calls them. The volumetric criterion holds for them all. Before ecosystem was added to the hierarchy, J. K. Feibleman wrote twelve laws of integrative levels.[8] With this volumetric consideration, Rowe rewrote one of Feibleman's laws so that volume and space relationships are included. This law holds that the object of study, at any level whatever, must contain, in the volume sense, the objects of the lower level, and must itself be a volumetric part of the levels above. Each object on any given level constitutes the immediate environment (in the sense of impinging surroundings) of objects on the level below. Each object is a specific structural and functional part of the object at the level above. The ecosystem passes this test as an object because it consists of individual organisms plus the nonliving world that connects them. (What the next natural "chunk" or "slab" beyond ecosystem in nature is, I can't say. Perhaps it is bioregion or continent or ecosphere.) What is important for agriculturists is that Rowe seems to have made the case that the next integrative level above organisms is the ecosystem as the space-time unit. To repeat, species, population, vegetation, or community are not "environment" for individual plants, and they are not any specific volumetric functional part of the ecosystem.

However, the ecosystem does differ from the other categories in the hierarchy because the human being defines the boundary. The boundary of an organism is natural and well understood. The same is true of an organ or a cell. And there are certain natural ecosystems, such as bogs, in which the boundary is clear. But for most natural ecosystems it is difficult to know with much precision where the boundary lines are. Particularly problematic is knowing where tall-grass prairie ends and mid-grass prairie begins or where mid-grass prairie ends and short-grass prairie begins. Yet few prairie ecologists would deny the existence of the three prairie types.

With agriculture ecosystems, where we place the boundary is more suggested by a human-imposed pattern on the landscape than by nature. A deed can define the boundary of a farm. A fence line may define a pasture or a field. We could think about a farm community as an ecosystem or a farm or an alfalfa field or even a cubic meter of soil. We can place mental cubes around anything we want, because our purpose is to be better accountants of what goes in and out through the boundary and, at the same time, to appreciate the dynamics of the ecosystem as a structure that obeys certain laws common to the other levels in the hierarchy.

Laws of the Integrative Levels

Before we dwell on the ecosystem level as an integrative level, we need to consider the other laws of integrative levels distilled by Schultz to apply to the ecosystem. Schultz has also derived these other laws and their corollaries from Feibleman's twelve laws. Next, we can't ignore species and populations if we are to talk about agriculture because we can't ignore populations of cows or wheat. Even though species and populations did not attain the status of being part of the hierarchy of structure that Feibleman, Rowe, and Schultz have discovered, they were regarded seriously as candidates. They are, nevertheless, part of another kind of hierarchy with its own laws. Species and populations exhibit some dynamic properties fundamentally different from those of individual organisms. They generate species diversity and experience adaptation. Species adaptation is of a different order than individual adaptation. Perhaps knowledge of these dynamic properties and the ways in which they impinge on the ecosystem will be useful in the effort to discover the unifying concept for sustainable agriculture. But first let us look at the other laws of integrative levels that Arnold Schultz, writing with the ecosystem in mind, developed from J. K. Feibleman's scheme.

Schultz combined some of the laws and corollaries of Feibleman into seven categories that he felt were the most relevant to the development of the ecosystem concept. I have already mentioned the seventh law, which deals with the criteria for "thinghood" and makes the ecosystem an integrative level. The first six laws follow, almost as Schultz has stated them, but not in the same order. I am listing the self-evident laws first. They are not necessarily trivial, but an elaboration on their relevance to agricultural ecosystems may not be necessary at this time.

1. In any organization, the higher level depends on the lower. Just as the organism depends on organs, organs on tissues, tissues on cells, and so on, so the ecosystem depends on organisms, soil, and water. What is implied here is that the lower the level is, the more enduring it is. Atoms are more lasting than molecules. The physical and biological components of an ecosystem are more lasting than the ecosystem.

142

2. The higher the level, the smaller the population of instances. There are fewer molecules than atoms and fewer ecosystems than organisms. The levels form a population pyramid. This law still holds for agricultural ecosystems. The variety of farms in Kansas may be greater than the number of natural ecosystems, but the total number of ecosystems still does not exceed the number of organisms associated with the farms.

3. Complexity of the levels increases upward. Complexity is partly the result of accumulating structure, but most of the complexity stems from emergent qualities that pile up. The emergent qualities are the interrelationships, which increase exponentially while the number of components increases linearly.

4. Each level organizes the next level below and adds emergent qualities (see number 3). If one knows only the properties of the lower level, the emergent qualities are unpredictable. Schultz points out that we couldn't have known from the gases hydrogen and oxygen that they could produce water. In this example more than one water molecule had to exist before the liquid property could emerge.

There are examples at other levels of organization where a "critical mass" is necessary before an emergent quality can arise. For example, one cell does not a tissue make. This "critical mass" idea may have great practical importance for sustainable agriculture. There is probably no such thing as a completely sustainable farm anywhere in the United States. Some farms are more resilient or can stand being weaned away from the fossil-fuel economy better than others. The Amish farms are probably the most notable, as a group, in this respect. But it is rare that an Amish man or Amish family will venture forth, alone, into a locality not previously settled by Amish people. When colonies are founded, seven families usually go together. The Amish know they can't make it in isolation. Although there are probably a lot of isolated good farmers whose farms experience no net soil loss, their ancestors were probably heavily dependent on community during the farms' establishment. A lot of back-to-the-landers learned that most individuals or even individual families who have made attempts at sustainable agriculture have fared poorly or failed outright. Perhaps a "critical mass" is necessary before the emergent qualities necessary for a sustainable agriculture begin to appear. For our purposes, the implication is that sustainable agriculture will need rural communities if it is to survive and flourish. In retrospect, it is clear that, once the systematic destruction or dismantling of rural communities was underway in the United States, the weakening of the family farm was inevitable.

5. For an organization at any given level, its mechanism lies at the level below and its purpose at the level above. This law may need to be restated. As it now stands, it presents a particularly sticky problem when we think about nature. Ironically, it serves us well in thinking about conventional agricultural ecosystems even though it does not apply to natural ecosystems. We may know the purpose of a cornfield, but what is the purpose of a tall-grass prairie? Our problem becomes especially difficult if we don't keep the origin of a structure separate from what we finally see as a finished product. For example, if we drop down to the organ level and consider the kidney, we might say that the purpose of the kidney is to remove nitrogenous wastes from the blood of an organism — to cleanse it. Here the purpose lies above the organ (at the organism level) and the mechanism lies below the organ (in the tissue). But few biologists would be satisfied with such an explanation, for in the evolution of the vertebrate kidney few of them would believe that purpose was "pulling" on one end, forcing the development of a mechanism to accommodate a higher purpose. Biologists, instead, speak of adaptation and say that those early creatures that had tissues fortuitously tilted in the direction of removing nitrogenous wastes, however slightly, were positively selected, in a Darwinian sense. Creatures that carried improvements on each former adaptation were further selected, and so on.

Only from our vantage point in history do we assign the words purpose and mechanism for what nature has produced. Even if we had been observers in the early stages of the evolution of the kidney, we probably would have considered the primitive or elementary kidney a finished product.

Perhaps part of the human condition is the result of the distance

144

from nature in which we place ourselves by dealing with the world in a language that emphasizes purpose and mechanism. An example from agriculture is a typical Kansas wheat field. If it is truly representative of a field on a typical Kansas farm, its purpose is to provide cash outright for the farmer. The bottom line, in other words, is production. The farmer needs a high yield. Since his emphasis is on production, he naturally employs mechanisms of "mass production," products of industry. Mass production features a huge capitalization of equipment and inputs and seeks to minimize labor costs. The logical outcome is larger and more expensive machinery and fewer people. But this creates vulnerability. If the crop is to get planted, tended, and harvested, breakdowns of equipment become less tolerable. For many farmers, this often means new equipment every two or three years and a need for higher yields to pay for it. The purpose of the usual American farmer, to produce cash, almost to the exclusion of everything else, dictates the mechanism for growing wheat.

6. It is impossible to reduce the higher level to the lower. Since each level has its own characteristic structure and emergent qualities, reduction is impossible without losing those qualities. There is no greater reality in the parts than in the whole: they are equally real. This concept is widely overlooked or ignored by most scientists today. In 1972, P.W. Anderson wrote a paper entitled "More is Different."[9] He emphasized that each level of organization is more than layers of atoms, that each level has its own laws every bit as fundamental as the fundamentals of physics. Nevertheless, we have been taught that many of the common sense observations all around us are an illusion and that the component parts are the reality. It is like saying that sympathy (an emergent quality) is an illusion since it cannot be located by the dissection knife.

When we look at the major problems of modern agriculture — soil loss, chemical dependence, increasing dependence on fossil fuel, loss of the family farm, more corporate farms, an expansion of agribusiness — we see that most of them are the consequence of too much reductionism. It is understandable. We live in a society dominated by scientific reductionism. The problem is deep and probably resides in the history of science and technology. Both have been deeply influenced by physics, which we placed fore-

145

most in the hierarchy because we believed that once we under-stood the building blocks of nature, all else would be chemistry. Consequently, the most acceptable explanations in science have been in physical rather than biological terms. One can see where this leaves the biologists. They were simply discouraged from pos-tulating scientific laws for the various biological levels because scientists in general regard biological phenomena as too indeter-minate for safe prediction.

This justification for and emphasis on reductionism in science and technology in general has been carried over from physics to biology to agricultural science. At the extreme, it appears that a license has been issued to an agricultural establishment of scien-tists and technologists to function as salesmen of industrial farm inputs. These salesmen of everything from fertilizer to computers push their products with an abundance of quantitative documenta-tion of their performance. They define problems for farmers — problems farmers scarcely knew they had — then sell them the remedies. On the slickest of paper, these salesmen may display impressive tables and graphs, products of highly mathematical econometric models developed and expanded by econometricians in the Department of Agricultural Economics back at the land grant university. In some respects, these academics are worse for the farmer than the salesmen, for they function as the agricultural priests who pass on the fundamentalist faith in reductionistic thinking.

Meanwhile, many farmers, along with the rest of society, have come to distrust their common sense observations. They have been made to feel that they are an illusion. Fewer and fewer farmers think about their farms as an ecosystem. A good farmer will con-tinue to look at a particular hillside and see what possibilities it offers in the total scheme of things, which includes his farm as a whole, its history, his family, and the aptitude of everyone in the family. An agricultural economist usually does not consider any of this because he, along with most of society, still distrusts many common sense observations.

We have also been warned away from analysis at higher levels of organization because, as we move up the hierarchy of the sciences from physics to biology, it appears that various attributes

146

become so complex and variable that, at best, experts in systems analysis are necessary to keep track of them all. But as Eugene Odum has said, "It is an often overlooked fact that other attributes become less complex and less variable as we go from the small to the large unit." Odum reminds us that there are "homeostatic mechanisms, that is, checks and balances, forces and counter forces, (which) operate all along the line, and a certain amount of integration occurs as smaller units function within larger units." The rate of photosynthesis of a forest community, in an example Odum provides is less variable than that of individual leaves or trees within the community, because when one part slows down another may speed up to compensate. Odum goes on to say that "when we consider the unique characteristics which develop at each level, there is no reason to suppose that any level is any more difficult or any easier to study quantitatively."[10]

As we move up the hierarchy, "more is different," partly because emergent qualities develop at each level. Although the findings in the study of one level may be useful in understanding the next level above, they never completely explain the next level. To refer to an earlier example, in water all the attributes of the higher level (the liquid quality of water) are not predictable by knowing only the properties of the lower level (the gases of hydrogen and oxygen).

The ecosystem, as a volumetric "thing," can be a useful conceptual tool when thinking about sustainable agriculture. We can put mental boundaries around whatever part of the landscape we want to examine. A good farmer is constantly making mental cubes or spheres that include the vertical as well as the horizontal dimensions of a field or farm or even a farm community. To call them cubes or spheres oversimplifies what a good farmer does. He is at once an accountant or acknowledger of what passes through the various boundaries. If he simplifies his farm by selling off the livestock, for example, he has simplified more than his work. Mostly because of the nature of the economic system, he has simplified his thought, a kind of tragedy, for what farms need now, desperately so, is more thought by their owners. But just as important, perhaps, is being able to acknowledge that the ecosystem obeys the same laws as the other integrative levels.

147

What eventually follows ecosystem, perhaps even next in the ranking, is Earth. It has volume. And now for the crucial considerations. None of the other categories in the hierarchy of structure come to be known by observing only one. To know about atoms we had to "observe" unimaginable numbers of atoms many, many times over. There are fewer molecules, but even so, before we could come to understand what molecules are, we "observed" many. The same with cells. Imagine two cells, an ostrich egg and the nerve cell of a whale. Observing only one would not do. When Schleiden and Schwann came up with the cell theory, they had looked at a great deal of cellular diversity and many times must have been quite perplexed. Had we only one organism to look at, we would be bewildered. Consider the difference between a blue green alga and an osprey. With only one, we would have no frame of reference. The same is true if there were only one ecosystem — tall-grass prairie, for instance. Do you see where this logic is headed? We have seen only one Earth. It is legitimate to compare planets and include Earth in discussing planethood, but because we have life on Earth and no life verified on the other planets, the comparison has, as yet, limited value. Isn't it likely that to call the Earth an organism is the result of our being organisms? An atom is an atom, a molecule a molecule, a cell a cell and so on.[11] If we were molecules within a cell, looking all the way to the organism of which we are a part, we might say the organism is a molecule.

To say the Earth is an organism must remain in the realm of poetry and it may even turn out to be bad poetry. We still don't know what the Earth is, beyond saying that it is a planet with oceans and land and life driven by the sun. It is our source probably and our nurturer certainly, but that is about where it stops. Organisms create something more or less like themselves, baby organisms. The Earth has been a creator but has never created little earths. Thinking of the Earth as an organism may create a kind of myopia.

* * * * *

And now I want to return to the first part of this paper. I have tried to show how out of "blanks" information can arise. Recall the "high fertilizer response" genes as the losses of discrimination. Remember that resistance to leaf blight was the result of lack of physiological resistance, and recall the long-lived Amish males with part of their Y chromosomes missing. Keep this in mind as we go through a very short course in the history of science.

We have long discussed "closed" and "open" systems in nature. We know that the paradigm of Newtonian mechanics dealt with discrete objects and that there are "laws" associated with a set of original conditions. This was a closed system ideal. Then along came the nineteenth century and the second law of thermodynamics, the postulate that when you expend energy there is going to be dissipation as heat. The consequence is entropy and disorder. But more importantly, now we are talking about "open" systems which extract energy from the environment and create order. That is how something highly ordered, like living organisms and social systems, came into being and are maintained. We are all familiar with how the Newtonian world view began to be eroded with relativity theory, quantum physics, and the Heisenberg uncertainty principle. Chance and probability took the place of Newton's world view of mechanical things and their properties. We all know this story. Now enters the Russian-born Prigogine, who has highlighted the notion that time is irreversible and that time is a very important variable. And though Newton's equations go forward and backward, organic processes are directed by time and there can be a change of state.

The old comfortable clockwork universe of Newton has given way, in other words, to feedback mechanisms, perturbations, and chance. Prigogine is trying to prove that, even in "far-from-equilibrium" conditions, a system can organize itself, that order can come out of chaos. One of the definitions of chaos is "any vast gulf or chasm; an unfathomable abyss."

The missing parts of the Y chromosome correlate with increased longevity; the absence of genes for physiological resistance grants protection from southern corn blight; high fertilizer response can be due to seriously altered or lost material: all are examples that not only further challenge the Newtonian mechanistic view, but also support the order-out-of-chaos notion from the ancients in the Judaeo-Christian tradition to Prigogine. Of course it is true that surrounding those blanks is a world of matter with which the blanks or damaged places interact. It isn't just at the molecular level that space or blanks become important. It is interesting that the volumetric criterion which gave the ecosystem standing in the hierarchy of structure forced us to consider the spaces between organisms to be as important as the organisms themselves. Gases are exchanged there. Water relations are dependent on space. Of course that space is filled with atmosphere. But from the vantage point of an organism space is a resource within an ecosystem and, as such, space becomes a source. I could not help but think of this as I considered those blanks on the genome that granted high nitrogen uptake, disease resistance, and longevity.

So there we have it. The absence of absolutes about the material basis of information helps provide us with the framework for understanding how information, a kind of order, can arise out of blanks, out of chaos. This leads me to my next and concluding subject.

The Cartesian world was one in which the parts of things had priority over the whole. Richard Lewontin and Richard Levins, Harvard biologists, have carefully outlined how this Cartesian world view has been responsible for problems for humanity. They argue that we should take a dialectical view and look again at the relationship between part and whole, arguing that part influences whole and that whole influences part. Our atomistic view, which suggests that the parts are immutable, causes us to say that trees, deer, and humans are "nothing but." This view has contributed to our alienation from nature, but there is some possible good news for us to ponder. Parts are being changed by the whole, and every example challenges the Cartesian assumption.

I have two examples. Gene splicers have spliced into the bacterium *E. coli* some hereditary material from a human cell. The nucleic acids in sequence make up the code for a specific linear arrangement of amino acids. The amino acid sequence in this chain is presumably the same in the bacterium as in the human cell. So far so good. Part has priority over whole. But eventually this linear chain will begin to bond to itself in various places, forming little loops here, little loops there, so that by the time it is through bonding, there is a three-dimensional structure which is capable of biological activity. It may be an enzyme that initiates a specific reaction. Now comes the rub. The sequence of amino

150

acids at home in the human cell, but now inside the bacterial cell, does NOT fold quite right. There is something about the *E. coli* internal environment that affects the tertiary structure of the protein and makes it inactive. The whole in this case, the *E. coli* cell, affects the part — the newly made protein.[12] Whole affects part and therefore removes the priority of part over whole.

The second example of how whole affects part comes from work done in embryology working on mammals.[13] Right after fertilization, in a normal mouse the egg cell contains two separate bodies called pronuclei. One is already present in the egg and contains the female complement of chromosomes, and the other is from the sperm and carries the male complement of chromosomes. If the male-donated pronucleus is removed and a female-sponsored pronucleus is inserted so that now both pronuclei had their origin in females, development is stopped. When the opposite condition is imposed, two male pronuclei in the egg, the result is the same. The conclusion is that regardless of whether the genetic material is represented in duplicate, it won't work unless there is one of each from each sex. In other words, mammals need moms and dads.

This interpenetration between part and whole can be illustrated by an example I have used too many times. The reality I am about to describe is that our values are able to dictate the genotype of our major crops and livestock. I think we can safely say that our major crops, for example corn, soybeans, and wheat, have genes that we might call "Chicago Board of Trade" (where a major share of the agricultural transactions occurs), or fossil fuel wellheads, or computers. Our values arrange even the molecules of heredity. That is interpenetration.

Gary Nabhan tells a story about a Native American woman in Mexico who had several ears of corn from her corn crop arranged before her as she shelled grain from each ear. There were ears that were tiny nubbins, and ears that were long; all had seeds of various colors. As she shelled grain from each ear to save for the next planting, Gary asked her why she saved seed for planting from the small ears. Her reply was that corn was a gift of the gods and to discriminate against the small in favor of the large would be to show a lack of appreciation for the gift. What she was doing, in genetic terms, of course, was maintaining genetic diversity. Values dictate genotype. James B. Kendrick at the University of California at Berkeley says that if we had to rely on the genetic resources now available in the United States to minimize genetic vulnerability in the future, we would soon experience significant crop losses that would accelerate as time went by. Roughly one-third of our current crop comes from four inbred lines, which is roughly the same as the amount of variation that could be found in as few as two individual plants.

As the Cartesian world becomes scaled down, what goes with it is the notion that the world is like the method. The dialectical or ecological approach acknowledges that our every act is involved in creating the world. It is inescapable for us to operate in our daily lives and not create the world that everyone must live in. What we desire arranges the genetic code in all of our major crops and livestock. We cannot avoid being participants in the creation which yet arises out of chaos as well as out of the material world. It is in agriculture, far and away our largest and most basic artifact, where human culture and the creation totally interpenetrate.

Nature does not have to be bent to our will as Bacon suggested; rather quite the opposite. Nature stands always ready, maybe even too ready for our own good, to meet our wishes. She seems to always be trying hard to give us what we want. Maybe that's why we have to be careful what we seek, for since the "fall," one way or another, she seems to respond to our ordinary requests, demands, and even prayers. This is a sobering thought, for too often her response has become our punishment through the Earth's desecration.

Notes

1. Richard Levins and Richard Lewontin, *The Dialectical Biologist* (Cambridge, MA: Harvard University Press, 1985).
2. Kirby Smith, "Why Do Women Live Longer?" *Science* 238 (October 1987): 158-60.
3. Jean L. Marx, "Oncogene Linked to Fruit-Fly Development," *Science* 238 (October 1987).

4. Arnold M. Schultz, "The Ecosystem as a Conceptual Tool in the Management of Natural Resources," in *Natural Resources: Quality and Quantity*, ed. S. V. Ciriacy Wantrup and James S. Parsons (Berkeley: University of California Press, 1967).

5. A. G. Tansley, "The Use and Abuse of Vegetational Concepts and Terms," *Ecology* 16 (1935): 284-307.

6. Cited in Schultz, op. cit., 141.

7. J. S. Rowe, "The Level of Integration Concept and Ecology," *Ecology* 42 (1961): 420-27.

8. J. K. Feibleman, "Theory of Integrative Levels," *British Journal of Philosophy of Science* 5 (1954): 59-66.

9. P. W. Anderson, "More is Different," *Science* 177 (1972): 393-96.

10. E. P. Odum, *Fundamentals of Ecology* (Philadelphia: W.B. Saunders, 1971), 5.

11. It is true that an organism can be a single cell. The parallel situation of the Earth as an organism, therefore, does have precedent in the hierarchy of structure.

12. Stephanie Yanchinski, "Boom and Bust in the Bio Business," *New Scientist* 22 (January 1987).

13. Julie Ann Miller, "Mammals Need Moms and Dads," *Bioscience* 37 (June 1987): 379-82.

7

JOHN TODD
NANCY JACK TODD

Biology as a Basis for Design

Introduction
Nancy Jack Todd

A number of us at this conference have invoked the thinking of Gregory Bateson in addressing the ideas of biology as a basis for design. Professor Ceruti, Susan Oyama, William Irwin Thompson, and Evan Thompson discussed him, and both Dr. Oyama and Professor Ceruti have referred to his phrase "the pattern which connects." It struck me at the time that the full Bateson quotation was so appropriate to the conjoining, if you like, of my husband's and my work in biological design, in the most physical sense, with the intellectual climate here, that I would like to remind you of the full quotation from Bateson's *Mind and Nature*. It goes like this:

"What pattern connects the crab to the lobster and the orchid to the primrose and all the four of them to me? And me to you? and all the six of us to the amoeba in one direction and to the backward schizophrenic in another?" And several paragraphs later he asks: "What is the pattern which connects all the living creatures?" He goes on to say that this is something that we may not know for a very long time.

I should now like to be so bold as to paraphrase Gregory Bateson and try and set in context our own particular kind of biological design. Given Bateson's introductory words about the connection of the crab to the lobster and the orchid to the primrose, the connection between all living things, I should like to ask: What is the pattern which connects the new mentality, the emergent and brilliant thinking represented at this meeting, and the desperately urgent dual crises of the suffering of humanity and the ecosystem destruction that is occurring over so much of the planet? Are we in the paralyzing position of being able to do very little until we have defined and articulated this emerging ecology of consciousness, or can we, as Dr. Zajonc suggested, work in paradox, work effectively in the paradox of both the simultaneously fading and emerging cultures? I think that one bridge between these two equally valid realities is the title that the organizers of this conference have chosen to work within, "Biology as a Basis for Design." It also sits very well with John Todd and me. The title of our last book, *Bioshelters, Ocean Arks, City Farming*, a catchy title, was chosen by the publishers. They insisted on that. We, in turn, insisted on the subtitle *Ecology as the Basis of Design.*

To give a visual image of the way we think of our work, I would like you to recall one of my favorite images from yesterday, a day very rich in images. Remember Lynn Margulis' "Mano de Gaia," the wonderful human hand with the picture of the earth at the center and the various life forms along the fingers, which Dr. Margulis referred to as the hand of life. That is the visual image I would like you to hold as we discuss our work.

A lot of the background for our work is now somewhat ancient history, so I shall be quite brief. Beginning in 1969, when we became most aware of the developing environmental crisis as we saw it, we spent some months working in what we called Doom Watch biology, dashing about giving speeches, telling people about lead from automobile emissions, etc., polluting the atmosphere, or seizing on the example of nitrates from fertilizer runoff in ground water affecting the health of children.

It didn't seem, however, a particularly creative way to spend the rest of one's life. Nor did it seem likely that it would do a great deal of good. So we turned the equation around, and began to ask ourselves whether we seriously thought viable alternatives existed, were possible. It was not whimsical alternatives we were

155

after as was so often the case in those days—of going off and living by yourself on a farm and planting a great deal of lettuce and hanging out with your friends. We wanted to know whether there were serious, viable, scientifically replicable alternatives to the technological and industrial systems that were causing so much ecological destruction. We formed an institute we called The New Alchemy Institute, and spent ten years working in organic agriculture, in aquaculture, in the integration of energy and architecture, mostly trying to articulate and answer a very basic question, if only for our own benefit. The question was: Are there viable alternatives for supporting human populations that in an ecological sense would be much less damaging?

After a number of years of very intense work and—I have to add—a great deal of work on the part of our fellow travelers and colleagues not only in the States but around the world, we came to the conclusion that, yes, indeed there are alternatives, not whimsical but serious, viable alternatives that, using biology as a basis for design, we can turn to. And that, in fact, such alternatives are impeded more by financial, political, and social realities than they are by any limitations inherent in the methods themselves. Some of these will be described by John.

With a satisfactory response to our initial problem, an affirmation that it is biologically possible to support human beings in a different way, we moved on from production to ideas of ecological restoration. Once again in conjunction with the work of a number of people, this research has proven more reassuring than we originally thought would be possible. I'd like to give you a quick idea of the kinds of related work that has supported our research. Wes Jackson's work in sustainable agriculture and beyond at the Land Institute is pivotal to biological design. Lindisfarne Fellows Amory and Hunter Lovins at the Rocky Mountain Institute in Snowmass, Colorado, have turned around the energy equation and proved that their maximum conservation, low-cost, energy efficient systems can do a great deal to continue to support modern life styles without devastating environmental side effects. Dennis and Donella Meadows are working worldwide on resource modeling. In a modest way it's a very hopeful scene. There is one person who exemplifies what is possible as much as anybody, an

American biologist working in Costa Rica. His name is Dr. Daniel Janzen. He has provided a model for an ecological turn-around that is instructive to all of us. Parenthetically, Costa Rica itself is something of a model country in terms of, as Dr. Ceruti said, a demilitarized economy. In Costa Rica is a remnant of forest, which was originally an enormous dry-land forest covering much of the western half of Central America from Mexico down into Colombia. Dr. Janzen has managed to preserve and protect an area of a few square miles on the west coast of Costa Rica, which he maintains contains all the same flora and fauna that existed at the time of the arrival of the Europeans almost 400 years ago. That being the case, with support from the Costa Rican national government, he has started to expand the protected area. They are taking advantage of every ingenious method of using its disadvantaged third-world economy as a basis for debt swapping. Outside agencies are buying the Costa Rican national debt and using it to fund national parks and nature preserves. As a result Dr. Janzen's forest is now endowed.

Dr. Janzen does not see his mission purely in terms of environmental ecology. He has worked from the beginning to integrate school children and local people into the project, providing educational programs and local employment, so that the park is not imposed on local people by outsiders, because then, of course, you run into a danger of vandalism and social resentment. Dr. Janzen has integrated the park not only into the local life of the area of Guanacasto in western Costa Rica, but also into the national life as well. He has begun to advocate looking at biological preserves as national treasures, the way we regard our symphonies and libraries and our great works of art and architecture. That idea is beginning to take hold. I think it is how we have to begin to learn to think about natural systems as well.

I like to use the analogy of emergence, in that so many of us here began our work in isolation. The New Alchemy Institute started at approximately the same time as Lindisfarne — but most of us remained isolated. Now, a great deal due to the impresarial talent of William Irwin Thompson, we have come together. I begin to see that, as we move towards an ecology of consciousness, the image is a series of springs, slowly becoming tributaries, and now

157

moving towards a great river, which is, in turn, flowing towards something larger. That embodies my sense of emergence toward which we are all working. For me, and I am constitutionally an optimist, as Dr. Lazcano said yesterday, both he and the bacteria did not choose to be like Violetta in *La Bohème* and say goodbye to the past; no more should we turn our backs on the past than should we say goodbye to the future. I think as we work towards this emerging ecology of consciousness our options open up enormously. My colleague John Todd represents one kind of thinking, imagining in the sense that Dr. Thompson referred to it, imagination, imaging, that I think is essential to this shared sense of emergence. Like Wes Jackson, he has the genius which Jim Lovelock pinned down very neatly the other day when he referred to it as a sort of planetary green fingers. (In the States we say green thumb, but I think the difference is minuscule.) It is a gift for working in the biological world in a creative and coevolutionary manner. Again, as Dr. Lazcano invoked John Lennon, I describe this kind of talent in John Lennon's words as some kind of "druid dude." John Todd will describe to you the specifics of the biological design that we have been working with. I should like to conclude by saying that a number of years ago, again in a Lindisfarne context, Gregory Bateson first heard of not only our theoretical but also our hands-on work in biological design. His response then was encouraging enough to keep us going for the next fifty years at least. What he said was: "Well, now, there's an epistemology with a future."

And it is.

Water: Its Uses, Its Abuses, and Its Revitalization
John Todd

My approach to biology as a basis for design, the grand theme of this conference, is in applying ecology directly to human needs and in scientifically exploring new ways of creating ecological economies. I have worked in both tropical and northern industrial societies to develop a practice of ecological design and to uncover its underlying principles. We have designed and built energy, food, shelter, and transport systems inspired by the workings of nature. We have designed and redesigned human settlements and developed biotechnologies for the restoration of damaged environments.

Today, however, I want to focus on one subject, that of water: its uses, its abuses, and its revitalization. There are a number of reasons I want to choose water as the theme for my talk. First and, perhaps, most important, water is the basis of all life. It is absolutely essential. A further reason is that water, much of it, is deeply threatened. For example, there are close to a hundred thousand chemicals manufactured by modern societies. These chemicals, through various pathways, get into the water and interact in ways that we hardly understand. Usually only one chemical is studied in relation to its effects on life forms — on occasion two, sometimes three, but never combinations of chemical compounds in their complex formulations. The U.S. Environmental Protection Agency has, on its critical list of compounds, some 54 carcinogenic substances that are turning up in the drinking water throughout the country. If, in fact, water is contaminated, it means that all of the organisms dependent on and using that water are, by definition, contaminated. We are, in essence, poisoning the seventh generation into the future. Ironically, in the U.S. since 1974, the laws have become increasingly strict with regard to the discharge of sewage and other toxic substances. The response of the water pollution industry has been to eliminate those dangerous substances by applying even more dangerous substances to the task of water purification. It is, literally, a horror story. If, for example, a community wants to eliminate phosphorus from the water, the local sewage plant will use toxic aluminum to precipitate the phosphorus that it puts into sludge, which is then disseminated in landfills or into the water table. What you have is the mass spread of aluminum throughout the environment, at a time when we are learning that, under conditions of acid rain, aluminum is toxic to trees and forests. That is just one example. There are many more. The point is, as EPA rules have become stricter, the chemical companies have responded by treating water with chemicals which have not yet been regulated. What we are approaching, from what we know now, is a "silent spring" of water. The crisis, on a global scale, is equally serious.

Flipping the coin psychologically with my dear friend Evan

Thompson: for me the discovery of bringing light and water together to explore what you might call emergent properties has been an extraordinary journey, a fusion of science, art, and planetary stewardship.

I want to begin by describing an ecological experiment, in this case an experiment in food production. The rationale behind this experiment was to find intensive methods of growing foods with minimal inputs of energy, nutrients, and resources, and to do so in a nonpolluting, ecologically recycling way. To do so, we used a series of translucent, cylindrical tanks, five feet tall and five feet in diameter. The idea was to raise water above ground level and expose it to light, much like a still waterfall. The water and light was to be the basis for the culture of aquatic foods. We wanted to create inside these light-exposed tanks an above-ground aquatic ecosystem which, at the top of its food chain would produce human foods. Since there had never been anything quite like that particular ecosystem inside those tubes, we had to develop a theory and, more importantly, a practice of what we call seeding, placing inside that new environment organisms from many different areas and watching them ultimately interact to produce what we hoped would be a steady biological state. We found that, even though the ecosystems were exposed to a lot of light, light remained a limiting factor. To overcome that, we placed tanks or ponds inside courtyards with reflective surfaces. Subsequently, we went to many different sources of water: lakes, eutrophic lakes, streams, slow-moving rivers, even pig wallows. We gathered vast numbers of organisms and micro-organisms, brought them back and put them into the tanks. We made sure that we had added a full complement of microbes, the idea being that the bacteria are the driving wheel which provide the links between the various elements in the food chain. Organisms from old forest soils, compost heaps, sludge, and rich lakes were seeded into the tanks. We tried to make sure that small protozoan animals which prey upon bacteria and algae would also be part of the dynamic pond system. Then we placed fish at the top of the food chain. Over the years we cultured about a dozen species of fish in this light environment. I should add that we added one technical input, that of nocturnal aeration becaue the ecosystems had to be aerobic—able to withstand seasonal fluxes with short days and nights. We worked with extremely dense populations of fish. One was a filter feeding fish called tilapia, originally from Africa.

During the course of the experiment we found that we had increased the productivity of the standing bodies of water in the tanks by an order of magnitude. In doing so we proved that a large number of fish could be grown to an edible size in ecosystems powered by the sun. The dynamics of the systems were extraordinarily interesting: when two of three species of fish were used in combination, they produced their own kind of system dynamics, regardless of whether the fish were catfish or tilapia or trout or carp from China or mirrorcarp from Israel. Equally interesting was the fact that at no instance did we have less than twelve to fifteen species of algae interacting in some kind of dance. But even after years of modeling, the dynamics of those ecosystems are still not fully understood. The point is they were both stable and productive.

The input of feeds for the fish caused a buildup of accumulated organic matter which, up to a point, the ecosystems had the intrinsic ability to respond to and correct. But every so often, unpredictably, they would collapse. Almost inevitably we could trace the collapse to the buildup of a compound toxic to fish at very low concentrations — ammonia. The critical element in the system was definitely ammonia. The next question became, if the algae cannot balance the system, is there another element with more benefits than costs that can be introduced into the ecosystem to protect us from ammonia buildups? Our inspiration for this solution originated with the ancient Mayans of Mexico, who developed a form of semifloating agriculture in which food crops were grown on the surface of water bodies so that the heavy nutrient loads that were the waste products of the large population of the time were recycled back into their food crops. We began to experiment with growing vegetables on the surface of our pond ecosystems to take up ammonia. We found that they took up ammonia almost as quickly as it was produced. They did so through two pathways: one was by direct uptake by the plant; and the other, which we did not expect, was via the root systems of the floating plants, which provided a biological substrate for two groups of bacteria that nitrify ammonia into nitrites and then nitrates. It was, in fact, the root systems of the floating plants that were driving the ecological nutrient bus. We experimented with a number of vegetables including lettuce, tomatoes, and cucumbers. From an ecological point of view, those food-producing aquatic ecosystems became stable to the point where they could withstand the short days and low temperatures of North American winters.

One of the most interesting things about working with ecological design – unlike working with nuclear power, for example – is that although side effects are often equally unpredictable they are almost always beneficial. For example, we found that the rich algae soup contained in our aquatic ecosystems was able to absorb radiant energy from the sun so efficiently that the water in the tanks remained relatively warm, even outside during the winter. The tanks had double walls and a two-layer cover on top; they stayed relatively warm and the fish survived winter temperatures. This led us to try similar tanks inside greenhouses we called bio-shelters to reduce dependence on fossil fuels for heating the buildings. We then introduced the ponds as an interior architectural element to ameliorate internal climate. One such building or bio-shelter with thirteen interior ponds without fossil fuels provided a climate that ripened bananas in New England in February. We built another bioshelter in a much more rugged climate on Prince Edward Island in the Gulf of St. Lawrence in Canada which is surrounded by ice for a good portion of the year. It, too, used solar pathways in thirty-three ecosystems to provide a year-round microenvironment for a laboratory housing a variety of horticultural and agricultural research projects – all of which were sustained by the warmth of the ponds.

Returning to the theme of water purification, a number of years ago, Falmouth, the town in which we live in Massachusetts, south of Boston, started to show extremely high cancer rates – five, six, seven times those of towns to the north and west. Our water was undrinkable. We had to buy bottled water. The day we bought our first bottled water in order to protect ourselves was when I began to shift my emphasis from using water to culture foods to studying ecological pathways to purify water. Using aquatic ecosystems comparable to the food-producing ones, I designed a theoretical sewage treatment plant that would take raw sewage from a town or a community, expose it to light and air, and process it through the series of ecosystems in which plants, animals, and bacteria act in concert to produce ecological by-products ranging from gases and fertilizers, to animal and human foods and, most important, potable or drinkable quality water. It was necessary to determine if it was possible to pass water loaded with pathogens, poisons, and organic nutrients through a food chain and to find pathways that would transform the harmful material into useful by-products. There were not many precedents for this kind of thinking: a former student of mine working with the city of San Diego; a small group at the space agency, NASA; another small group associated with Epcot in Florida; a few groups of scientists in other parts of the world, particularly at the Max Planck Institute in Germany. But it was and is a small tribe working on questions of ecological restoration.

I got involved in this rather quixotic task of trying to restore contaminated water partly because of the encouragement from people like James Lovelock and Lynn Margulis who believed that somewhere there are organisms and associations of organisms capable of extraordinary things. They were finding such organisms in their Gaian research, and the rich Gaian soup that they were exploring suggested that nature has many organisms, methods, and pathways that can be applied to such difficult problems. I decided to design an artificial river — made up of discrete components that, as the water flowed along its pathway, would sequentially purify certain contaminants. Each component would set the stage for the next phase of purification, which in turn would set up another phase.

Our first project in this field was in a ski resort in northern Vermont not far from the Canadian border. The odds were badly stacked against us in that the system would have to treat maximum inputs of waste in the middle of winter when available light was very low. In late December the sun goes down behind the mountain at 2:10 (or 14:10) in the afternoon, and it doesn't come up till 10:30 in the morning. We undertook the project there because it was the only community that wanted us then, and we had to take the chance. The community is Warren, Vermont. It was in

163

violation of the discharge permitted for sewage because of its location on a mountain spring. State law mandates that you can only discharge pristine water. The existing sewage treatment plant was very high tech, an advanced facility about ten years old, capable of removing many, not all, nutrients, pathogens, organic matter, and suspended solids. But it was typical of most modern treatment plants. To break up and get rid of ammonia — which is very high in the wintertime there, about 60 milligrams per liter and sometimes higher at a breakpoint chlorination plant — it used eight hundred dollars a day of chlorine. The pH was elevated to about pH 11. Even so, the plant only eliminated the ammonia most, but not all, of the time. As a by-product it also produced chloramines, known carcinogens, not to mention sludge so filled with aluminum that the town could not find a legal place to put it. One farmer would accept it, but even those days were numbered.

I wanted an alternative way of removing these extremely high levels of ammonia. To do so we built a structure, a transparent envelope or bioshelter designed to trap solar energy, which behaves in micro in much the same way as the atmosphere does in regulating global climates. Like the Earth, the bulk of what is inside the structure is water, a relatively stable thermal compound. Inside we created three types of aquatic ecosystems. The first was flowing water. The second was artificial marshes, which have uncanny abilities to do beneficial things. The third was the same solar ponds or tanks that were part of the agriculture experiment described earlier. The plant component was made up of floating and potted plants which created a beautiful garden. A visiting state senator responded by saying, "Not only is this place beautiful, it doesn't stink. I can now get interested in the subject of sewage."

Raw sewage enters the plant on the left and is discharged into the base of 3.5 meter-tall translucent cylinders or tanks where it is exposed to light and aeration. It is being shifted there from an anaerobic to an aerobic environment. At this point, it then rises from the bottom to the top of the tanks where it is exposed to light. It then starts on a journey lasting several days. It flows around a corner and up into a marsh. From the marsh, it is discharged through three silver cylinders, after which pure water is returned to the environment. Between 10 and 20 percent of the now pure water is directed back toward the beginning of the cycle where it is discharged into the 3.5 meter-tall solar tanks, in which there are large populations of trout, small mouth bass, and 200 species of plankton. In terms of understanding the overall system and its ability to withstand perturbations or shocks, it is important to remember that it has a recycling as well as a discharge component. The treatment plant is just a small one, 50,000 liters capacity. It treats up to 15,000 liters a day.

The interior ecosystem was started in late March. We literally combed the countryside for organisms to introduce into it. There were few swamps, rich lakes, streams, or even other sewage plants that we didn't gather materials from. We had no idea what organisms would be there. We did know that we needed certain classes of organisms that would allow the organic loading known as biological oxygen demand to be reduced from hundreds of parts per million to 20 in order for other groups of bacteria such as the nitrifiers to be able to work. Aeration was the first phase; then exposure to light; then the bacterial breakup of organic matter, a very rapid process in a viable ecosystem, followed by a nutrient uptake cycle; then an ecosystem building cycle; and finally polishing and denitrification.

It was interesting to watch the behavior of the plant for the first three months. It would start to work or metabolize, then it would give the equivalent of a hiccup. There were days when there was foam on the surface of the water and it looked awful. On other days it was crystal clear. We couldn't quite figure out why. It was unquestionably an unstable system in part because it was loaded at full strength from the day we started and also because the water was relatively cold. After about three months of seeding however, the level of water purity improved from that of primary to secondary treatment and then to that of advanced waste water treatment. After three months our plant was producing pristine water. We will never fully understand the ecological dynamics, although a fairly large research group is working on it. An important component that we have taken into account is the terrestrial plants, some having economic value, which we grew on the surface of the water. We didn't know when we started which plants would be happy on the surface of the water; we did hedge our bets. The river willow was one of the most successful of those plants, as one would expect. The plants which adapted best developed extensive root systems. There was aeration on the bottom of the first raceway that causes organic matter to rise and be trapped in suspension and to be consumed by generalist types of bacteria like Bacillus, and by large populations of zooplankton, microscopic shrimp-like creatures which then went to work on the plant roots. Within less than a day, the biological oxygen demand went from above 700 milligrams per liter down to levels of about 20. The rate of purification was extremely rapid. Within the first day, or first half day, the biochemistry of the ecosystem was such that nutrients already were being transformed and removed.

Among the more successful plants were the umbrella plant and the eucalyptus. We decided to work with eucalyptus because the botanical literature of Napoleon's time described a particular species that was planted to reduce disease in areas surrounding villages prone to malaria and other diseases. Those eucalyptus thrive in a wastewater environment. The trees spend nine months as seedlings and water purifiers floating on the pond surface. They are subsequently potted and can be used to improve air quality or give an aromatic essence in a room or office.

At the far end of the river inside the plant, the water is absolutely clear. We are not exactly sure why it was crystal clear; we assumed it was because of the grazing of the microscopic animals. Then, through the work of Kathe Seidel at the Max Planck Institute, we learned that there are inherent properties in the root systems of some water organisms that enable them to flocculate organic matter and clarify water. At that stage of the cycle there are swarms of snails that eliminate sludge. There is almost no sludge production in the treatment plant, which means that organic material is quickly absorbed by the biological pathways. The snails are fed to the fish and provide a large part of their diet.

Sludge is becoming a major problem. Removal is a social issue, costing billions of dollars, but it need not be part of the waste stream. Sludge can be eliminated by channeling into pathways that can be controlled and can even become economically productive.

Now the second-to-last part of the story is the treatment plant's marsh ecosystem. When I started working with marshes a few years ago, I knew very little about them, but I have since discovered that they're extraordinary ecosystems. The types of things they can do boggle the imagination. Once you've realized it, you want to restore marshes everywhere.

In our marsh we have grown cattails, watercress, and water iris, which Kathe Seidel discovered will eliminate Salmonella, Staphylococcus and other dangerous human pathogens. It does so by producing a powerful antibiotic, which it releases into the environment. Our results showed 10^6 and 10^7 coliform bacteria coming into the plant in the influent and as low as 2 to immeasurable amounts in the effluent, suggesting that pathogens were effectively removed from the system. We're going to work next with viruses. The role of the cattail in the ecosystem is to remove heavy metals such as lead, cadmium, and other dangerous compounds. There are a variety of other plants that are very good at removing heavy metals, including the umbrella plant. There are other plants called Scirpus or bulrush, whose genus includes whole groups of hollow-stemmed marsh plants that break down organic compounds like phenols into nontoxic end products. The hollow-stemmed water plants have a phenomenal ability to remove organic carcinogens. A study done in San Diego using only one species of hollow-stemmed plants showed that very few carcinogens get through. *Phragmites*, which is considered a weed, is a generalist in water purifying and also has the ability to flocculate substances out of water.

We are beginning to find that the marsh system serves two functions. It eliminates the poisons, either by destroying them or shunting them into particular pathways. It also provides an anaerobic phase in the last part of the purification process. As the water flows through the marsh and heads downward, it reaches a zone in which bacteria that can function in the absence of oxygen predominate. At that point, any remaining nitrates which can be toxic in drinking water, particularly to infant children, are broken up and vented out into the air as nitrogen gas, completing the denitrifying cycle.

It is possible then to make pristine water from very poor water. That much has been demonstrated. It is further possible to remove bacterial pathogens. We don't yet know about viruses.

167

Furthermore, as the purified water leaves the plant it provides a habitat suitable for the culture of valuable fishes, providing an economic component. For some reason there is a process that occurs in marshes which seems to prevent disease in fish. Currently we have three references in the literature indicating that if water passes through a marsh before it reaches the fish, it protects them from becoming disease prone.

We are beginning to work with an ecosystem, the whole surface of which has economic potential involving medical and horticultural plants, as well as fishes that can be cultured, grown to a small size and then stocked out. Instead of sewage treatment being one of the most expensive costs for society, it can be turned around to become a basis of economic activity.

The evolution of our water purifying ecosystems has not been without crises of a serious order in the plant. The first crisis came when, unknown to us, the operator of a neighboring plant for several months backflushed aluminum sludge into our plant. One day we noticed a greatly reduced ability of the nitrifiers in our system to eliminate ammonia. Then we discovered that the aluminum had bound up the phosphorus and made it unavailable. There was less than 0.002 mg/1 of phosphorus available, and many of our bacteria were starved and dying. It took both stopping the influx of aluminum and the addition of phosphorus to bring the plant back to life.

I have mentioned the amazingly dangerous chemicals being used these days to purify water or to sterilize environments like hospitals and sports centers. We found we had a compound called quaternary ammonium coming into our plant. Every morning, when the nearby sports center was disinfected, a wave of death passed through our plant, killing the bacteria. We were also receiving bromine, which is used in swimming pools and in hot tubs as a substitute for smelly chlorine. Fortunately for us, the water from the marsh that passed over the fish (which was 10-20 percent of the influent volume) was able to maintain sufficient biological metabolism to allow them to survive the perturbation. Recycling the water through the marsh provided the ecological redundancy to keep the biological processes of the plant alive.

We have not yet been able to eliminate as much of the phosphorus from the system as we would like. Phosphorus tends to be bound up with organic matter. Although we are producing drinkable quality water, we would like to be able to eliminate even more phosphorus from the system.

It is a constant throughout all of these processes that if you are going to eliminate ammonia ecologically, you have to have enough alkalinity in the water to do so. In Vermont we thought we had enough to do the job. We had alkalinity from sand because the swimming pools at the resort were sending us the diatomaceous earth through which they filtered water into our waste stream. We thought this gave us the alkalinity necessary to drive the ecological cycles. In fact, the alkalinity required by the bacteria in our system had to be calcium carbonate. Through ecological detective work and troubleshooting, we thought to add calcium carbonate in the form of baking soda. The system responded amazingly quickly.

Smallmouth bass grow very rapidly in our plant's ecosystem, and we plan to culture them in our newest plant in the city of Providence, Rhode Island. Providence has a particular waste problem in that much of its economy is based on the jewelry industry, by-products of which are a lot of toxins. Providence is situated on one of the most beautiful estuaries in the eastern United States, Narragansett Bay, which is currently being bombarded with so many different chemicals that its shellfish and fishing industries have been largely shut down. Our idea is to test a prototype of our water purification plant in a city to see to what extent toxins can be removed. A by-product of the operation there will be about a half million striped bass a year. Striped bass are a much loved sport and commercial fish in the eastern United States, but populations have been so badly decimated by pollutants that they are now beginning to disappear from much of the eastern coastal waters. Since life proceeds by ironies we like the idea of using waste treatment plants to restock the ocean.

It is increasingly obvious to me that in the ultimate sense, nature is unknowable. However, the patterns in nature and imitative ecological strategies will, in years to come, prove the basis for design. I will never know enough, I don't think any of us will, to build a space colony that will be able to travel through time and space without continuing influence from the richness and natural wisdom that is Earth. I remember once a few years ago, Rusty

Schweickart, the Apollo 9 astronaut, asked a group of us to conceive of the smallest ecosystem capable of remaining stable and functioning over time. It was Lynn Margulis who answered, "There's only one that I know of—and that's Earth."

We have to be very careful approaching the question of moving ecosystems out into space. From working with water purification, my sense is that while working on the problem of moving out into space, we will learn more about how the Earth works. The more we find out how the Earth works, the more we are going to revere it and to treat it as fundamentally sacred, and the less inclined we are going to be to leave it. This is a co-evolutionary story. Maybe the story that we're all involved in is the co-evolution of nature and society. Maybe that is the next turn on the spiral of human/planetary culture.

8

SUSAN OYAMA

The Conceptualization of Nature

Nature as Design

The controversies I find most interesting are the ones that are notable for the questions they raise, rather than for the solutions they produce. One can argue about whether computers have minds or not, for instance, but the intriguing question is what it means to have a mind — and whether a mind is something one can "have." By the same token, one can wonder whether apes have language or not, but the real challenge is to say precisely what language is. Yet another example is the endless debate over whether some trait is "in" the genes or not. I have spent considerable effort trying to understand just what this last phrase (or its opposite) could possibly mean. What sorts of things does it show about the way we think about the nature of organisms and their development?

Examination of these questions reveals some unspoken assumptions. To begin with, all three have spatial implications. Minds and language are thought to be things we possess or not; they are assumed to have a location, typically in our brains. "Genetic" traits (or programs for them) are in the DNA. Behind these assumptions is the image of isolated individuals whose properties (possessions!) can be enumerated without paying much attention to their activities or surroundings.

Perhaps the question underlying the title of this symposium

offers us this kind of opportunity to reflect on assumptions. "Biology as a Basis for Design" could lead us to deliberate about just which designs are biologically natural and which are not. Or it could lead us to ask whether nature has a design "there" for us to imitate. To turn Gertrude Stein's dismissive comment about Oakland, California, into a query, Is there a there there? Does Nature have a nature, an essence, independent of us but knowable by us?

Small-n-nature, big-N-Nature

There are several ways in which my reflections on this question will be a departure from my past work. In my investigations of the relation between the internal and external domains, I have concentrated on the concept of internal biological nature. This I have called "small-n-nature," as in "human nature." I now turn my attention to Nature "out there": "big-N-Nature" rather than "small-n-nature." Secondly, my writings have often been characterized by a certain impatience with ambiguity. I have warned of its dangers and urged greater precision in the use of particular terms. Here, however, I will not just tolerate ambiguity of a certain sort, but will celebrate it. Finally, my work has always been characterized by an emphasis on constructive interaction. (1981, 1982, 1985, in press; "small-n-nature" and "big-N-Nature" are from Oyama 1987). On this third count, I will not depart from my former habits; the emphasis on constructive engagement remains. This time, however, it is applied not to the ontogeny of organismic designs, but to the designs we see in the external world.

By insisting on construction, however, I don't mean that we simply project our internal designs on a passive, chaotic Nature. This would be to accept the objectivist-subjectivist split so ably criticized by Maturana and Varela (1987), by certain feminist theorists (Harding & O'Barr 1987, for instance), by Lakoff and Johnson (1980), and by others who are dissatisfied with seventeenth-century notions of objectivity. Rather, external Nature, like internal nature, is co-constructed over time, through intimate engagement with the world. Nature is multiple but not arbitrary, and design is brought forth with the world in that fusion of knowledge and action also described by Maturana and Varela. Just as I have denied the validity of traditional notions of immutable biological nature inside us, written in our genes at the moment of our conception and existing independently of our interactions with our developmental contexts, I now deny that big-N-Nature has a unitary, eternal nature, independent of our lives in the world. In fact, the kinds of interactions in which we participate influence the Nature we design. (The ambiguity in the preceding sentence is intentional: I mean to refer both to our conceptualizations of Nature and to the kinds of concrete changes we bring about in the world.)

I am going to make some comments that may seem subversive to the theme of this conference, but ultimately I don't think they are. Along the way, I will discuss concepts of design and nature and the virtues of multiple perspectives in elaborating these concepts. I will touch upon biology as a way of knowing, the relationship between knowers and knowledge, and the necessity of taking responsibility for our contributions to the knowledge (and therefore the Nature) we construct. This may seem rather a lot, but my comments on each topic will be brief. I wish only to sketch a set of issues, not to provide an exhaustive treatment.

Design in Nature

The word "design" is multiply ambiguous in English. It can be a noun or a verb, and can have multiple meanings in both roles. In creative activity, the word refers to the originating intention: One conceives a design, a plan or scheme. It also refers to the finished product: A completed design may be placed on display in a museum. Finally, it is the act of creation that fulfills a design: One designs (makes) a table.

In working from a pre-existing model, on the other hand, as is implied by the idea of using biology as a basis for design, "design" refers to the pre-existing external model: Replicas can be made of an original design. The finished product may also be called a design, though we usually take pains to distinguish the original from the copy. The activity itself, however, is not called

173

"designing," because the design is already there. Instead, we speak of imitating, of copying.

Our vocabulary thus reveals our assumptions. Subjects are treated as radically separable from objects. Design, or form, originates either inside or outside the subject-agent. A strict distinction is made between active creation and passive imitation, between originating a design and serving as a conduit through which it passes. (On the conduit metaphor, see Oyama, in press, and Maturana & Varela 1987.)

But we are not committed to these assumptions in order to consider nature and design. We can admit our active and interactive role in the definition of problems, in the choice and conceptualization of model, in the mode of investigation, in the construction of knowledge itself. I would even playfully suggest that we should increase the ambiguity of "design" by including "imitation" or "study," or even "perception" in the semantic complex that already embraces the creation of a design, the design created, and the design that guides our work. Who knows, this little exercise in creative muddling might even dignify imitation. (Being of Japanese descent, I admit I may have a somewhat personal and exaggerated interest in such revisionist semantics.) Interestingly enough, a recent exhibit of drawings in New York City was entitled "Creative Copies." In any case, it should help to undermine some of the traditional assumptions about knowledge and activity that are now being strongly challenged from many directions.

Multiple Perspectives

Let me start with two prompts to my own thinking about these issues. One was Mary Catherine Bateson's comment at the 1987 Lindisfarne meeting in New York. Speaking about the metaphor of the Earth as mother, she offered some alternative metaphors — the Earth and ourselves as coparents, for example, or the Earth as child — and made the gentle suggestion that we needn't insist on only one. There might be some virtue, that is, in a kind of tentative flexibility in our thinking about this relationship — or rather, these relationships.

The second prompt was a recent story in the magazine *The New*

174

Yorker by Ursula Le Guin (1987). Entitled "Half Past Four," it was not so much a story told from several points of view as it was a story that was itself transformed. In a series of scenes, people and events shift. Ann is first presented in an encounter with her father, Stephen, and with Toddie, the retarded son of her father's new wife, Ella. In the next scene Ann is Todd's sister, and the two siblings discuss their absent father, who has started a family with another woman. Then she is Ella's daughter, meeting Ella's suitor, Stephen, and so on. Identities, histories, and even sexual orientation are progressively permuted and transmuted, while the many-dimensioned space is bound together by recurrent themes and images.

Reading the story for the first time, I found myself backtracking hurriedly. In the careless reader's attempt to recover what the initial scan had missed, I fussed: Are Toddie and Ann siblings or half-siblings? Who is this Ella, anyway? It was only after several of these truth-gathering forays that I realized that getting the facts straight once and for all was not the point. Rather, the concatenated scenes could be read for their richly proliferating relations, including the relations between those relations.

These two experiences led me to reflect on the value of multiple perspectives — not as several lines of sight converging on the same object, where the goal is a single, more accurate view, but rather as paths to richness, to curiosity, to a sense of possibilities and myriad connections, divergences, and discontinuities. Anthropologists Gregory and Mary Catherine Bateson speak of diversity of reference, of point of view, in ethnographic knowing (1987, 185). (It is perhaps only coincidental that Le Guin is also the child of anthropologists.) This kind of mobile multiplicity can encourage compassion and empathy, for it fosters the appreciation of both particularity and commonality. Trying to see the consequences of one's actions through another's eyes, after all (perhaps even including the "eyes" of Nature), has long been an exercise for increasing moral and emotional responsiveness. It might even give rise to the sense of extended responsibility embodied in the work of so many of the Lindisfarne Fellows. Bateson and Bateson write, "Empathy is a discipline" (1987, 195). It can be a corrective to the exclusionary absolutism of much traditional science and, incidentally, much traditional religion. Both, after all, are involved in legitimating only certain knowledge, in sanctioning only certain knowers and ways of knowing.

In scientific knowledge, the knower paradoxically disappears. The ideal of scientific objectivity is based, in fact, on the inter-changeability of knowers. Sandra Harding has written about Baconian objectivity as universal subjectivity — knowledge by anybody — and about the corresponding scientific division of the world into the real (public, shared) and the unreal (merely private) (1986). An influential contemporary version of this division is the distinction between the biological (objective, real, physical, basic) and the merely psychological or cultural (subjective, less real, eva-nescent, and arbitrary); it is biologists' roles as arbiters of the bio-logically real that lend them special authority in today's world.

The disappearing knower supports the myth of the absolute autonomy and separateness of the world. That that separation may involve a degree of discomfort and insecurity is a possibility explored by Bordo's account (1986/1987) of the rise of Cartesian rationalism. She compares this historical development to the drama of separation in psychological development and notes that one way of reducing the pain of separation is to choose aggres-sively to pursue separation; the pain is then "experienced as autonomy rather than helplessness in the face of the discontinu-ity between self and mother" (p. 259). I would read this, by the way, as Bordo herself does, not as a developmental psychopa-thology of science, but as "a hermeneutic aid," enabling us "to recognize the thoroughly historical character of precisely those categories of self and innerness that describe the modern sense of relatedness to the world" (p. 253).

Biologists as Knowers

Biologists are heirs to this tradition, and they share the tradi-tional reluctance to recognize their own contributions to their knowledge. Such recognition threatens to make knowledge "merely" subjective, a solipsistic projection on the world. The scientific method, after all, is about eliminating subjectivity, protecting pure factuality from "bias." These fears about the con-tamination of truth assume just what I wish to question: the separation of knower from known, the opposition of active creation to passive reception, the conception of pattern and design as things with an independent existence. If we take the virtues of multiple perspectives seriously, we must own up to our concerns and sensitivities. We can, and should, embrace a more interactive view of knowledge and action. Despite our fears, I believe that neither we nor the world will disappear.

Note that I am not just complaining about "bad science," a science infected by extraneous interests and points of view. This implies that a pure depersonalized science can exist. Rather, this storymaking from a particular point of view is what science is — not only "bad science" but also what Helen Longino and Ruth Doell have called "science as usual" (1983/1987). (On the relationship between the two, see Harding 1986. This is a complex and difficult problem; Harding believes it is possible, and necessary, to take a critical stance toward both.)

Information

"Information" is the modern, technological incarnation of the notion of design; it is thus central to the issues at hand. Information is usually conceptualized as a kind of stuff that can be found both inside and outside of us. The information in us is supposed to be revealed in "biological bases" — the instinctive core of our being, a prescribed inner reality. This is small-n-nature, typically thought to be encoded as genetic information, information that is "translated" in development into bodies and minds. Phenotypes are treated more or less as readouts of genetic programs. Information "out there," on the other hand, comes from the external world; it is supposed to be acquired through perception. It then appears in the mind as representational knowledge. Somehow information moves from big-N-Nature "out there" into our heads.

But information is not some mysterious stuff, capable of being transmitted from one place to another, translated, accumulated, and stored; rather, it grows out of kinds of relations. Information is a difference that makes a difference (G. Bateson 1972). This invites questions: difference in what (what are you paying attention to?), about what (what matters, what is problematized?), for whom (who is asking, who is affected?). Asking these questions leads us to focus on the knower, a knower who always has a particular history, social location, and point of view.

Ironically, the science that was based on the democratization of knowledge has produced a technocratic elite, so that knowledge-by-anybody is actually knowledge by a very few. The habitual disembodying of scientific knowledge, however, tends to obscure the specialness, the exclusiveness, of this class of knowers. This mystification-by-depersonalization is exemplified by the frequent use of the passive voice in scientific writing.

If we acknowledge that our interests, perspectives, cares, and worries are part of the complex in which information is generated, then the knowing subject can't disappear as easily as it does in conventional science. It should become harder to mystify knowledge and action. It should become easier, that is, to detect the politics of knowledge: the subtle power involved in defining problems and evidence, in legitimizing knowers and knowledge. Many have commented on the exclusion of women and non-Western peoples from the inner circle of scientific knowing, and Wes Jackson (1987) has commented on the way farmers' knowledge has been largely excluded from scientific agriculture. (On the importance in agriculture of nonscientists' knowledge, and on alternative research methods that use existing conditions in underdeveloped areas rather than requiring expensive and inaccessible equipment and techniques, see also Richard Levins 1981.) In addition to highlighting the usually invisible power relationships that partially structure our knowledge, recognition of our active role in knowing may lessen our chances of getting reductively stuck in one perspective or at one level of analysis.

Biology as Basis for Design

All these considerations lead us to ask: What kind of biology? What kind of basis? What kind of design? If we mean a biology that is fixated on a small-n-nature written in the secret code of base pairs, if we believe that Nature designs organisms by giving them genes for things, so that we can imitate her by inserting those genes into other organisms ("reprogramming" them) to make them produce the same things, then we already have a certain kind of

178

biology as a certain kind of basis for a certain kind of design. Just as surely, our concepts of design and of ourselves have served as bases for that kind of biology. (See Haraway 1985, for a spirited commentary on the modern constitution of organisms as information processing systems: as "cyborgs," cybernetic organisms.) Or if we mean a biology that is fixated on a single vision of big-N-Nature, perhaps as ruthlessly competitive or as inherently cooperative, as a perpetual race or as a harmonious equilibrium, and if we believe we can order our own lives and activities by this vision of Nature, then we already have this kind of biology as well; it is a basis for, and a reflection of, our ideas of (or aspirations for) our own design.

Can we envision another kind of biology, one less tied to a search for the single timeless truth that will structure our lives, a biology that recognizes our own part in our constructions of internal and external natures, one that appreciates particular embodied perspectives as vehicles for empathy, investigation, and change? If a metaphor is something through which we can think (Bateson & Bateson 1987, ch. 17), and perhaps through which we can create/discover ourselves, can we find different metaphors for our world, and thus construct different ways of being in it?

Taking Responsibility for Nature

We must take more responsibility for the Nature (and the biology) we construct. We do not, however, manufacture either our own natures or Nature out there as detached, Godlike subjects. Our responsibility, then, is not the responsibility of unmoved movers, absolute originators projecting order on chaos. Rather, the construction is mutual; it occurs through intimate interaction. By the same token, we do not simply record facts about external Nature, any more than we are simply manifestations of an internal nature encoded in some genetic text. "Information," that is, is not given independently of us, and because this is so, we cannot disclaim a kind of ownership. Our cognitive and ethical responsibilities are based on our response-ability, our capacity to know and to do, our active involvement in knowledge and reflection.

So the productive ambiguity of subjects and objects, of multiple perspectives, of design as pattern, of ourselves as nature's designer and as nature's designs, as designers of our designs of (and on) nature, of our own natures as products of our lives in nature and of the life of nature in us — this ambiguity represents the rich confluence of biology, cognition, and ethics captured in the program of this gathering. If Nature is our technical or moral teacher, it is not as a radically separate, independent source of information-stuff, but rather as a source of news of difference, a world we interrogate with particular questions and particular concerns in mind, and whose responses we interpret in the light of our own history with it.

I very much respect and value the work on alternative biologies represented in this volume, but think we ought to be cautious about claiming one true account of Nature's nature (though I have in the past come close to doing this myself). I am suspicious of quests for single truths; there is a strong tendency to take what is prescribed ("already written," whether in the genes or in the language of the Earth and streams, and therefore in no way dependent on us) as prescription, that is, as a received formula for action. We should resist this temptation to seek "the natural" as an authoritative guide to our lives. It is, after all, the temptation to deny our presence in every truth we see. Our presence in our own knowledge, however, is not contamination, but the very condition for the generation of that knowledge. Biology is an activity among many, and its varieties are ways of acting in the world that reveal us more than we may realize. Design is the pattern that emerges with that activity. Finally, this includes even our conceptions of Nature's own design.

Donna Haraway writes of science as fetish: "an object human beings make only to forget their role in creating it, no longer responsive to the dialectical interplay of human beings with the surrounding world" (1978/1987, 219). Elsewhere, she calls on us to forsake our search for a totalizing unity, to give up our "dreams for a perfectly true language, of perfectly faithful naming of experience" (1985, 92). In place of the quest for a lost innocence, an original wholeness to make our lives intelligible and to ground our politics, she advocates a politics of coalition. Such a coalition would be based, not on a common language, but on a "powerful infidel heteroglossia" (p. 101).

180

Much of this could be seen as a denial of the desirability, or even the possibility, of doing what some of my colleagues are doing. I may seem to be saying that biology can't be a basis for design. In fact, once our terms are reworked in a way that fits the enterprise, just the opposite is true. It is "biology" as timeless truth that I reject, not biology as a human activity entered into with responsible awareness. The first defines reality once and for all; the second is intimately connected to the persons and life circumstances of scientists and does not claim transcendent truth. We can't help revealing our notions of biological design in our other creations, just as we can't help showing ourselves in our practice of biology. Probably the most common and intuitively appealing way of conceptualizing natural design, in fact, is by analogy to our own activity. To acknowledge our part in constructions of Nature is to accept interaction as the generator of ourselves and of our interrelations, of knowledge, and of the world we know. Both we and the world are expressed in this dance, even as we are created and know ourselves in it.

If any of this makes sense, then the perspectives of the contributors to this volume are extraordinarily precious. Their sciencing shows us moral/esthetic/intellectual selves both responsive and response-able (and so, responsible) to a different conception of Nature, and thus, to a different conception of ourselves. If there is special value in the sensibilities revealed in their work, and I think there is, it is perhaps not so much due to their having found the one true essence of Nature, but rather to their having developed and enacted a "knowledge of the larger interactive system" — what Gregory Bateson called, simply, "wisdom" (1972, 433). Such knowledge is not in any absolute sense truer than the partial knowledge of cause-effect arcs that Bateson says our conscious purpose cuts out from the loops and circuits of larger systems, but it may well be crucial to our particular, nonabsolute contingent, and increasingly endangered existence.

Concerns, Cares, and Generative Complexity

What sorts of concerns are expressed in these alternative ways of questioning Nature? In what may be a foolish attempt to speak for

181

my colleagues, I will venture a few guesses. One thing I see is worry, both about the excessive power of traditional science and about limitations on its power. Science's ability to predict and control (the twin goals of contemporary science — whatever happened to understanding?) often seems inadequate to the cascade of unintended consequences that frequently follows technological advance. These two, excessive power and inadequate power, are not contradictory. Far from being mutually exclusive, power and vulnerability are both aspects of our embeddedness in the world, an embeddedness denied by conventional accounts of objective scientific knowledge. As an example of this denial, consider the idea of objective truth as truth that is grounded in no-ground, no-body, and no-place. Quantity of power, furthermore, is not necessarily the same as adequacy or appropriateness of power. A little delicacy and discernment can go a long way.

In addition to worries about power and vulnerability, I sense in my colleagues a certain discontent with the feeling of estrangement that seems to have been fostered by establishment science's obsession with detachment, isolation, and independence. Metaphors of engagement, connection, and interdependence crowd our language, as we struggle for different ways of knowing and being in the world. This emphasis on interconnection is related, in fact, to my points about power and vulnerability. Attending only to consequences of powerful techniques without attending to the consequences of those consequences is just what allows mainstream science to advertise power without giving comparable time to danger and mishap. Often associated with the paralyzed dismay that can accompany our glimpses of what Donella Meadows calls "Awful Interconnections," these metaphors of wholeness can also show us that "solutions are as interconnected as problems" (1988, 16). Solutions in turn point to other problems and solutions, not only technical, but psychological, cultural, economic. There is thus a moral-esthetic-political dimension to this preference for inclusion over exclusion, the personal over the impersonal, mutuality over domination, systems of influences over single causes, openness over closure, loops over lines.

This dimension exists whether we recognize it or not, and it is a source of difference in our approaches to science. Differences, however, do not necessarily preclude common goals. We return, then, to the theme of multiple perspectives, not as an exercise in arbitrary and empty relativism, but as a discipline in flexibility and empathy. I suggest we try to respond to Haraway's challenge to forge a coalition of diverse tongues and visions, generative of the kind of complex and multiple truths required by our complex and precarious designs with, of, on, and in Nature.

REFERENCES

Bateson, Gregory. 1972. *Steps to an Ecology of Mind.* New York: Ballantine Books.

Bateson, Gregory, and Mary Catherine Bateson. 1987. *Angels Fear: Towards an Epistemology of the Sacred.* New York: Macmillan Publishing Company.

Bordo, Susan. 1986/1987. The Cartesian masculinization of thought. In *Sex and Scientific Inquiry,* ed. S. Harding and J. F. O'Barr. Chicago, IL: University of Chicago Press, 1987, 247-64. Reprinted from *Signs* 11 (3).

Haraway, Donna. 1978/1987. Animal sociology and a natural economy of the body politic, Part I: A political physiology of dominance. In *Sex and Scientific Inquiry,* eds. S. Harding and J. F. O'Barr., Chicago: University of Chicago Press, 1987, 217-32. Reprinted from *Signs* 4 (1).

Haraway, Donna. 1981. In the beginning was the word: The genesis of biological theory. *Signs* 6 (3): 469-81.

Haraway, Donna. 1985. A manifesto for cyborgs: Science, technology, and socialist feminism in the 1980s. *Socialist Review* 80: 65-107.

Harding, Sandra. 1986. *The Science Question in Feminism.* Ithaca, NY: Cornell University Press, 74, 227-28.

Harding, Sandra and Jean F. O'Barr, eds. 1987. *Sex and Scientific Inquiry.* Chicago, IL: University of Chicago Press.

Jackson, Wes. 1987. *Altars of Unhewn Stone.* San Francisco, CA: North Point Press.

Lakoff, G., and M. Johnson. 1980. *Metaphors We Live By.* Chicago, IL: University of Chicago Press.

Le Guin, Ursula K. 1987. Half past four. *The New Yorker.* September 28: 34-56.

Levins, Richard. 1981. Class science & scientific truth. *Working Papers on Marxism & Science* (Winter).

Longino, Helen, and Ruth Doell. 1983/1987. Body, bias and behavior: A comparative analysis of reasoning in two areas of biological science. In *Sex and ScientificInquiry*, op. cit. 165-186. Reprinted from *Signs* 9 (1).

Maturana, Humberto, and Francisco Varela. 1987. *The Tree of Knowledge*. Boston: New Science Library.

Meadows, Donella. 1988. World interconnectedness also works in our favor. *Annals of Earth* 6 (1): 16.

Oyama, Susan. 1981. What does the phenocopy copy? *Psychological Reports* 48: 571-81.

— 1982. A reformulation of the idea of maturation. In *Perspectives in Ethology*. Eds. P. P. G. Bateson and P. H. Klopfer. New York: Plenum Press, 5: 101-31.

— 1985. *The Ontogeny of Information*. Cambridge: Cambridge University Press.

— 1987. Looking for nature. Opening address, 15th Anniversary Meeting of the Lindisfarne Association, New York City, November 7.

— In press. Ontogeny and the central dogma: Do developmentalists need the concept of genetic programming in order to have an evolutionary perspective? In *Systems and Development: Minnesota Symposia on Child Psychology*. Vol. 22. Eds. M. Gunnar and E. Thelen. Hillsdale, NJ: Lawrence Erlbaum.

9

GIANLUCA BOCCHI
MAURO CERUTI

Emergence and
Transcendence in Evolution

T he Pantheon of Indian gods is not organized into an ordered hierarchy, a product of a unitary, consistent, and continuous view of the world. It is a complex microcosm which faithfully reflects the degree of complexity of the society which has thrived in the Indian subcontinent for the last five thousand years. Among the many events which compose its dramatic history, an important encounter stands out in the foreground — that in which the urban, agricultural, and maritime civilizations of the Indus valley opposed the onslaught of the nomads coming from the steppes of Central Asia. These nomadic Aryans of Indo-European tongue eventually succeeded, however, in triumphing over and almost canceling, up to this century, the very traces of what had been a refined and technologically advanced world. This encounter dates back more than three thousand years and is still permeating contemporary Indian civilization. It has shaped the unequal caste system which has been regulating for countless centuries the lives of millions of people, down to the smallest details. It has given rise to the principal linguistic European languages of the north and the Dravidic languages of the south, generally considered today to be the descendants of the languages spoken by the civilization of the Indus Valley. It was at the origins of the characteristic traits of the

Indian religion, which, behind the all-inclusive label of Hinduism, conceals a group of heterogeneous cults, often incompatible and hostile among themselves.

Not even the vertex of the Indian Pantheon — the Trimurti of Brahma, Vishnu, and Shiva — is immune to these divisions. What is seemingly a reasonable division of work, with Brahma as the creator, Vishnu as the preserver, and Shiva as the destroyer, actually conceals within itself a profound asymmetry. Whereas Brahma and Vishnu are gods of the religion of the Aryan invaders, of that world of deified heroes which has a distant parallel in the Germanic gods, the cult of Shiva is autochthonous. It dates back with all probability to the civilization of the Indus Valley and is still practiced today in its fullest form, especially within a Dravidic context. Shiva was opposed for a long time by the Aryans. Even after it had been integrated into the official Pantheon by public acclaim, Aryan hostility continued to manifest itself towards it with a series of hardly gratifying appellatives, such as "god of tears," "god of the mountains and the forests," "god of sickness," but Shiva is, above all, *Nataraja*, the god of dance. It is with the garment of the cosmic dancer that he animates movement "where everything, beauty and ugliness, creation and destruction, is expressed or concentrated in a sole, complex yet symmetrical journey," which expresses a universal symbolism — a patrimony not only of the Indian civilization, but of all humanity.

In his dance, Shiva is the destroyer who purifies. Surrounded by a ring of flames, he takes fire in his hand and hurls it into the world, thus annihilating everything in its path. But his destructive power strikes blindly. It is not directed against something or someone, not against any enemy in particular. It is not inspired by ethical rules, nor does it wipe out those sinners who may have strayed away from their predestined pathways. On the contrary, the dance of Shiva makes us realize that such predestined pathways simply do not exist. Even that which is "good," even that which has functioned and remained unaltered throughout the unfolding of the ages, is, nevertheless, destined to be regenerated by the purifying fire. The dance of Shiva is not only destruction, it is also destruction/transformation/creation. It is the expression of a Gordian knot which inextricably binds together both protection and terror, being

186

and void, creation and destruction. It indicates the inevitable alteration of the ecological conditions, incarnates the idea that the new is possible only thanks to this change and, therefore, thanks to the giving away of part of the old. It symbolizes death understood as rebirth, which is a universal theme in all human religions.

The peaceful distinction of the roles distributed among Brahma, Vishnu, and Shiva is contradicted in the dance of Shiva. Down to the smallest particulars, all his iconography tends to represent a *unitas multiplex* of creation, preservation, and dissolution which cannot be broken down any further. The followers of Shiva interpret the interrelationships among the gods of the Trimurti in quite a different manner than do the followers of a more conventional view of the world as envisaged by the Aryan victors. Brahma and Vishnu express single polarities: hot and cold, solar and lunar, male and female, yang and yin. Shiva, however, has the duty of transcending them, of revealing the coproduction and the joining of the opposites. In a certain sense, Shiva, then, is god the creator par excellence. Whereas Brahma is creation according to rules, a predictable, controllable unfolding, Shiva is the process of emergence, of the creation of the new, of the unpredictable, of that which is not deducible from the rules, of the uncontrollable, of that which cannot be subdued. The dance of Shiva is the Indian Trimurti proposed to us by an image of change, which, for the Western world, is clarified in counterpoint to the developments of evolutionist thought.

The dramas, apparently so distant in time and space, of the conflict among the conceptions of the world from within the Indian microcosm help us comprehend the fundamental aspect of the transitions of contemporary science, of our impressions of the history of nature and about the nature of history. Our science, in its subsequent developments, has been able to comprehend Brahma and Vishnu quite well, but has in a certain sense resolved into them the same Shiva. In the universe of modern science, creation drew its own sense from the rules that found its own predictability, its own deducibility and its own conceptualization. Much more problematic is the relationship that binds change and creation with chance, the contingent, the unpredictable — the dance of Shiva. Twentieth-century science has begun asking itself about the

changes and the creation which take place due to chance occur-
rences, contingency, randomness, transcendence, the dance of
Shiva. Science has taken account of the irreducible and constructive character of the singular and of the event. Contemporary thermodynamics and biology are becoming the fields of study of the
multiple interactions between reversibility and irreversibility,
between stasis and change. Behind the simplicity of the presumed
first elements of the universe, a gulf of interactions has opened
among systems of entangled hierarchies. The domain of regal
order has been substituted by the internal conflicts of the tetra-
gram: order/disorder/interactions/organization.

The history of science in the modern age is the history of the discovery of deep space and deep time: from Galileo who turned his
telescope to the study of satellites orbiting Jupiter, to the astrono-
mers who today scan the skies with their telescopes looking for
quasars, neutron stars, and black holes; from the eighteenth-cen-
tury naturalists who scoured for fossils, to those communication
physicists who have recently discovered a fossil residue far more
ancient — the fossil radiation at 3 degrees K which seems to testify
to that original explosion which, more than fifteen thousand million years ago, marked the origins of "our" time and "our" space.
While reading the many chapters of this history, one is struck by
the radical nature of the process of decentralization which man has
embarked upon in the last few centuries. For medieval man, the
farthest heavenly body was Saturn, and the fixed stars were nothing but set pieces on the inside of a huge container which marked
the atemporal limits of the physical universe. As far as history was
concerned, everything had taken place within the narrow confines
of a mere 6000 years as dictated by the biblical chronology, a
length of time which seemed to be in accordance with what was
held as irrefutable truth regarding the history of both nature and
humanity. Today, science talks quite unabashedly in terms of thousands of millions of years, multiplying by a factor of at least
2.5×10^6 the traditional chronological scale of our civilization. For
the space scale, the comparisons are slightly more difficult, but
perhaps the divergences would become even more gigantic. One
cannot help but be struck by the enormous abyss which separates
the term *a quo* from the term *ad quem* regarding the spatial and

temporal dimensions of our universe. Our astonishment grows further when we realize that even when the Copernican revolution had been accepted by, and incorporated into, the realms of science and later by common sense, the traditional temporal chronology was still well in force. The multiplication of time by the huge factor we have just mentioned has been done, after all, for little more than two centuries, having really only been started as late as the middle of the eighteenth century.

Biological evolution was comprehensible only with great difficulty in the terms of the traditional chronology. If the world was created 6000 years ago, the species literally have not had the time to transform, and their fixedness is more a fact implied by that same image of natural history than a dogma superimposed from the outside. One of the more general cosmological hypotheses of the Darwinian Theory of Evolution — both its consequence and its postulate — was, therefore, that every traditional chronology should be radically put in discussion. As a result, the temporal scenario of the history of life (and of the cosmos) was decisively amplified. If evolution is a fact — demonstrated independently by a series of morphological, behavioral, ecological, geographical, and paleontological phenomena — then the various organisms may have had sufficient time to evolve and to develop an enormous diversity beginning from common undifferentiated ancestors. In the period of its victorious affirmation, Darwinism converged readily with the newborn field of geology and with other sectors of paleontology in the formulation of a history of life on Earth measurable at least in hundreds of millions of years. It is therefore significant that one of the most persistent opposers of this new chronology of natural history was one of the leading physicists in the scientific disciplines of that period, Lord Kelvin. Based on purely physical and chemical reasoning, he argued that the Earth could not have had such a long history, because otherwise it would no longer have been able to display autonomously produced heat so spontaneously: It would have dissipated into space a long time beforehand. Hardly worth mentioning is the fact that the controversy ended with the biologists in the role of sound victors, seeing that other sources of heat had been discovered, which were not even within the realm of hypothesis for Lord Kelvin (e.g.,

189

radioactivity) yet were easily compatible with the new evolutionary chronology. Worth serious note, however, is the radical divergence between the two schools of reasoning in conflict. For Darwin and the biologists of his time, evolution, the idea that the whole of life may have had a history and that this history may have required a scenario of an adequate period of time in which to develop, was a fact proven by a myriad of convergent and independent sources of evidence. If certain physico-chemical data were in apparent contrast, they did not, however, succeed in invalidating the reality of this other all-pervasive fact. Rather, it was more probable that the very same contrast may have been due to the presence of then unknown physico-chemical processes. This, in fact, was the exact result of subsequent analyses. For Lord Kelvin and other physicists and chemists of the time, the line of reasoning was exactly the opposite. The tribunal to which our images of natural history were to be submitted was, of course, constituted by general laws of the physico-chemical order. These laws even had the authority to confute an idea which was by then sufficiently popular, that is, the Theory of Evolution.

This conflict turns out to be, then, the particular expression of a much more general conflict between the cosmology implicit in the discovery of deep space by the modern scientific tradition and the cosmology implicit in the discovery of deep time. Instead of being defined as chapters of the same history, the history of deep space and that of deep time reveal the nature of concepts, world visions, and schools of metaphysics and cosmologies, which, in the modern era, have been in perennial contrast and have contributed to the creativity and the polyphony of our scientific tradition. From this point of view, "classical" science — the science of planetary motion and billiard balls — appears as the result of the energy that modern man has poured into it with the intention of regulating the deepness of the space in which he has found himself immersed. In contrast, a conspicuous part of the developments in twentieth-century science — which has tended more and more consciously to present itself as a truly "new science" — may be interpreted as the fruit of the discovery of the irreducibility of the cosmology of deep time regarding the cosmology of deep space, and as the result of the retraction of the first on the second. Only today can we clearly discern the key points of this conflict, and can we likewise comprehend in which way certain presuppositions concerning these cosmological approaches may be able to cooperate to produce a new cosmology.

The cosmological tradition has, in the course of the modern era, tried to regulate the important events of the history of the discovery of deep space by presupposing the homogeneity of space and the possibility of extrapolating from one of its parts to the whole, from small regions to the entire universe in general. It has also tried for a long time to do likewise with the crucial events regarding the discovery of deep time. This tradition has even enjoyed, if only in part, a sound heuristic success, inasmuch as the attributes with which such a cosmology tended to represent time in natural history — "uniform," "gradual," "progressive" — have indeed become incorporated into the fundamental theories of the first historical sciences of nature, from geology to evolutionary biology. However, during the last hundred years, developments in these same sciences have demonstrated the unsustainable nature of this idea of time as proposed by the tenets of natural history. Not only have these attributes demonstrated wide and significant exceptions, but the very idea of the homogeneity of time in natural history has been questioned, not to mention the idea that an extrapolation — no matter how accurate — might be useful as a guide to better understand its various stages of development.

Against this traditional stance has appeared the image of a plurality of "times" in natural history, and the game of interactions and retroactions among these "times" is presented today as the fundamental reason for the irreducible unpredictability of every historical development.

The cosmology of a radically "evolutionary" nature (which in the modern sciences has far surpassed its sphere) originally confined within the human world of the living, to touch upon the universe, is inextricably bound to this irreducible unpredictability. In all his experiments, any researcher eager to predict the destiny of a stage of development of the universe, would not have any reason whatsoever to paint the actual scenario in which the events would have constructed themselves. Contemporary cosmology, in fact, proposes this assertion in even stronger terms: such an observer

191

would not even have any probable or plausible grounds for doing so. The great events of the history of the cosmos, life, and humanity are not only intrinsically unpredictable, they are also intrinsically improbable. The creation of more articulated or more complex structures, the creation of the new, cannot be inferred from a logical analysis of pre-existing structures. Every time the whole of contemporary science gives rise to a science of the genesis of structures, and of increasingly new structures, it encounters the problems inherent in the unlikely nature of this genesis, not to mention those regarding the stability, conservation, and invariance of the same pre-existing structures. Perhaps the most general product, in cosmological terms, of the interaction between the discovery of deep space and that of deep time is constituted by what Jean Piaget defined as a common itinerary of the sciences of our century: the interaction between a structuralism without a genesis and a geneticism without structures has produced a genetic structuralism which is the widest context in which it remains possible to redefine in complementary terms (competition and cooperation) the traditional dichotomous character of the relationships among the terms of each of the philosophical pairs that give rise to the epistemological controversies within the contemporary scientific disciplines. In particular, these pairs concern the study of living organisms and include: temporal / atemporal, the singular / the generalizable, diversified / homogeneous, irreducible / reducible, discontinuous / continuous, variance / invariance, and homology / analogy.

The cosmological conflict, primed, as it were, by the constitution of a historical science of nature, appears in all its radical nature if we consider that in the course of the last hundred years, from the moment in which the Darwinian Theory of Evolution became the consistent conceptual framework within which to outline a history of life, the development of biological thought has been characterized by the coexistence, at times peaceful, at times in conflict, of "two biologies." These biologies hinge on different types of questions, so different in fact that many questions, while fundamental for one, were felt by the other to be pure nonsense, and vice versa. Ernst Mayr defined the relationships between these two biologies as the opposition between "the study of proximate causes, the subject of the physiological sciences (broadly considered) and the study of the ultimate (evolutionary) causes, the subject matter of natural history."[1]

However, this divergence of the types of specialization and of the fields of investigation of the "two" biologies has had even more general epistemological and philosophical implications. It has also been accompanied by a series of contrasts: between a conception of science turned exclusively towards the elaboration of formalized and quantified theories, and one that retains the useless and misleading, if not indeed impossible, reduction of biological concepts to theories of this kind; between a constant search for explanations in general and unchanging laws and a reappraisal of historical narrations considered to be the only possible means of comprehending many phenomena and many different classes of phenomena; between a biology which calls upon physics to supply models to apply and to generalize, and a biology which is convinced that physics has very little to say about many of the topics characteristically studied in the fields of the evolutionary and behavioral sciences. This (relatively) peaceful coexistence ended up in open war when one of the two competing traditions (the physiological tradition in a broad sense, definable also as physicalist), after the great success represented by the discovery of nucleic acids and by the subsequent deciphering of the genetic code, thought that the base and the model of biological explanation had been thus located. Many of the issues posed by evolutionary biology were then easily translated into the conceptual framework made available by the physicalist tradition. However, many others were simply abandoned, held as they were not to be significant according to the pre-established criteria. If this idea of life and its study had a rapid success, obscuring as it did alternative ideas, just as rapidly did it reach its own "physiological" limits, as it were, just when there appeared in the foreground the necessity of a revision of the criteria which determined significance, and more generally, the untenability of the thesis of a unilateral unification of the two biologies. Fortunately, however, the subsequent, important developments of evolutionary biology have not given rise to a reductionism in the opposite direction. They have, on the contrary, questioned the very idea of reduction as the only means of contributing to overcome the duplication of the traditions, while pointing out the utility, and indeed the necessity, of various points of view and different logic systems in the study of the living organism.

The very workings of these events have also witnessed the development of a sort of *reductio ad absurdum* of the claims of the physicalist tradition, which has explicated the contrasts among the evolutionary sciences and the totalizing claims of a conception of knowledge based on classical physics. The problem of integration between the historical dimension and the molecular dimension of the sciences regarding the living organism has been interpreted in the very sense of the search for the actual way in which the invariance of the biochemical laws of the living organism can exhaustively define the fundamental mechanism. Seeing that it was also thought that the fundamental invariants in the universe of the living organism had been discovered thanks to the "molecular revolution" in the middle of this century, the problem of change in such a universe and belonging to such a universe could be considered substantially resolved. Jacques Monod, for example, was able to write, about twenty years ago, that "not only are the elementary mechanisms of evolution understood in their general outlines, but they are also identified with precision," and, therefore, "as far as the essential outlines are concerned, the problem has been resolved and evolution is no longer at the frontiers of knowledge."[2]

This attitude has been seen to be a direct threat to the survival of the evolutionary tradition as such, and even more so as an affirmation of the irrelevance of those disciplines intent on elaborating certain historical narrations and understanding the functions of the singularity of the events in natural history, the most salient example of which is paleontology. In this context, the most recent developments of the evolutionary sciences have provoked some profound reflection on the very tenets of their theories, and have considered from a new point of view the problem of the rapport with those disciplines which has been developed within the framework of the physicalist tradition. These developments have also very clearly pointed out that the phenomenology of biological organisms and their history shows a diversity and a variety, both characteristic and irreducible, which cannot be studied or adequately filtered through the homogenizing historical approaches of a generalized molecular biology. The proposal is not the substitution of a science of invariance with a science of change. On the contrary, the proposal is the construction of a science which would, in the study of the life of organisms and of historical events, make continual reference to the interaction of two "eternal metaphors," in the words of Stephen J. Gould, of two world visions at the same time competitive, complementary, and cooperating. These world conceptions emphasize respectively the homologies and the analogies, the leeway present in historical processes and the harmonies of the processes of optimization, transformation and persistence, and the moments of stasis and those of catastrophe.

One of the most interesting by-products of the developmental tendencies in the evolutionary sciences, and in the sciences of living organisms in general, has been the profound reappraisal, both historical and cosmological, of the same tradition in which the evolutionary sciences developed and of the same great conceptual turning-points which are at their origin. More precisely, there has been an epistemological and historiographical awareness that this same tradition has been powerfully and repeatedly influenced by heuristics and by strategies which have tended to translate the temporal into the atemporal, the irreversible into the reversible, the singular into the general, the historical narration into the necessity derived from a law. In particular, Stephen J. Gould has unequivocally pointed out the way in which the so-called "fathers" of contemporary scientific geology (James Hutton and Charles Lyell) were profoundly motivated by the attempt to insert the irreversibility of historical phenomena into a cyclic cosmology directly inherited from the medieval tradition, as well as into the universe admirably represented in the stained glass windows and the sculptures in the Cathedral of Chartres. More generally, this reappraisal has underlined the ambivalences in the work of Darwin, in which a substantial methodological pluralism and reference to a wide variety of tempos, modes, rates, directions, and mechanisms regarding evolution coexist side by side with the search for a fundamental point of observation and explanation of the evolutionary processes. In this light, it has been possible to analyze from new points of view the very way in which this irreducible ambivalence of Darwin's work, this plurality of themes, was rapidly reduced and translated into a series of "philosophies" of history and cosmological extrapolations. These, in turn, have unilaterally interpreted the science of evolution as the discovery of the fundamental direction and factor of evolution (whether biological or not) time and time again identified within the concepts of "selection," adaptation, recapitulation, and so on. Furthermore, the attempts to integrate the multiple dimensions of the history of living organisms and the search for the fundamental level and dimension for the explanation of evolutionary phenomena into unitary models, into a perfect synthesis,have accompanied the development of biological evolutionism throughout the entire twentieth century, through, however, the multiple reorganization which such development has undergone following the creation of new research areas (genetics, population genetics, molecular biology, etc.).

This reappraisal of the history of evolutionist thought has disclosed the crux of a general, recurring conflict. This conflict exists between a methodological attitude inclined to consider the actual phenomenological complexity of the events of the biosphere and of evolving populations as the pertinent starting point for natural history, and a methodological attitude determined to construct an image of them filtered into the terms of something "invisible and simple," or, as it were, of a philosophy of history. The developments of the Darwinian tradition last century did not succeed in settling this conflict, which was already, nevertheless, implicitly active within the assumptions of "philosophy of history" which constituted the nucleus of Darwinian thought (or, however, of a Darwin interpreted tendentiously), and the discrepancy between these and the fossil evidence which seemed to indicate a history of nature rather different in many ways. And in fact, where possible, this conflict became progressively more acute. Twentieth century evolutionary biology, from the 1930s to the 1980s, has been developed through the great controversies on nature and on the rhythms of evolutionary change. The "philosophy of history" associated with the dominant Darwinian tradition wanted this change to be slow, gradual, and uniform, while paleontological documentation demonstrated it to be sudden, irregular, and discontinuous. In a similar fashion, the very nature of the transitional processes between a species of ancestors and a species of descendants has been questioned. "Classical" Darwinism and neo-Darwinism presented them as processes of gradual transformation of the first into the second, where the fossil evidence seemed rather inclined to support their being considered similar to the processes of filiation inherent in multicellular organisms. The descendant species would then appear in a relatively sudden manner (on a geological time scale) and could even coexist for long periods of time — although usually in different habitats — with the ancestral species.

For about a century these conflicts were resolved by turning to principles of both authority and hierarchical ordering concerning the various branches of knowledge. A case in point is fossil evidence, the scenario of world history, which paleontology suggests might be imperfect and should be integrated and interpreted therefore within the framework of reference as defined by the basic Darwinian assumptions. In a certain sense, the history of nature would thus be duplicated in an "empirical," blind, and deceiving history and in a "philosophically" oriented, simplified but truthful history capable of grasping the hidden order and the invisible yet simple nature of it all. The contemporary developments of the evolutionary sciences can well be read as the tendency to question the necessity and the utility of this duplication. They can also be seen as an attempt to reconstruct the history of life within the sphere of life on Earth and in the universe. It too can be considered as being a refusal of those strategies of a priori hierarchical ordering in the fields of research into evolutionary phenomena and as a contemporary effort to construct the theory of evolution of biological organisms through intercommunication and hybridization among a whole array of disciplines.

We can understand the consequences of the contemporary developments of this conflict only by comprehending the meaning of the evolutionary sciences' answer to the challenge issued by the totalizing claims of the tradition as a consequence of the developments of molecular biology. The conceptual framework responsible for these developments has, in fact, endeavored to define the new fields of research via procedures of extension and extrapolation of the patrimony of classical physics. It has also underestimated the importance of singular events in the scientific investigation of living organisms (and has aspired to the utmost to their dissolution). It has even judged as impossible scientific research on the origin of life. However, most of the developments of the modern evolutionary sciences can well be read as a radical move away from such presuppositions. Physics itself (and in particular the thermodynamics of Ilya Prigogine) has reflected on whether an important stream of biological research in our century (especially in the field of embryology) was not in fact in the right when it pointed out a certain incompatibility or, in any case, a certain heterogeneity between the two orders of explanation of classical physics and biology. It also questioned itself on whether the same strategy for getting over this incompatibility was not indeed the reappraisal of certain physical processes in the light of new conceptual patrimonies elaborated to account for the specificity of biological processes.

Meanwhile, the biological theory of evolution of Darwinian inheritance has reappraised and broadened its epistemological borders through an intense cooperation with other scientific approaches. These other disciplines are mainly those which share the same central interest for the history of life on Earth (and in the cosmos). Other scientific approaches include ecology, biogeography, the unitary science of the living and non-living Earth which James Lovelock defined as geophysiology, and paleomicrobiology. Still others are the symbiotic theory of cellular evolution which demonstrates how eukaryote cells — shared today by polycellular organisms on the Earth — derived from the cooperation and the integration of simpler organisms, still distinct if not indeed hostile in the past; the newborn science of hierarchies and of differing levels of reality; and the approach to the universe of living organisms which Humberto Maturana and Francisco Varela elaborated in the notion of autopoiesis. These converging themes outline an approach to the history of life and to that of the Earth in which not only is the same reference to events irreducible, but so too is it indispensable for shedding light on many of the mysteries and riddles created by a history of nature more in harmony with the particular philosophies of history than with the complexity of the actual phenomena themselves. The double-sided studies on singularity—physical on the one, biological on the other—have allowed for the defense of the pertinence of biophysical investigation, for the advancing of new hypotheses on the origin of life on Earth, for dialogue with astrophysics and physical cosmology so as to open a meaningful debate on the relative diffusion of life throughout the cosmos, and on the possible varieties of this life. The discovery of contingencies, hidden at every turning point in every evolving structure, does not pose an end to the important research on the general rhythms underlying the phenomena of the cosmos, but, in fact, broadens our horizons in quite a decisive manner.

This complex game of interactions—always in the process of becoming and never quite accomplished—among approaches, modelizations, and various disciplines has already produced an extremely prominent result for the cosmological tradition of the modern age. It has brought about a reappraisal of the nature of that conceptual couple, "chance" and "necessity," which was defined as the limit of the knowable universe within the realm of "classical" science. It was, in fact, the ultimate criteria of scientific quality. As such, science was only that which considered the necessary. When it occurred, chance had to be reduced to the level of insignificance; it had to be dissolved. If this was not possible, then it was permissible and quite a matter of duty to present a final admission of ignorance about the phenomena in question.

The modern evolutionary sciences have breached such a limit in several fields. Above all, they have demonstrated how behind every significant event of natural history—from the origin of the universe to the origin of life, from the origin of the eukaryote cell to the origin of the various phyla and species—the same inextricable knot of chance and necessity is in play, albeit in everchanging configurations. "Classical" science wanted to undo this knot once and for all by separating the two polarities through the imposition of limits to rigid (non-historical) criteria of significance. However, the impossibility of undoing this knot has hardly become a weakness. On the contrary, it has become a source of strength in the modern sciences which have searched for more suitable conceptual instruments with which to account for these ever-changing interactions. This has brought about important transformations in the expectations and the perspectives of science itself. The study of the potentiality of evolutionary systems is not to be identified with the search for a precise and exhaustive predictable nature of their future. Also the same limits incurred by our own capacities to predict become, in a positive sense, new sources of knowledge in the history of nature and in the nature of history.

Yet the modern evolutionary sciences show us something else as well: not only the recurrent, changeable interactions of chance and necessity, but also the relationships of reciprocal coproduction of these conceptual polarities. They point out how behind every intervention of chance there is also the presence of necessity, and how behind every intervention of necessity there is the presence of chance. The modern evolutionary sciences tend to break those comfortable "black boxes" within which one has often taken refuge to conceal the gaps in our explanation.

The hierarchical theory of evolution constitutes one of the most significant roots and outcomes of such a mutation of perspective. Such a theory, which is the conceptual framework within which the evolutionary sciences of the 1980s have articulated their research in a progressively more conscious fashion, springs forth from the awareness that, in the sciences of biological evolution, the search for the "invisible and simple" component has brought about simplifications and illegitimate conceptual subordinations. The theory is also born from the demand to study evolutionary phenomena from new points of view as complex networks of interactions among systems, hierarchical levels, and indeed, among various hierarchies.

Hinged on the classical pair "mutation/natural selection," the entire Darwinian and neo-Darwinian tradition has, in effect, put forward an image of biological organization embryonically structured on two levels, in which the raw material of evolution would be provided by the mutations produced at the genome level and would then be organized by the processes of natural selection among the individual organisms themselves. Furthermore, this conception has witnessed the parallel emergence of extrapolations which, on the one hand, would seem to exclude the possibility of extending this embryonic hierarchy to levels above that of the

200

organisms themselves (whose existence would have to be considered then as purely conventional), and on the other hand would tend to consider the dynamics of the genome as a sort of lower limit, a sort of black box out of which evolution would only extract the results. Elizabeth Vrba and Stephen Gould have strongly pointed out some sufficient reasons for questioning both these assertions, and have, in fact, proposed the demand for a reorientation of perspective as a challenge for future evolutionary studies.[3]

The fundamental hypothesis is that even the higher levels (the species) and the lower levels (the genome) of the individual organisms may in fact be the site of selective processes (selection of the species and molecular selection) analogous but not reducible to the processes of natural selection. Such processes can have significant effects even at the individual level and combine in a creative way with the effects of a more strictly defined natural selection, which operates on this level. This involves a new approach to the problem of the determination of evolutionary phenomena, which in many instances completely restructures the traditional ideas concerning the interactions between chance and necessity. Indeed, the dynamics belonging to the various levels of the hierarchy can have significant effects at the level of individual organisms, in which the site of the production of new evolutionary characteristics has traditionally been placed. However, it does not necessarily follow that they need have them. For example, many processes of molecular selection whose results are indiscernible, or, at most, neutral at the individual organism level, coexist with many other processes of the same type whose results manage to pass through that "threshold of discernibility" which renders them significant even at a higher level. The contemporary theory of evolution wants to confront this irruption of the singularity and the contingence of events by developing a theoretical framework capable of taking account of its effects. Let us read then, for example, what Elizabeth Vrba and Stephen Gould write concerning their theory of exaptation:

We coined the term "exaptation" for features arising for one reason, and then, fortuitously available and co-opted by selection for another reason (Gould and Vrba 1982). Form-function

201

correlations may be ubiquitous in nature, and may express the good design of organisms and other entities, but they need not arise directly by "adaptation" (sensu Williams 1966) — that is, by direct selection for current utility. We originally restricted our discussion of exaptation to features arising at one level and later co-opted for a different function at the same level — feathers evolving for thermal regulation and later co-opted for flight, for example. But the scope of exaptation becomes vastly expanded under the hierarchical perspective — because all upward or downward causation to new characters may lead to exaptation. Mutations arise for their own reasons at their own level. If they affect phenotypes in a way that selection upon organisms favors, then these mutant phenotypes are exaptation at the level of organisms.[4]

The hierarchical theory of evolution has led not only to this reappraisal of evolutionist ontology (from the unity of evolution to the hierarchy in evolution), but also to a deepening of the relationships between the genealogy of living organisms and their ecology, which, in the Darwinian tradition, had been neglected to the advantage of the genealogical aspect considered as the only pertinent and fundamental component. Furthermore, it is important to reveal that the evolutionary dynamics of an ecological and economical type (related, that is, to the exchanges of material and energy with the environment) are quite distant from those of a genealogical and informational nature. Every ecological system (no matter what scale it may be on) is, in fact, composed of multiple species and/or multiple interactions. Moreover, a single species (which is defined as a reproductive informational community) can partake in several different ecosystems and play different roles in every one of them. The leopard, for instance, is spread over a wide variety of habitats, from South Africa to Indonesia, and in Asia it feeds on animals, such as deer, which do not exist in Africa.

The revision of the problem concerning the fundamental evolutionary units and the explicit connection of the genealogical and the ecological aspects of evolution has led to a new scenario in which not one, but two parallel and reciprocally interacting hierarchies operate. Niles Eldredge observes:

This revised ontology [of evolutionism] automatically forces us to consider an alternative approach to the very structure of evolutionary theory — simply because it presents us with an alternative description of the organization of biological nature. That structure is hierarchical. Genes, organisms, demes, species and monophyletic taxa form one nested hierarchical system of individuals that is concerned with the development, retention and modification of information ensconced, at base, in the genome. But there is at the same time a parallel hierarchy of nested ecological individuals — proteins, organisms, populations, communities and regional biotal systems — that reflects the economic organization and integration of living systems. The processes within each of these two process hierarchies, plus the interactions between the two hierarchies, seems to me to produce the events and patterns that we call evolution.[5]

It is in this context that the demand to explore the relationships of circular causality connecting the genealogical and ecological aspects of the living organism becomes ineludible. Because, if it indeed be true that the constituent materials of ecosystems are the species themselves (and therefore, ultimately, the informational material contained in their genetic pools), it is also true that never are the selective advantages of any evolutionary characteristic presented in abstract, but only in given phenotypes which interact within the spheres of given ecosystems. In multiple situations ecosystems exert a causal influence on evolutionary processes because a character can be advantageous in some types of ecosystemic interactions and not in others. The same species can therefore thrive, flourish, and develop in one ecosystem and disappear or become extinct in others. This, of course, can alter the composition of its genetic pool and its reserves of variability with all the possible consequences for its evolutionary future. Not only that: often the extinction of a species — in its real sense, or in the narrower sense of disappearance from a particular habitat — depends on global ecological dynamics, with respect to which the local selective advantage of this or that character is not in question. These extinctions provoke, however, a radical reorganization of the reserves of genetic variability available for future evolutionary developments, in a process which is clearly of an exaptive nature, in which causes operating at the ecological level have important consequences for other levels, and even for the levels of another hierarchy — the genealogical one.

The study of extinction demonstrates how far the irruption of singular and unpredictable events may transform the directions of evolution and, more specifically, the same great regularities and legalities of the biosphere. Not only can the extinction of certain individuals have a decisive effect on the evolutionary path of a particular species, but so too does the extinction of certain species not confine itself to playing a decisive role in the evolutionary path of only one particular genus. In a more radical manner, the extinction of several species is found to be one of the protagonists in the history of living organisms under the guise of mass extinction. Extinction of this kind is not selective, nor does it aim for this or that organism, nor for this or that species in particular. It is not directly caused by the inadequacy of this or that morphological or behavioral character. It happens in the same way in which Shiva strikes: by chance and in huge numbers. It literally creates, in a manner of speaking, a void in the biosphere. The most catastrophic of instances of mass extinction occurred in the Permian Age, eliminating from the face of the Earth more than 90 percent of the species. And considering the extreme variety of species eliminated, there does not appear any a priori reason for the disappearance of certain species and the preservation of others.

Contemporary paleontology has pointed out how mass extinction is an extremely relevant and relatively recurring phenomenon in the history of multicellular organisms. Mass extinction appears indeed to be more frequent, more rapid (in geological terms), more profound (due to the number of species eliminated), and much more faceted (regarding the rhythms and directions of evolution valid under normal circumstances) than that which was first suspected. But, above all, paleontology has pointed out its ambivalence: not only its destructive role, but also — if not indeed principally — its creative role. Perhaps many of the great turning points of biological evolution, not to mention many of its most radical innovations, have not yet taken place to the same extent in the present biosphere, crowded as it is by the species in competition under normal circumstances, as they have in the imbalanced and desolate biosphere in the periods following the large shocks of mass extinction. Therefore mass extinctions appear as a series of fundamental events following which the dynamics of an ecological nature — the history of the planet as a whole, with all the determinations at a meteorological, geological, and even cosmic level which this history involves — profoundly influence and determine the dynamics of a genealogical nature, that is, strictly speaking, the very same evolution of the species. According to Vrba and Gould the study of mass extinction is, today, one of the most important stimuli which brings us to a radical change in the very same ways of conceiving the idea itself of the time of evolution.

[The principle of] exaptation also works for downward causation. Mass extinction, for example, may generate a pervasive realignment of life's diversity. The new proportions and types of creatures available for adaptive molding to renewed ordinary environments after such an extraordinary event form a largely fortuitous pool of exaptive potential. This expansion of the role of exaptation versus adaptation contains an important lesson for our basic attitude toward history. Hypotheses of adaptive optimality represent the extent to which we can ignore history and treat form and ecology as a problem of unconstrained equilibrium in a timeless world. Exaptation embodies all the quirkiness of historical contingency — you only get to an advantageous place if some other process for another reason gave you the goods. Hierarchy and the exaptive status of cross-level causation teach us that we inhabit a world of enormous flexibility and contingency — a world built by irrevocable history.[6]

This flexibility, this contingency, and the irreversible and creative character of the history of life and of the history of the Earth become even more apparent when we discover that the necessities and invariants of today's biosphere are, in actual fact, the product of evolution. They are the result of the actualization of determined possibilities and of their having been fixed in the form of interlinking constraints in more or less remote periods in the history of life on Earth. The research carried out in the above-mentioned field of micropaleontology has greatly contributed to this change in point of view. This is due to the fact that it has enabled us to discern the process through which these "life necessities" (the eukaryote cell or the multicellular organisms themselves) were fixed. It has also made us realize that in such fixing processes a decisive role has certainly been carried out by singular, unrepeatable, and formerly unpredictable events. This reinterpretation of the invariants and of the "necessities" of living organisms, seen as the outcome of real creative processes, has progressively redefined the "hinge" role of those disciplinary spaces — biochemistry and biophysics — which the physicalist tradition naturally considered as the fundamental instruments with which to carry out the reduction of the temporal to the atemporal, of the singular to the general. The problem has been posed, therefore, of the very origin of these biochemical and biophysical invariants considered to be the product of the closely interwoven presence of both necessity and chance, of pre-existing bonds (e.g., of a specifically physico-chemical nature) and of singular events. Such a problem takes shape, for example, in the questions posed by the investigation into the origins and evolution of the genetic code. For what reason does a particular cordon of DNA bases translate into one particular amino acid? And why only this one? For what reason did, out of all the existing or possible amino acids in nature, only a small select group become part of the structure of those proteins shared by all the beings living today on Earth? One can outline then the idea of a natural history of necessities and invariants, which makes it plausible even to pose the question of the nature and origins of the association among proteins and nucleic acids whose necessity and invariance constitute the nature of life as it appears today on Earth. From this point of view, such an association does not seem at all to be dictated by an atemporal and predetermined necessity. It is likely though to be the outcome of dramatic, catastrophic events, the final product, as it were, of a long history of the biosphere.

In the very idea of a natural history of necessities and biological invariants, there is, in some way, the implicit discovery of a nature

206

and a history of nature which are the origin of its own forms, its own laws, its own necessities, its own invariants. The perspectives opened by physical cosmology widen the horizons of this discovery as they are pushed to the limits of our space and time. This is so because physical cosmology outlines a natural history of the necessities and the invariants: the same physical constants, the same masses of particles, the same general regularities of our universe, such as gravitation, electromagnetism, nuclear interactions that originated in the most remote ages in the history of the universe. It is also the same origin in which certain singular, contingent aspects of the first events in the history of our universe may have played a decisive role.

Such outcomes in the contemporary sciences provoke a reinterpretation of the same notion of law. Laws are constraints resulting from the history of the universe which has in itself beginning and origin regarding the creation of form (or law), not, however, predetermined and atemporal necessities. Furthermore, these constraints are not simply imposed "from the outside onto a preexisting reality, but participate in the construction of an integrated structure and determine for the occasion a spectrum of intelligible, new consequences."[7] This interpretation of the notion of law makes it possible and indeed necessary to reconcile the universal aspect of scientific explanation with the recognition of the singular characteristic of the universe itself and of the same constraints which constitute it. The outcomes of scientific investigation and epistemological reflection converge in proposing the plausibility of the idea that the universe could have been quite different and indeed even the plausibility of other universes.

We will be able to evaluate the distance separating the currently emerging evolutionary character of cosmology from the cosmological images characteristic of the modern tradition if we comprehend and take seriously the various interpretations of the notion of law in agreement with them, and if we comprehend and take seriously the different role which, consequently, the notions of possibility and change play in them. The formulation of the cosmological problem beginning with the search for an "invisible, simple" component, considered the notion of possibility as being subordinate to that of necessity, and the notion of change as subordinate to that of invariance. Taken as a whole, the possibilities of an evolutionary course came out to be all given a priori and fixed once and for all. The idea of possibility was totally laid aside, however, to the full advantage of the opposing poles of necessity and impossibility. The recognition of the fact that the universe of the possible is redefined repeatedly throughout the course of natural history in a variable, unpredictable way is the very element which characterizes the image of nature and history supplied by the sciences of change in our century. It is the same element which best characterizes the rediscovery of the potentialities of the idea of physics. Through the study of the origin and the becoming of the constraints which regulate our universe, one can also outline the idea of a natural history of possibilities, in which new universes of possibility are produced in connection with the great turning points of the evolutionary processes. Within the course of this natural history, certain possibilities become fixed and are in turn transformed into constraints which eliminate certain other possible alternatives, but which also produce some new ones. Obviously, the natural history of constraints and the natural history of possibilities are closely interwoven and constitute a history of the reciprocal coproduction of both possibilities and constraints.

Contemporary science deems the following question pertinent: do autonomous ontological orders really exist? It is also trying to explore the meaning and the consequences of a positive reply to such a question. Hence, we can plausibly say: ontological orders "become," and this becoming — with all the history of the creation of these orders, and of the interactions among these orders — radically transforms the cosmos: it endows it with its very own history. The cosmos, understood in the fullest sense as a unitary and integrated universe, is not given *ab initio* or *sub specie aeternitatis*, but it becomes. The key problem of most of the cosmological tradition in the modern age, that concerning the infinite nature of the cosmos, is progressively defined in the problem of its incompleteness, of its transformation, of its continual creation.

This new tendency to question the very roots of the cosmological problem has, of course, outlined an entire series of interrogatives on the nature of nature, laws, and history, and even on the ways of understanding and influencing the course of human

history. Are the laws (the forms) of nature atemporal and predetermined once and for all? Or is it indeed possible to talk about
a natural history of the laws (of the forms) of change and of the
creation of these laws (forms)? Is this creation of forms (of laws)
for itself? These are the questions contemporary science is pos-
ing from within its own developments, while outlining the possibility and the necessity of a science of the new and of the
emerging, which would also overcome the opposing forces
between nature and history, between invariance and change, and
between laws and events.[8]

Notes

1. Ernst Mayr, *The Growth of Biological Thought: Diversity, Evolution and Inheritance* (Cambridge, MA: Harvard University Press, 1982), 67.

2. Jacques Monod, *Le Hasard et La Necessité*, quoted from the Italian translation, (Milan: Mondadori, 1970), 114.

3. Elizabeth S. Vrba and Stephen J. Gould, "The Hierarchical Expansion of Sorting and Selection: Sorting and Selection Cannot Be Equated," *Paleobiology* 12 (1986).

4. Ibid, 225.

5. Niles Eldredge, *Unfinished Synthesis: Biological Hierarchies and Modern Evolutionary Thought* (New York: Oxford University Press, 1985), 7.

6. Vrba and Gould, op. cit., 225-26.

7. Ilya Prigogine and Isabelle Stengers, "Vincolo," *Enciclopedia Einaudi* 14 (1981): 1076.

8. On these topics by the same authors, see also Gianluca Bocchi and Mauro Ceruti, "Modi di Pensare Post-Darwinian," *Dedalo*, Bari, 1984; Gianluca Bocchi and Mauro Ceruti (eds.), *La Sfida delle Complessita* (Milan: Feltrinelli, 1985); Mauro Ceruti, *Il Vincolo e La Possibilita* (Milan: Feltrinelli, 1986), and Mauro Ceruti, *La Danza che Crea* (Milan: Feltrinelli, 1988).

From Biology To Cognitive Science

General Symposium
on the Cultural Implications of the
Idea of Emergence in the Fields of Biology,
Cognitive Science, and Philosophy

William Irwin Thompson Because of Francisco Varela's work on self-organizing systems and his particular work in developing the concepts of "autopoiesis" and "autonomy," I thought it would help us get right into the heart of the problem of Emergence, if Francisco were to open our symposium by giving a comment on Jim Lovelock's lecture.

Francisco Varela Well, this is both a pleasure and a very challenging thing to do. I do have three points I would like to make, which get down to the more "nitty-gritty" level of it all, but before I do I would like to make a more general, introductory remark about how I see Jim Lovelock's work. Frankly, I think Lovelock's work will be looked at, in the future history of science, as one of the great ideas of twentieth-century science. I look upon Jim as a scientist of the highest standard, so my three points should be seen as suggestions for refinement, not as a basic disagreement. I wish to use the grains of my "nitty-gritty" approach to polish and sharpen rather than erode or disintegrate.

Having made that clear, let me then make three remarks. First of all, Jim has made it very clear in his publications up to this time that Gaia cannot be described as other than having the quality of life. It is Gaia, living organism. Now this whole question has been tossed around and around, and around, for it is an important and difficult issue. But it seems to me that this difficult issue can perhaps be helped and clarified by making a distinction, a distinction that I hold as the important one. It is the difference between being alive, which is an elusive and somewhat metaphorical concept, and a broader concept, which is perhaps easier to tackle, that of autonomy. The quality we see in Gaia as being living-like, to me is the fact that this is a fully autonomous system. So, what is an autonomous system? I think that one can make it all more precise by saying that it is a system whose fundamental organization corresponds to operational closure. Now, operational closure is a technical term which I explicitly developed and formalized in my 1979 book.[1] Indeed, the book is about operational closure. Briefly stated, operational closure has to do with the fact that, when you build a system, you are in a situation where this entire "spaghetti" so to speak becomes its own identity mechanism; it specifies its own identity.

It is this quality of self-identity that I see in Gaia. So, operational closure is a form, if you like, of fully self-referential network constitution that specifies its own identity; but also specifies the way in which it comes to terms with whatever comes its way. That is, it establishes a sense of copulative world around it. This is the other side of Gaia, a part that is so clear in the theory. So it seems to me that autonomy, in the sense of full operational closure, is the best way of describing that living-like quality of Gaia, and that the use of the concept of autonomy might liberate the theory from some of the more animistic notions that have parasitized it. Now, when you say, "operational closure," what you have to do is to specify fully what kind of a closure it is, and this is, of course, empirical work; but it is the kind of work that Jim and many other people are carrying out,

211

and is where you do begin to get a clear sense of what this "spaghetti" is all about. In the cell, for example, we know what this closure is like; we can point to the biochemical mechanisms and so on and so forth. For the nervous system we can also say how it works, and for the immune system as well. The empirically attractive quality of the idea of Gaia is that the mechanism, the precision of this form of closure, is open for investigation.

So, that was my first remark: the distinction between living-like autonomy and the operational-closure quality of Gaia. My second point is about Jim's models of "Daisyworld." I'm afraid that here I do disagree a bit with Jim, if I may say so, for I think that in some sense Jim is selling himself short, far too short. I mean this in the following sense: Daisyworld, in the best tradition of feedback engineering, which Jim has referred to, is not the same thing as a fully plastic network, that is, a network which has some way of changing itself. This concept of network is one that comes out of recent research in cognitive science and Artificial Intelligence. Here there is a distinction between a single, linear feedback mechanism, or circumstance where you have one, two, or three feedback loops, and a network. A whole bunch of feedback mechanisms added together does not amount to the same thing as a network, for a network has a distributive quality and has its own dynamic. Network behavior, as we have seen, can be stable, or it can have a way of changing itself in order to achieve stability in the circumstances in which it finds itself. So I propose, I hope not too boldly to its own inventor, that the best model for Gaia is not one of the old tradition of feedbacks added together, but one of a fully distributed network. In the terms of the theme for our conference, "Biology as a Basis for Design," this is an area where biological research can provide great insight into the nature of our designs. In the same way that you will not get a cell by just adding together the regulatory circuits of enzymes and substrates, you will not get Gaia out of the regulatory circuits of Daisyworld. I believe that one will not have a fully convincing argument for Gaia until the full plastic network qualities of Gaia become apparent. For then, you see, you will actually be able to put your finger on the learning capacity of Gaia to show just how it becomes adaptive. If I may be technical for one moment, the Kupka-Smale

Theorem of 1976 shows that the attractors in such a phase-space are somewhat dense, so it is not hard to find a system that will behave stably; what is interesting is not that one finds such stable regimens or attractors, but that the system itself is able to find them. And that is much more easily explained by a learning mechanism — that is, not just by a group of equations in the tradition of feedback engineering, but by a system that has dynamics. Now, of course, variables are changed, but the way in which the systems change variables expresses a metadynamics, a learning principle. This is what I was trying to show in my talk on the immune system.

So, that was my second point, that Gaia has to be seen as a learning mechanism, and for that shift in perspective we need to move from feedbacks to distributive networks. We know what the learning mechanism of the nervous system is and what the learning mechanism of the immune system is. My last point is about chaos. Here again, I'm afraid that I tend to disagree a little bit with Jim. I think that when we talk about chaotic regimes, technically speaking — but perhaps I should back up a minute to explain the technicality. As the folks who work in this domain know, there are fundamentally three modes of behavior in a dynamical system: stability, the form of a point attractor; oscillation, the form of a periodic attractor; and aperiodic behavior, the form of a chaotic attractor. These are the three kinds of attractors known so far. Now, the fact that the third kind of attractor of behavior of a dynamical system has been called "chaotic" is giving rise, I believe, to a lot of misunderstanding, because we tend to think that chaos is bad. If we change the terminology and use that of Mandelbrot, so that instead of talking about chaotic regimes we talk about "fractal attractors," then we can remove the chaotic overtones. Then we are in a different world, and I am becoming more and more convinced, along with a few other people, that while in fact "fractal attractors" — formerly known as chaotic attractors — can be problematic in some circumstances, wherever they appear — and they seem to be very common in biological systems — they are not destructive but rather creative. For example, let's not forget that one of the first fractal attractors found was in ecological data by Robert May in 1976. Recently, we have been able, in a tour de force with colleagues from Stockholm, to demonstrate that the immune system normally has chaotic attractors, or fractal dimensions. Furthermore, there has been recent work carried on by Walter Freeman at Berkeley which is perhaps the clearest example.

If you measure the dynamic activity of the olfactory bulb, which is the part of the brain — in this case of a rabbit — which has to do with smell, at least in its sensorial side, you actually find chaotic attractors, and the system fluctuates and goes in and out of these chaotic attractors. Why? Because each time the animal goes through a breathing phase, the entire lamina — which is an enormous amount; it is like a huge population of neuronal activity — stabilizes into some form of attractor, and then lapses back into a chaotic regime. And then at the breath, a full non-chaotic regime sets in. This in and out of chaotic attractors is the way — Freeman believes, and I agree with him — of actually keeping, as it were, an open mind. That is, the rabbit can go through this nonstructured state, which we see as behavior, as sniffing, and then go back into this more open-minded state. This is the basic idea of a fractal dimension, that you are not trapped into a caged dimension, that you actually have access to a much more diversified state. So, I submit in brief, that fractal attractors do exist in biological systems — there is evidence for that — and I am sure that they exist in some of the dimensions of Gaia and that this is the way for good old Gaia to keep its own mind open. So there is no need to shun chaotic regimes as necessarily bad. Of course, it still is very much an open question, but I do think that we should not overlook this possibility. So, these are my three points.

Thompson Thanks, Cisco. Looking at this from the point of view of a cultural historian, and one who was at M.I.T. when Warren McCulloch was still alive, I see your comment on Jim's talk as a generational development. The first and founding generation of cybernetics, names associated with the famous Macy Conferences, such as McCulloch, Von Neumann, von Foerster, and Bateson, gave us basic concepts for systems guidance and correction, the feedbacks you're talking about. Now your generation comes along with its connectionist language of "Net Talk," "Hopfield neural nets," or your own "autopoiesis," and says, "Our generation wants to take it another step, from feedback to the metadynamics of the system as a learning one." It is like the movement from a one-dimensional line to a two-dimensional square. We do need places to look to find these complex systems of learning and the stabilization of an identity over time, and that is why I thought that both the immune system and Gaia were interesting places to look, and why I thought it would be interesting to have Varela comment on Lovelock's work. Of course, part of the force of Daisyworld is that it comes at complexity through simplicity, that it serves as a parable. Do you feel, Jim, that the metaphoric force of your argument is lost if the simplicity of feedback is immersed in the complexity of networks?

James Lovelock   Thank you, Bill. Yes, in a way, for it's the vastness of Gaia that can put people off, particularly scientists, so Daisyworld does serve as a simpler way for an engineer to get the hang of it. You see, as I said at the meeting, I'm essentially an inventor, and inventors are intuitive people who get ideas of things, and then when we make them, we find that they work. They may not always work commercially, but they usually do work. And then we have to spend years trying to explain to people why they work, and that really is hard work for inventors, and sometimes they just never succeed at it.

Can I start off, Cisco, by asking a few questions which will betray my complete ignorance? But don't hesitate to tear me to pieces; I don't mind at all, as long as that helps me to understand where I went wrong. So my first question is about "Emergence." I love this word, emergence, it's a beautiful word and it really means something to me, but first I want to take it down to the very lowest level. One of the simplest cybernetic devices ever made was Watt's steam engine governor. Do you know the thing? It's a couple of balls that go round and round, centrifugal force pulls them out, and as they go out this closes down the steam valve on a steam engine, and slows down the engine so that it can settle down to a steady speed. It's called the governor. It works very well. There's an apocryphal story that this was shown at a Royal Society Conversation in London in the middle of the last century and that one

215

of the people who went round and looked at it was James Clerk Maxwell, who, as you may know, was no slouch of a mathematician. Maxwell is reported to have said, at the Royal Society Council meeting three or four days later, that he had spent three sleepless nights trying to analyze Watt's steam engine governor and it totally defeated him. But, nevertheless, he had no doubt that it worked, and that it was an excellent invention.

Now, what I want to ask is: Is a cybernetic device as simple as that — one that shows emergent properties? That is to say, I look at emergent properties as being described by a condition where the whole is more than the sum of its parts. Certainly, the steam engine governor is doing something that you would not expect simply from the collection of its parts. It only does it when it's working; it doesn't do it when it's still. Now this is a very elementary level, but it's important to me to know whether this is "emergent" in the context that we have been talking about here.

Varela   I think that is really the right place to start. Let's see if we can exchange some impressions on this, because I certainly do not have a position to defend on this issue. Perhaps the place where I would begin is by reminding us of something that Evan suggested, something that I think is very, very important, and that is that if we are going to make sense of emergence as something interesting, then we have to distinguish between an emergent property and an emergent domain. Now, what could this mean?

Let me say what it means to me. Watt's steam engine governor, for example, certainly exhibits an emergent property, in the sense that, as with many other examples one could give, you have something that closes onto itself. Maxwell had a bit of trouble with it because the mathematics of his time never had, shall we say, snakes eating their own tails — this is something that does entail a different mathematics. But it is not all that hard, and you don't need a few years to figure them out. But there is an emergent property, which is the regulator of your set-point. Now, that I would call an emergent property but not an emergent domain. Why? Because to me an emergent domain is one that creates or specifies or gives rise to a new identity or a class of things. An absolutely dramatic case would be the emergence of the cell. From this point of view, our little notion of autopoiesis is useful, I think, because it specifies the circular mechanism. As Antonio showed in his presentation, you have the membrane, which by itself is an emergent property; you have lipidic liposomes or microcellular structures that can become a membrane. OK, that's an emergent property, right? On the other hand, you can have these lovely RNA-type molecules that have catalytic and replicative properties, and that in itself is an emergent property. Now, you put those types of RNA molecules inside liposome-type containers, and you bundle them together; you buckle them together so that the membrane now becomes integrated or is a result, in some sense, of the production of the RNAs and vice versa. The RNAs can have their enzymatic and replicative property because they're containing. Now, at this point, this bootstrapping activity gives rise to these coherent unities that, in my view, are the minimal living structure, which is why, with Humberto [Maturana], I wanted to give this activity a specific name, autopoiesis, for they are self-producing in that specific sense of being buckled together. There is no set-point here. There is no sense of just a one-dimensional property arising, but what arises, what emerges is a class-identity, and that gives rise to an emergent domain, which is life. And that, you know, is pretty dramatic. Now my feeling is that with Gaia it's much the same sort of thing: one can take regulatory loops of gases or particular calcium concentrations, whatever; but it seems to me that what your work shows, and clearly points out, which to me was a great revelation, is that in fact this whole thing is in itself an identity, in the same sense that the cellular identity can be called that. Therefore, Gaia is a proper emergent domain.

Now, as with any domain, therefore, showing a single loop or an emergent property won't do as a complete analysis, or even as an adequate or reasonable analysis or demonstration. I can look at a cell, a bacterial cell, and look at these metabolic loops; and I can control the cell via enzymes and the steady state of glycolysis or whatnot. But that is not the totality of the coherence of the cell. For that, you have to close all the loops, at which point the descriptions of feedback simply don't work for me. That's where I would agree with Bill and would call this second generation cybernetics; it's this post-cybernetics type of work that

I'm very fond of. Let me say one more word about this, and then I'll shut up.

The main difference, as I see it, is that in order to analyze this class-identity in a way that is not loops upon loops but has this quality of the emergent domain, one has to add the quality that I tried to capture in my presentation, and that is the metadynamics. Metadynamics is the system described not just in a way that explains how the parts begin to relate and give rise to the whole as more than the sum of its parts, but also in a way that explains the process by which the whole knows how to change itself in such a way so as to maintain that quality, that emergent property. That to me is the "click" that makes the whole thing take one more step. So, my comment after your talk, Jim, was, in a sense, my desire, my wish, my fantasy, to try to see in Gaia its learning mechanism, its network properties. What are its network properties? Are they like the brain? Are they like the immune system? Are they like the cell, or something totally different? This seems to me to be the fascinating question about Gaia, and maybe you have an answer for this. Certainly, I would love to hear more.

Lovelock   Thank you, Cisco. You have cleared up a lot of uncertainties, at least in my mind, but you've also landed me with this big problem. You've said a lot, and so let me start at the end, so to speak. I think we have come by different paths to the same point. We now do not describe Gaia as a hypothesis, but as an evolutionary theory. And I think that evolution is another way of discussing what you are talking about; in other words, a time-dependent process in which information is stored and changes are allowed. And we certainly do see Gaia as a tightly coupled evolutionary process involving the biota and its environment together. This brings me to the second point, which again takes me back to my practical side as an inventor. I have a strong intuition that an essential part of all living processes is the solid state. I cannot conceive of life occurring in a fluid — this dissipative-structure of the Prigogine type — for the living system needs a memory, and that will always be expressed in the solid state. I think that Prigogine's work has largely been to demonstrate that where you have a flux of free energy, you can get order to appear in the form of dissipative structures, like an eddy in a flowing stream, or an anticyclone or cyclone in a meteorological system, or a flame burning, or a chemical sort of order. These things have structure and form, and the entropy within them is reduced and excreted as the system operates. So far, these resemble life-forms, for they also have boundaries usually, but they never last. They are dissipative, they have no future, they never evolve. And I wondered why that was. What was the difference between them and the life-forms of every sort, from bacteria up to Gaia? The only thing that I could see, and as I said, it's no more than an intuition at this time, was the presence of the solid state. It is the solid state which can constitute a memory, so that learning becomes possible. And I would include a nuclear gas as a solid. In other words, in the solid state the atoms are tied together in a nondissipative molecular or literally solid structure. In a cell, the DNA and the membrane are solid. In Gaia it could be the mountains, all sorts of things, as well as the solid parts of the biota. So I put it to you as an intuition that the solid state is a very important part of what we're talking about here — memory or learning ability — for without the solid state you cannot have a memory or a reference to go back to.

Varela I fully agree with you that in the case of the cell the stability of the DNA is the key for its learning-evolutionary strategy. However, Jim, let me put it to you that there are other cases where this doesn't seem to be so. And these cases are very important in the current work on network research, work inspired, say, from research on the immune and nervous systems. In these cases, the memory is precisely nowhere — it is everywhere. I love to tell the story — it's a lovely story actually — of the earliest days of cybernetics, when all the boys, John Von Neumann, Warren McCulloch, and Norbert Wiener, used to get together at McCulloch's house. McCulloch was a bachelor and lived with his mother all his life. So they would get together and discuss things, particularly memory; they would talk about memory for months. Now McCulloch's mother was a very nice and quiet lady who would sit there and knit or sew. She never would say anything, but finally at one point she interrupted all these silly boys and said: "I don't know why you boys worry so much about memory. I know what memory is all

219

about." And so they all turned toward her and said, "Oh, well then, please tell us!" And she answered, "I just keep a little bit of everything everywhere." And, in fact, she did. She would keep one needle and one piece of thread and a little money in her purse, in her pockets, on the table, under the seat cushions; she kept a little bit of everything everywhere. So here is your principle of a distributive memory. And she was right, for in the brain there is no solid state in that sense of the DNA. That is, if you try to find the memory of Mrs. McCulloch, you will discover that it is in fact the totality of relationships of the system, the totality of the activity of the dynamic state. In mathematical terms, one would say the "attractor," which is one level higher up, is where the memory resides, if anywhere. So, it could be, Jim, that in Gaia you are absolutely right, that memory is a more concrete and tangible form, a stable structure like DNA. But it need not be. There are other examples: In the immune system it is the totality of the pattern and the memory; a little bit of everything is everywhere. It is not this one active connection, not this molecule, this transmitter, but the pattern which constitutes the memory.

Lovelock   My response to that would be that if you could produce for me a gaseous computer, I might be convinced.

Varela   Not a completely absurd notion.

Lovelock   No, there will be solid parts somewhere in the architecture. Well, this can go on indefinitely, and I think it's not really constructive for us at the moment. If we want to discuss the next level up from life — mind or intelligence or whatever — I think we should make it clear that a separation has been made. But, let's call it a truce at this point, Cisco.

Margulis   Let me approach it from a different angle. I completely agree that memory is not just solid, but solid and fluid. The fluid phases have to move things, and the solid phases have to store them. You start with a membrane and nuclear gases as the storage and the catalytic phases, but the next solid pieces are starches, polyhydroxybutilate, or, in other words, storage products. And when you add these solids to your perception of the system, you add a temporal dimension to your entity. In other words, as soon as you have solids that are sources of food, of energy, then you, if the you is a cell, can do things over time. The more you can store, the more you can do things over time. The solid state is absolutely essential, but by itself would be nothing. Let's take life at 0° Kelvin; it's frozen. All the components are there, right? Autopoiesis must be in there somewhere, because when you bring the temperature back up everything comes alive. I'm not sure if everybody here knows this, but you can take cells and store them at 0° degrees Kelvin for months, for years, and if you are careful about bringing the temperature back up, then you can get everything back to life; so, therefore, they weren't dead; they were stopped. Now that tells you that with total solidity the properties of life are inhibited; they are just stopped. So solidity by itself won't work completely as an explanation, and the absence of solidity won't work either. You have to have both solid and fluid; systems have to be heterogeneous to work.

Ricardo Guerrero   I think the solution between Jim and Lynn, the solution between solid and liquid, is gradient. The frontier between solid and liquid is gradient, and gradients are necessary to transmit or to change energy. So a solid state acts as a gradient to a liquid state.

Thompson   And this frontier between solid and liquid crystals or amorphous crystals seems to be the frontier of science fiction's imagination of the computers of the future, so maybe you are all right at the same time, Cisco, Jim, and Lynn!

Wes Jackson   There are so many things going on here, that if I respond to all of them, I run the risk of becoming incoherent. But I do want to talk a little bit about this business of an emergent property versus an emergent domain. And I would ask Cisco this question: Would you consider an epidemic to be an emergent domain?

Imagine a natural ecosystem, before agriculture began, an ecosystem with lots of species diversity, so much diversity that no insect or pathogen could possibly have an enzyme system able to break all the plant diversity down. A human looking at that ecosystem would never see an epidemic. With an ecosystem that's a monoculture, any number of species could mow it all down: a virus, a bacterium, a fungus, an insect, or even a cow. None of these groups of organisms that I've mentioned as agents in the epidemic was probably classified as such until monoculture came along. Would these be creatures which have entered an emergent domain, or did they display emergent properties within a larger emergent domain? What is the difference between an emergent property and an emergent domain?

Varela   We put it this way, Wes. I think that this distinction between property and domain is not a recipe, as far as I understand it, but is a sort of heuristic principle that has to be seen and analyzed in each particular case. The one who addresses the analysis has to know the details. I'm happy, for example, to make the distinction between property and domain in the case of a cell, where I have a little knowledge about these things, or for the properties of the nervous and immune systems. But for ecosystems, I'm so ignorant that I wouldn't know precisely what to say. So it's not a matter of a recipe, or of a little conceptual machine, but of a guiding idea that has to be looked at in the specific situation.

While I have the floor I cannot resist, because of my Latin temperament, making a comment about what Lynn said. She was speaking about something totally different from what I was. Maybe this is part of the misunderstanding of the last exchange — not the first, where I think we agree. Yes, fluidity and solidity in the sense of the material realization are always necessary; but that's not the point. The point is that a cell is a cell, not because it is both fluid and solid, which every bit of matter is, but because it has the pattern, the autopoietic pattern, the way the things are put together. The fact that you can crystallize it and then bring it back to life is true, but, from our point of view, not the relevant issue. It's a nonrelevant observation to the question of what is the pattern that, when you have it gives you the emergent domain of life. So, in the same way, yes, in every computer that we invent, we're going to have solid components, but that is trivial and does not address itself to the pattern of connections that would give the damned machine one capacity or another. In the classical Von Neumann machines, the pattern of the qualities they had was based on storage. But there are machines that you can buy or build today whose pattern is not one of storage but of distributive properties. And this is an invention; it's as tangible an invention as Watt's governor or any other invention. So, let's not confuse levels. Let's not confuse the level of realization with the level of pattern. Emergence is always a pattern relative to a level of realization, and if we stick to the level of realization, then we miss the emergent property.

Now, to go back to your point, Wes, this is precisely the point: What is an epidemic? You would have to give me the nitty-gritty of it to enable me to make a distinction between property and domain.

Jackson   All right, if we have an organism that is able to create an epidemic because humans created a domain of monoculture, is it fair to say that monoculture makes it possible for us to manage our own epidemic behavior? Is that what agriculture is? And does the emergent property show up in the individual while the emergent domain is where the pest population flourishes?

Lovelock   I am glad you raised the point about epidemics, Wes, because I think it is an interesting one in the discussion of domains and the phenomenon of chaos and similar things. I think it might be helpful to consider what has happened in the science, if you can call it a science, of population biology. The field was quite prominent in the discoveries of the mathematics of chaos. Robert May, a famous population biologist, has contributed greatly to the mathematical formulations of chaos, and in so doing, I think, he has revealed how dreadful a biologist he is, because he has come out with such statements as the more species you have in an ecosystem, the more fragile and less resilient it becomes. He states this quite firmly in his book, in quite unequivocable terms. But this is so contrary to natural experience that one intuitively feels that he is hopelessly wrong. Now this relates back to epidemics where you have two-species ecosystems that, in a sense, are failed

223

domains, or domains about to fail. The mathematics of epidemics will quite frequently show chaotic behavior. Indeed, Robert May first discovered chaos in his mathematical model of two or sometimes even more species ecosystems, foxes and rabbits and the like, for these are very prone to chaos indeed. But his models are not domains, because the environment is not included in that kind of model. Now in the real world, say with your epidemic of spruce worms in the monoculture of spruce forests in Canada, and this is a classic example, you have something that is completely out of touch with the world environment. This monoculture is not about Gaia; it's an artificial human construction, and the pathology of chaos is what you seem to find in it. The point that I wish to make is that chaotic phenomena are all too frequently, I notice though I wouldn't want to push the point too far, associated with pathology, not with health. Health seems to be a representative main-state where chaos is remarkable by its absence. I leave out of account the constructive use of chaos in neurophysiological systems in brains, and that's why I think we need to be clear about the various levels we're talking about, whether species in an environment, or brains perceiving an environment.

Jackson   Robert May was summarizing lots of studies and concluded that the diversity-stability principle did not hold. Some ecosystems are not very diverse but are, nevertheless, quite stable; others are very diverse but unstable. May did not, so far as I can tell, deal with the diversity within the species.

Thompson   May I interject two points here on epidemics. One is that this word "chaos" is being used in opposite ways, archetypal and mathematical. Ralph Abraham says that a healthy heart shows chaotic behavior, and when it doesn't you're in trouble because you're having a heart attack. This use of the word is the same as Walter Freeman's that Cisco mentioned, where the rabbit has to loosen up to scan widely enough to discriminate between sniffs, for if he systematizes, his process of cognition will be too narrow. So here chaos leads to creativity and flexibility in cognitive skills. Now an epidemic seems to me to be a judgment of a perceiver who takes a slice out of life for his purposes, be it field or forest, and

224

calls it a monoculture. Says who? Maybe that field is a patch in the real ecosystem in transition over time, only the perceiver is not looking at the real rate of time for the event because of his arbitrary threshold of perception. In one of Lynn's early papers on symbiosis, before her book came out, she quotes Jeon's work showing how an infecting bacterium can become an endosymbiont in a surprisingly short time.[2] So it's a question of bookkeeping. If you look at the individual or a population, you may for your agenda as an observer yell, "epidemic!" but the environment or evolution may not be keeping the books in that way. Chaos dynamics tells us that the addition of noise pushes a system toward a different attractor. So infection or epidemics can be added noise that is moving the system toward a different attractor. Maybe the next attractor is the symbiosis of the eukaryotic cell, a conglomerate that looks pretty "chaotic" and messy from the point of view of a prokaryotic cell, but we wouldn't want to call this cell a pathology. The difficulty comes from this damn buzz-word "chaos," and I argued with Ralph Abraham about this in Los Angeles. When you scientists take these archetypally poetic words, such as "Gaia" or "Chaos," the words themselves seem to become basins for projections.

Arthur Zajonc I would like to make a comment on this matter of the epidemic that Wes was talking about. I couldn't help but think about the problem of water purification that John and Nancy Todd talked about, when the neighbor upstream flushed all the aluminum into their solar aquatic purification system and the plants went into toxic shock from all that aluminum sludge, but because of multiple feedback loops from the extra set of tanks, the system was able to stabilize itself. If one thinks about monoculture and epidemics, one can see that monoculture is a situation in which one begins to cut the feedback loops that would normally stabilize the situation. So noise, instead of being damped out, in fact grows exponentially until one falls, as it were, into a larger stabilizing system, a domain of the species or a new strange attractor, such as Bill was talking about.

I think one also sees this kind of thing in the economic realm, the case of pharmaceutical companies — this is my classic example. Whenever I think of the old apothecary on the corner, manufacturing his own drugs and giving them to the neighborhood clientele, I think of what a stable situation that was. If he was a diabolical sort of individual and started putting carcinogens or poisons into his drugs, the community would find out very quickly, and they would get rid of him. But if you have companies which distribute hundreds of millions of bottles of these things all over the country (think of the Tylenol scandal) it only takes one person, not very much noise in the system, to create a situation that is catastrophic. All over the world the system crashes, until they invent new capsules or whatever. So with this tendency to monoculture, despite its powerful and gigantic economies of scale, you paradoxically end up with a very unstable and weak situation. That's one comment I wanted to make.

The second is about this idea of memory. I really think there are two forms of memory: There is the form of memory which is conscious, in which I remember specific facts or events that took place. Through a conscious act of will I can call these back. But there is another kind, which I think is not localized, but is more the distributive kind. Here again I have a tendency to see this in terms of organs in Goethe's theory of language and of faculties. That is to say, if I am in school and I have to remember every movement of my hand as I write, it would be impossible to write. That kind of memory would actually be so rigidified that it would be impossible for me to be a participant in society; so that kind of memory somehow has to become transparent to unintentionality.

Finally, and this is by way of a question, in trying to contrast Minsky's idea of intelligence,[3] let's say, with the kind of thing that Varela and Maturana or Lovelock might be looking at as a higher order, I think it basically comes down to the issue of "metadynamics." I think this is a very important aspect, very important. Think of the way Minsky looks at this problem of mind: You have a society of parts, they are functions, which one can identify; one picks up something, one moves it towards one's mouth. These functions are made up of a whole variety of little discrete building blocks, which one then moves together in some way, couples them together to create a society, and these now will seem to display the higher order functions, which we might think of as living functions or intelligence, and so on. So, my question, Cisco, is: What

is your opinion of Minsky's basic analysis? How does metadynamics bring in another level? As a biologist you have a tradition
that goes back at least as far as Aristotle, where you see in living
organisms a meta-level. That is to say, that Aristotle would make
a category distinction between the animate and inanimate worlds.
So Aristotle could say that this metadynamic of the animate is the
new realm. Does Minsky bring in the realm in some other way? Or
is he basically trying to create mind out of the nonliving, inorganic
realm, without bringing in a new metadynamical level of structure,
the living inanimate world that Jim presented in his first talk?

Varela   A fascinating point. I would love us to get into this, so
I'll stick my foot into my mouth straightaway by saying that, in
fact, with particular reference to the point that you're raising, I
tend to agree with Minsky. Epistemologically speaking, of course,
we couldn't be farther apart, but in terms of a connectionist architecture for emergence, "K lines or societies of agents," we overlap.
    Lynn said yesterday that both she and Jim are speakers for the
labor union of the bacteria. They are syndicalistas, which I think
is great; it is about time bacteria had one. But I want to join this
syndicalist movement and become the speaker for the little lymphocytes and the neurons, because they are just as alive as the little
bacteria. For now it seems to me that we can look at life in all of
its manifestations, at the cellular level, the immune level, the brain
level, or the Gaian level, and notice that all of these tell us a little
bit of what is going on with the organization of the living. So in
this sense I want to disagree a bit with Jim when he says, "Well,
that's another level, a separation has been made." I don't know
why it should be another level, since we have brains too, just as
much as we have cells. And this leads into the point of Minsky's
work; I'm not sidestepping, because I think that the valid part of
Minsky's analysis, which I and many others share, is that, in fact,
he does understand emergence. A "society of agents," as he calls
it — this is his language, I prefer to talk about networks with metadynamics — when they come together give rise to something that
pops up in the middle, in a distributive way. This is Minsky's idea
of mind, and it is a damned interesting one, if you think about it.
That is, mind, just as much as memory, is something that emerges

227

but is not localized anywhere; it is only in the enactment of the totality working together that you have mind. The valid part of Minsky's analysis is that this mind is not a single, unified thing. As an emergent property, it has many sides and it tends to appear and disappear; so, for example, you have your model memory, what the psychologists call "performative memory," the one you use in driving a car or playing the piano, and you have your "episodic memory," the one, for example, in which I recall the story about McCulloch's mother. These two types of memory, it seems to me from a neurophysiological point of view, are based on exactly the same type of processes, distributive networks in which a little bit of everything is everywhere and at work on the job. Where is that memory? Nowhere.

Now where I disagree with Minsky, and it is as important to say where I disagree as to say where I agree, is that he makes two hypotheses which I think are dreadful. The first one is that these different emergent patterns are doing something as a way of getting to know the world out there, that the world is out there. So you have these brains that have developed this capacity through evolution to know the world well (representation) and to fit into it optimally (adaptation). The brain is enslaved to a pre-given solid world, you see, just as evolutionary theory before Lovelock was the organism's enslavement to a pre-given environment. Now, Arthur, in your talk about perception and participation, and in Evan's talk about color vision, it is clear that this way of looking at the brain as an information-processing machine, performing computer-like computations that construct representations of an independent and objective external world, that this epistemology is naive.[4] So I don't have to explain all that to you.

My second point of disagreement with Minsky arises when he begins to articulate emergence as a form of nihilism. He literally says in his book (and Evan and I have written a critique of this in our book[5]), "My God! we are stuck in a situation of having to say that this mind doesn't exist, for it is nowhere; there is no 'me' in the solid sense of localization, and yet even though there is no such thing as a self, we all have to live as if we had one." So, from Minsky's nihilistic point of view, we all have to live unauthentic lives in that we have to pretend to something that we know not to be the

228

case. This is what I think is absolutely silly. This nihilism is the flip side of absolute materialism. There is no absolute material world out there independently, and there is no absolute self in there independently and locked in its place. The world and the self are brought forth in the pattern of relationships. Minsky sees emergent patterns in his "societies of mind," but he wants to ground the patterns on objects, on agents, and when he can't, when ground is not an appropriate idea for ideas like pattern, emergence, metadynamics, he becomes frustrated and gives up in nihilism. I don't wish to give up. I wish to pursue the metadynamics down to a technical level of connectionist, distributive patterns, architecture, whatever. The exciting thing is that in some cases, such as with the immune system, you can take it down to some levels of precision, even mathematical precision. Whether such a metadynamics can be equally explicit and precise, say, in a Gaian context is what brings us all together to think and explore. It's a fascinating area, but very much still an open question. Certainly in the cases of the brain or the immune system, as I tried to describe in my talk, we are getting a little closer; and I think even Minsky would agree with me, but he wouldn't like my terms, which are completely different from his.

Lovelock   Cisco, may I just come in at this point for a moment about this matter of the different levels, because I would like to get it clear. I don't want to be dogmatic, but I do want to learn here. So let us consider this case. Nowadays there is a great deal of hoo-ha going on about the existence of minute self-replicating programs within computers. They are called viruses, and they cause an endless amount of trouble. They show some, but not all, of the properties of living, self-organizing systems. They have emerged, if you like, in this niche that we have created for them. Now, I've often wondered whether it is the case with our own minds, which are as impressive a piece of hardware as computers, if there is an analogous situation, a separate life-form which you could call the soul, if you like, the self, or whatever, that appears in this niche of our bodies. Now if the soul or self does exist as a kind of program-entity, it is existing within a space, perhaps within our nerve cells, which are alive at a lower-level sense. So, we are dealing, to my mind, with two separate levels, the level of the life of our cells, and the level of the life of us, our minds, our selves, our souls. But if you think these levels are the same, I'd be glad if you would say so, so that this confusion can be cleared in my mind. I admit that this postulated soul, or self, or whatever may not exist at all, but I put it forward as an example. If it does exist, does it represent a separate domain upwards from the living domain of the cells, or not?

Gianluca Bocchi I would raise some epistemological problems about this concept of Gaia. As a student of social phenomena, I have also been very interested in the Gaia hypothesis, since I have been most influenced by biological studies in general. Diverging from the majority of activities in the studies of social phenomena, I consider that there are very tight connections between biological and social phenomena. This seems to me to be particularly so with the notion of emergence of which we are speaking. We need to understand that social phenomena are not disjoined from phenomena of the living, from the thing that is evolution. Having said that, I really think that the human social world in which language is so vital is itself an emergent domain in which we give internally a sense to all the things that we say, that we do. I am also very interested in the evolutionary theory of Gaia, as an emergent phenomenon of our language, of our social communication, of our social trophallaxis of knowledge; and for this I would like to return for a moment to a brief exchange between Francisco Varela and Jim Lovelock. Varela said to Lovelock "It seems to me that Gaia is an emergent domain," and so I say to myself, "Let's call this new system a learning system." The reply of Lovelock was "Gaia is an evolutionary theory." As a sociologist, I have the impression that biologists and physicists have the tendency to read this response in a different way than would a sociologist. For a student of sociolinguistically produced phenomena, the reply, "Gaia is evolutionary theory," is equivalent to saying that it is an emergence of our language, that if there had never been human beings Gaia would not exist, that prior to Jim Lovelock, Gaia did not exist.

Perhaps Jim Lovelock does not agree, but as a sociologist I tend to maintain, therefore, that Gaia is not, as Francisco said if I have not misunderstood, a system comparable to the cell, although with much more complexity, and that therefore the problem of how to learn is not analogous. The problem of how to learn in the case of the system of Gaia is the problem of how an evolutionary theory learns, not any evolutionary theory as such, not just any theory in particular. Let's say the class of phenomena to which the Gaia system belongs is not simply the class of phenomena that we can call theory in general, that is to say, human socio-linguistic productions of a certain type. Gaia is another class, or perhaps a subclass, of a particular type of theory which does not disjoin the metaphysical from the physical, the reasons from reason, from the reasons of the heart, after the thought of Pascal. These kinds of theories do not have as an ideal the separation of fantasy from truth, as Mauro Ceruti said yesterday; they are a new kind of theory, in that they are not simply new theories, but a new way of theorizing. They live through our social communications, they evolve through our social communications, and therefore they are, in this sense, an emergent domain. Also, in this sense, the cognitive domain we here constitute among ourselves, imaginatively and intellectually, seems almost separate from us, yet is an emergent domain that we have produced, that we have coproduced. It seems at the same time broader and more restricted than was experienced at the beginning among ourselves. But then we are at the same time other things, members of other groups. If the sum is more than its parts, then Gaia, as evolutionary theory and emergent domain for the Earth or for us here, seems to be a name for many different parts.

Lovelock   Thank you. You put an immense responsibility on me, so I am relieved that you're obviously wrong, because if Gaia didn't exist before, then we wouldn't be here talking about it. Also, I would like to correct one point. Gaia is truly emergent, but it emerged between Lynn and myself, so Lynn will have to share the responsibility for the continuing existence of the world. Anyway, I'm glad to have the responsibility shared.

The point that really started all of this was, I suppose, the one on memory and Gaia and evolution, Gaia being an evolutionary theory. So let me just add a few words of clarification before passing the microphone to Cisco. If one looks at Gaia as an evolutionary theory involving the species and the environment, then the way it would be so crudely seen as working would be that those species that are able to sustain the environment at a favorable rate tend to survive to leave more progeny than those who don't. And in this process there is also a memory involved in the change of the environment, but there is also a memory involved in the selection of the kind of species. As the process goes along, the solid-state of the planet, the environment, is the physical memory of all these events, so you have an evolutionary memory system operating on two levels: the short-term memory in the species with their genes, and the long-term one in the solid part of the environment. And I'll stop there.

Varela Since Jim and I are both natural scientists rather than social scientists, we were understanding the idea of learning, of evolutionary learning, pretty much in the same way. And I agree with what Jim has said. But your point, Gianluca, is also, I think, interesting, and we'll take it in the sense that there is another meta-level. So let us come back to all these "meta's." Before Jim and Lynn talked about Gaia, nobody saw it, in much the same way that before people talked about natural selection, natural selection wasn't there. So you are right that we cannot extricate ourselves from the socio-linguistic context in which we are. This would be part of what we naturally consider the history of science, and I think that both levels have to be addressed simultaneously. Both the relativity of the theory to the human situation, and the fact that there is a sense in which we are grounded on a nature are correct.

But I would like to connect this linguistic point that you raised to the last comment that Jim made, about whether I see the sense of self or mind as emergent. This is an important point. The answer — and I do have an answer to it which I don't have to hold on to, but it is the answer I had been trying to find for years and it was expressed with Humberto in our book *The Tree of Knowledge*[6] — is that life and cognition are inseparable things. The moment that you have a living system, in the sense of the cellular autopoietic, or perhaps a Gaia-living-like system, you have cognition. Now here by "cognition" you should understand, not the representation of the world in a mental form, but some kind of enaction. From this point of view, the appearance of the nervous system

232

does not invent mentality or cognition at all. It expands it, much in the same way that language expands it. And here I agree with you, Gianluca, that language is a beautiful example of an emergent domain, a domain and not a property. It is an emergent domain because it creates the domain of social communication with its science and theories and so forth. Now in much the same way, "self" is also an emergent domain. This sense of self, as we humans experience it with these funny little things called eyes and "I's," is an emergent domain. I do agree with Jim, concerning levels, that it is one step removed from the more Gaia-cell-like phenomenon of life. So, therefore, one has to separate the level of the socio-linguistic self as an emergent domain from cognition in the larger sense. Cognition I would squarely put down with the cells and the plants and all the rest of it.

Evan Thompson I would like to say something about this idea of emergence by going back to the point Arthur was raising about Minsky's "societies of mind." There is one way in which I think Minsky has not understood the idea of emergence, and that is where he writes as if emergence is some kind of one-way stream. Recursiveness, I think, is crucial to emergent patterns. Minsky talks about agents and about putting them together and connecting them, and he does see that what is important is the relations among the agents, and he also sees that those relations can be treated as having an integrity in their own right, that is, having a unity. But he still thinks of it all as a kind of process of accumulation, in the building blocks fashion. If we take the case of, say, a multicellular organism where you have second order autopoiesis, you can distinguish that the first order autopoeisis of the cell is subordinate to the maintenance of the second order autopoiesis of the multicellular organism. Now here you have a clear case of the kind of tangled hierarchy of relations where the higher order autopoiesis in fact constrains the possibilities of the lower order. And in this process there is a dynamic of circularity, and I don't think Minsky sees these qualities of emergence at all. Since he doesn't see the circularity he can say that the world is in fact fixed and out there, because he hasn't appreciated the logic of self-reference that is involved in the notion of emergence. Now it is this kind of

233

circularity that is related to the point you were making, Gianluca, about the relationship between our cognition, perception, and action, and Gaia. This is what I am trying to get at by talking about perception and color vision. Obviously, Gaia is something that acts as a domain within which we move, and in that sense it extends beyond us and doesn't depend on language; but we can't separate that kind of outerness or exteriority from the fact that we are inside the domain, involved in the kind of circularity that brings us forth, as Francisco would put it. It is this pattern of circularity that is, I think, really at the heart of the idea of emergence, whether we are talking about Gaia, the cell, mind, or language.

Thompson   I would like to say something here about this social quality of natural science, because there is also a circularity to the way in which our ideas of nature are part of the perceived nature of the self. The nineteenth-century narratives of nature, and the nineteenth-century novels that explore the nature of the self are related ways of knowing. There is a book called *Darwin's Plots* by Gillian Beer that explores this in some detail. In the sociology of knowledge when we move historically from nineteenth-century Darwin to twentieth-century Maturana and Varela, we are moving from lines of descent to patterns of reflexive self-reference or emergent patterns of circularity in the metadynamics of the system; we are moving out of the world view of Darwin and Dickens, the world of movement from ape to man in nature and from rags to riches in culture. Evolution is, after all, a world of "Great Expectations." But the "metadynamics" that Cisco is talking about when he says that Gaia is a brilliant example of it even though the lines of feedback in Daisyworld do not capture the essential novelty of the emergence, is itself a new way of thinking. In this sense, metadynamics and metafiction, the works of Italo Calvino and Jorge Borges, are related. Now I don't think we can appreciate this metadynamic without a new geometrical imagination, a new way of appreciating the movement from lines of descent and ascent— be they Darwin's plots or Minsky's "Klines"— to the metadynamics of circularity. Cisco in his lecture tried to explain all this algebraically, and he lost just about everybody. This is why I keep emphasizing the coeval cultural emergence of chaos dynamics and the phase-portraits of the geometries of behavior, for if we get the wrong picture in our head, we are going to waste a lot of time defending turf.

I see Daisyworld as a twentieth-century way of trying to explain a twenty-first-century phenomenon, sort of like explaining Einsteinian relativity in Euclidian geometry instead of Reimannian geometry. Gaia is a myth, a metaphor, an evolutionary theory, and a linguistic domain that we as a group constitute, but in all of these there are patterns of circularity, in all of these there are patterns of emergent behavior that are not, as Evan said of Minsky, accretive, not linear.

Jackson A side comment before I get into my main comment. In the summer of 1964 I sat in a boat off Puerto Rico with H. T. Odum. He had been studying a rain forest in Puerto Rico; he was funded, I think, by the Atomic Energy Commission. He and his workers had put a huge canopy over part of the forest and were looking at nutrient cycling. The reports that came out of these studies would fill half this room. Lots of deadly dull data was accumulated, but Odum made a comment that I have never forgotten: he remarked that a Puerto Rican rain forest had a "low order of mind." He explained that when a huge tree went down in one part of the forest it affected the croaking pattern of frogs ten miles away. This was the low order of mind. For a young biologist that was indeed something to think about. Odum's group introduced radioactive trace elements into that ecosystem and then followed them through the forest. This monumental work is now a classic. Much of the work in system ecology goes back to that particular era and the eventual erosion of the diversity-stability principle is the result of this type of system work. I'm satisfied with May's summary work, Jim, but back to Gaia.

I do not believe in Gaia and here is why. As we go up that hierarchy of structure from atoms to molecules to cells to tissues to organs to organisms to ecosystems, and, finally, to the next category, Earth, one thing characteristic of all levels is that, in order to know what each is, we had to see lots of examples. To know what a molecule is, we had to "see" lots of molecules. The same with atoms, organs, organ-systems, organisms, and now ecosystems.

235

But we have seen only one Earth. It is not good enough to say that we've looked at a lot of planets. We have to think of planets plus life, and so far we have an inference base of one.

I'm glad, Jim, that you have rejected the notion that Gaia is a hypothesis. I think we'd have to count it as bad science to formulate a hypothesis around an inference-base of one. Consider the range of variation at the various levels in the hierarchy. At the atomic level, for instance, hydrogen has one proton and a nucleus: a molecular weight of two units. The helium atom has an atomic weight of four units. Uranium has ninety-two. Imagine that we were part of one of those elements and were trying to define what it was. Cellulose has a molecular weight of up to a trillion. If we were within or a part of cellulose trying to decide what cellulose is, we would miss the notion of moleculehood.

Where this leads us, I think, is that before we can know what Gaia is, we will have to look at a lot of planets with life. I can imagine a planet which, like a balloon that is blown up, has life on the inside, on the inner surface. Such creatures may be like flies on a ceiling. Maybe when that planet's sun is hot the planet expands, and at night, it decreases. I don't think that this falls outside the range of variation we see in the other levels of the hierarchy. A bacterium is a cell, but so is a whale's neuron. Or consider a redwood or a Holstein cow; both are organisms. A tropical rain forest and a prairie meadow are both ecosystems. I would not be surprised to see even more diversity among other planets in the universe. What I think you are studying are some of the commonalities among ecosystems. And so, Jim, I think your field is ecosystemology. What you're looking at in your field are some of the commonalities among ecosystems. So what I would ask you to consider is a new identification of your field, and by the way, I realize that it's too much to ask you to do this, because there is now too much intellectual capital accumulated in the notion of Gaia to give it up. And that is an emergent quality in the sociology of knowledge that we ought to have.

Lovelock Wes, if you had not existed, I would have had to invent you. And that would have been difficult. Well, before I answer, could you define for me what you mean by ecosystem?

236

Jackson   Ecosystem can be defined at least as readily as Gaia can be defined. To study an ecosystem, we can draw a boundary wherever it is convenient for our purposes. We can draw it around a cubic meter of soil, one meter underground. All we want to do is measure what goes through the boundary and study the dynamics within. Or, we can take a farm and enclose it within a cube or a sphere, and call that farm an ecosystem. The student of ecosystems simply wants to know what goes through the boundaries in both directions as well as the dynamics within them. Now, I know that there are those who will protest this...

Thompson   You can count me in on that.

Jackson   ...because we think that when we look at a cell, we're looking at a discrete natural entity. On the other hand, if we were to apply the electron microscope to the place where cells come together, and then take a vote as to where one cell ends and the other begins, we might have a problem with the determination of the boundary. So, Jim, an ecosystem is a volumetric unit which allows us to become accountants of what goes through a boundary, and scientists who study the dynamics of what occurs within that boundary and what crosses it are ecosystemologists. I've been telling young people in college audiences that the most exciting field in the next century is going to be accounting. So I tell them, quite seriously, to take double-entry bookkeeping as their first exciting course, and then come back and apply it to these other systems. So, does that answer your question, Jim, about what an ecosystem is?

Lovelock   It's not going to be easy to answer you, Wes, because you are using a different logic from the one that I would use. To go back to your first point that you can't really consider Gaia as an entity because there is nothing to compare it with, I disagree totally. There have been a whole series of Gaias existing throughout the history of the Earth. To start with, that of the Archaean Epoch was a system that was run by bacteria and nothing else. And it existed in a reducing atmosphere, probably — though we are not sure about it — an atmosphere of 100 parts per million of methane, and only traces of oxygen. This is a totally

237

different system from anything that we know now. It existed, survived, and was our progenitor. The Proterozoic Era was yet another Gaia, and so on; and there will be successors to us. The evidence is weak because geological evidence is fallible. That's point number one.

Point number two is that, in a simple-minded way, one of the characteristics of living domains is that they are open in a thermodynamic sense, but still bounded. The Earth is very much an open but bounded system. Its energy transactions are almost wholly in radiations. It receives visible and ultraviolet radiation from the sun and it excretes fairly low-energy infrared to the outside, and that is its principal energy exchange. There's very little matter in the exchange at all, apart from astronauts and meteorites, and they don't amount to a hill of beans as far as mass goes. But I wouldn't differ from you too much in that you could consider the whole lot as the ultimate ecosystem. It's a stronger one than the others, because its connections are so much stronger. It has a common atmosphere running right around, linking everything; it has the oceans as a transport system, and, on a long time scale, it has the somewhat fluid dynamics of the Earth's crust. It's a little less arbitrary as an ecosystem than when you set up a sphere around your Land Institute in Kansas.

Thompson I see a danger here of "misplaced abstractions" in arbitrary boundaries and arbitrarily generated statistics that tell us more about the agenda of the bookkeeper than about the subject of study. Studying life without an understanding of membranes and boundaries is highly suspect. The membrane produces the relationships we want to study, just as a vibrating instrument produces music. I can draw an arbitrary line across my waist and study what crosses it, but it won't teach me as much as studying the membrane of the lungs or the skin. And as for your second point that we need a whole lot of planets with life to discover Gaia, I disagree there too; we didn't need a whole lot of instruments or musicians to create music. Some Pleiocene mama started humming while she nursed, and some Pleiocene male added a rhythm section by slapping his thighs, and music was born. The same goes for Gaia; it took only a look at one planet, Mars, for Lynn and Jim to take an extraterrestrial look at Earth. But, in one way, your point is valid,

238

in that Gaia did develop in the context of NASA getting in on the act of the study of life.

Jackson   OK, let me be straightforward about what I think the dangers of the Gaia hypothesis might be. Sorry, Jim, the Gaia theory—I'm still caught up in the old language. There was a time when I was as breathless as everybody else about all of this, but I have decided to back out of breathlessness. For the New Age crowd, the ones that get breathless about Gaia, the ones that perform at the Cathedral of St. John the Divine and get others to be breathless about Gaia, this idea has the potential to generate a peculiar form of twentieth-century vitalism. I think we have done a pretty good job in the last century of dealing with this controversy of vitalism versus mechanism, but I am afraid that it has all been opened up again. So I think it is up to us to be careful about our language and to assume the responsibility for not allowing an undue amount of breathlessness to develop, but rather a deeper kind of understanding, perhaps even a reverence. So now I'm talking about reverence versus breathlessness. I guess I am in favor of reverence, but not this New Age breathlessness.

Susan Oyama   I'm not so sure we have put the vitalism-mechanism problem behind us. The contemporary versions of that problem are, in fact, very much to the point in discussing emergence. Vitalism is characterized, not just by a resistance to reduction, but more crucially by a totalizing impulse that matches reductionism in its arrogance. The difficult trick is to acknowledge the emergence of order at different levels without succumbing to the temptation to subordinate everything else to your favorite level (a higher-order reductionism, if you will). Whenever higher levels are seen as nothing but epiphenomena to lower-level activity, or when they are seen as independent from, or more worthy of attention or concern than the ones below, the desire to play epistemological (or ontological) favorites has won. Both moves are reductive in that they impoverish by transforming the momentary single-mindedness required for analysis into a general privileging of one level of analysis.

One sometimes sees a kind of fetishism of emergence, in which properties or entities at the generating level are dismissed as unimportant. Mere organisms are of no significance compared to Earth-wide processes, mere person-to-person conversation is irrelevant when planetary culture is the issue.

I think I understand some of the reasons for these particular emphases. Human chutzpah needs to be tempered, both for moral reasons and as a brake on our wilder depredations of the environment. One way to do that is to put humankind firmly in its place on the Gaian landscape. Ordinary institutional or even national identities obscure subtler, large-scale processes that cannot be contained by these traditional boundaries. These are certainly legitimate concerns, but I believe that one can emphasize emergent domains, for these and other very good reasons, without playing that old game of Combating the Other by Turning the Tables, of Finding Out Where Reality Really Lives. I thus use the term "generating level" advisedly; one should never imply that interactions among entities are somehow rendered causally impotent by a focus on the phenomena that emerge through these interactions.

Lynn spoke about a cell at 0°: she said autopoiesis must be there because all the components are there, and because the cell can be brought back to life by thawing. But surely the point is that presence of the components is not the same as the system of their interactions. It is the latter that constitutes life. Though we may not want to say they are dead (because death is usually considered irreversible), neither do they show the dynamic interrelations that autopoiesis implies. I think Cisco was saying something like this in his reply.

Varela   Yes, precisely.

Oyama   So this desire to see the emergent as somehow contained in lower-level constituents is the more familiar of the two kinds of "reductions" we ought to avoid. It is the familiar reduction downwards. "Reduction upwards" may seem an oxymoron, but what I want to convey is the similarity between finding autopoiesis in cell constituents and making those constituents irrelevant to cell processes. Though no one said this about cells, I wonder whether Wes sees something like it among Gaia devotees — a tendency to see Gaia as somehow transcending organismic processes, the way the life force supposedly transcended the material world. I rather doubt that most environmentalists, however mystical their rhetoric, really believe this. If they did, it would be hard for them to speak so passionately about Gaia's vulnerability, and about the urgency of the crisis that faces us.

Ricardo Guerrero   I would like to address myself to all of these points that have been made here. First, about the ecosystem. As a microbial biologist working with small ecosystems and as a lover of the history of our Mother Earth (whether we call it Gaia or not), I think the problem is one that Aristotle was also dealing with, and that is the problem of the synthetic and analytical approach to ideas. We start with different models, and when we develop them synthetically we are going in one way. But we can also take the departure point of studying only one thing and analytically defining the differences that we find. Once we have the idea of the triangle, we can try to identify things with that shape, things with the idea of the triangle. Another Aristotelian concept is the idea of the genus and the species in the philosophical sense. Let me give you an example concerning the evolution of ecosystems. On some islands mammals and birds practically do not exist, but for different reasons. Take a small island, one of the Baleric Islands, where only reptiles survive. This is very curious, because mammals and birds have not survived there for different reasons: birds cannot be maintained, and mammals never arrived. OK. Now on this island you have ecosystems where reptiles are the predators, carnivorous, primary consumers, and secondary consumers. The ecosystem there is archaic, like in the time of the dinosaurs, or, considering the bacteria, like in the Archaean. So the definition of Gaia is not a thing but the organization of the interactions between the living system and the ecosystem. Very early in the history of Earth, ecosystems were organized as ours is now. The thing is that the representatives of life, the particular organisms, were different from ours now; but the systemic relation of life and environment was not so different.

Let me give you a second biological example. In Australia plants are not very diverse in taxonomy, but they have a lot of eucalyptus. They have perhaps two hundred or three hundred

241

varieties of eucalyptus. From our point of view, even where the taxonomy is so limited, the ecological diversity is still pronounced. So, taxonomy is one thing, and diversity is another, and other kinds of diversity can serve the same function within an ecosystem. The main characteristics of the different Gaias in the history of the Earth were the integrations of the relationships. But I agree completely with both of you: an ecosystem can be, not just in a cubic meter, but a cubic millimeter. How big is the ocean? For a microorganism, it could be one liter; for a tropical fish, one coral reef; but for a whale, the entire Pacific. It's not size, but the relationships, the dynamics that constitute Wes's "ecosystemology."

OK, so the Earth is indeed one ecosystem in total. The Earth has also many, many other ecosystems. It's not a problem for me if we have not yet found other similar planetary systems; we can define the idea of Gaia, that is the idea of life, and I would define Gaia as the capacity to maintain the properties of a given planet. Take Mars, for example. The canals of Mars were made by liquid water some four billion years ago. Liquid water was running there at that time; perhaps life evolved there, or perhaps it did not, or it did but could not be maintained. But for whatever reason, Mars is now dead. It has gone through some sort of planetary evolution. But here, perhaps because it was the right place at the right time, life evolved and began to maintain its conditions.

So for me Gaia is really this interaction between life and Earth. It is tellurian, which is another classical idea, the idea of our connection with Mother Earth. And for me this is everything. These ideas are also expressed in our mythologies. As human beings, we are recent arrivals on this Earth, and we have only been here for the last three hundred thousand years or so, but we still identify with the Earth, and these myths remind us of where we came from. Adam, in Hebrew, means clay, from the Earth itself.

Margulis   I think that when we have succeeded in defining Gaia well enough — and I don't mean a precise technical definition, but in a clear enough way — Wes is going to become the leader of the Gaia movement. What we're seeing here is that we have failed somehow in our communications. For me, Wes is a functioning, practicing Gaiaologist. So somehow Jim and I have not expressed

242

the theory in the right way. As you know, I like my definition better than Jim's that "the Earth is alive." But I'll just let him have it; I love him to say it his way, but I don't say it that way. And I think it might be worthwhile to spend two minutes with the technical scientific definition.

I would say that Gaia is the property or capacity, or the phenomenon, that involves the sum of the biota — that's the flora, fauna, and microbiota, all the living organisms — by which the surface environment of this planet is regulated and maintained. Notice that I don't say all aspects of the planet; the aspects of the planet that are regulated are reactive gases of the atmosphere, the temperature, the oxidation rate, the pH, and, this is Lovelock's innovation, the salinity of the ocean. These aspects on the surface of the Earth are actively regulated by the biota and are different from what they would be if the Earth were simply a planet intercalated, passively, between Mars and Venus. In the search for Gaia, we have to see, on one extreme, argon and neon and lots of things, that is, the non-reactive chemistry that one finds hard to imagine as the inner part of the Gaian system; and on the other extreme, the carbon compounds, nitrogen compounds, and the radiant energy in the visible spectrum that are so clearly intrinsic to the Gaian system. Thus to summarize it, Gaia then becomes the phenomenon of the sum of the activities of the biota, with respect to reactive chemistry and surface temperature properties.

So Gaia becomes the sum of the phenomena, what the sum of the ecosystems do. And here I would deny completely that an arbitrary dividing anywhere on the farm gives you an ecosystem. Francisco did a wonderful job of defining what a minimal cell is functionally, not to mention Cargan and Warren. So I would say that the minimal ecosystem functionally has got to have a producer, in the fundamental sense, has got to have some organisms that take the source of energy, whether it's chemical on the one hand, or light on the other — and those are the only two possibilities that we know — and it has to take back energy and it has to convert it. The circulation of matter, and this has to be completely within the ecosystem, has to be faster within the ecosystem than it is from one ecosystem to another. It is just like the mail, which is, more or less, faster within one nation-state than it is from one nation-state to another. A nation-state has a self-maintaining border, maybe a loose border, as between Canada and the U.S.A., or maybe a tight border, as between Mexico and the U.S.A. And so an ecosystem has got to have some kind of border, and therefore I would agree with Bill that your arbitrary cube is not an ecosystem. Your farm, which has production and cycling at a greater rate within it than, say, between it and the forest next to it — that probably is an ecosystem. The termite hindgut that I showed you is not an ecosystem, it's a community; that is, it is a population of different kinds of organisms working in the same place at the same time. Why is it not an ecosystem? Because the source of energy, the conversion of energy, the prime production, is not present. So a pond can be an ecosystem, because there is some source of productivity, whereas in a termite hindgut there is only a community.

So, if you observe a community that is making the system and maintaining the natural boundaries, you will notice that they don't do it as well as a cell; that is, the natural boundaries of a cell are much tighter boundaries than the natural boundaries of an ecosystem. So I recognize an ecosystem as a natural unit, but when you, Wes, put an arbitrary square around something, that, to me, is not an ecosystem. That is just a bite out of something for the purposes of study. Anyway, Wes, I think there is a communication problem with Gaia for you, because I fundamentally agree with much of what you say, and I tend to think that there is a deeper agreement among us than you presented.

Thompson I think it's unfair, Wes, to blame the Goddess cult of New Agers at Findhorn or the Cathedral of St. John the Divine on Jim and Lynn. They are what Hilary here calls "the Gooey Gaia Group," and what they all have in common is that they have never read any of Lynn or Jim's books.

Lovelock May I make a small point of clarification? I agree with everything that Lynn said, but I don't know whether she meant one part or not, so I would like to ask her. Lynn, when you said regulated by the biota, I would rather say regulated by the system comprising the biota and the...

Margulis Yes! A very important point. We got into trouble for fifteen years with this, because we used to say that Gaia was buying for the biota at an optimum. We kept in an idea of an optimum, in other words, a temperature, oxygen level, and pH that were maintained optimally for life. What we ran up against, improperly I think, was the criticism that in the Archaean the optimum was one part per million oxygen, whereas the optimum in the present is 20 percent oxygen. So, the system is changing all the time; it's not an atom. Think of it this way: Any group of organisms, such as people, produce excrement. Now that's the end of the story if there are no other organisms, for eventually you drown from lack of food and lack of removal of the excrement. But this is where diversity comes in, diversity as a system of maintenance, because the dung beetles and fungi and bacteria eat the excrement and thus remove it. Therefore unless our behavior increases the probability of the next group of organisms, the system is going to stop. So the system, as Jim says, has its properties that are determined by the internal organization, the autopoiesis if you wish, of the system, and, therefore, we shouldn't talk about the optimum (or the best) paying for it. This is political talk — it's hierarchical political talk. Rather, we should talk about the organization of the system that determines the running of the system. When we do that we can go to the Mendeleevian Table of Elements and we can say, "Helium, not a Gaian element; hydrogen, an absolutely crucial Gaian element; carbon absolutely crucial; vanadium, maybe." Gaian elements have the following property: either they are required to run the system or they are poisons for the system and need to be removed; or they are virtually inert, and you breed them as much as you breed another. And then you can just organize the chemical information in the Gaian science.

Guerrero   I think any atom is a Gaian atom. All of them.

John Todd   Between now and the end of the century there is going to be a deep concern expressed by many people in many places about the extinction of species. I would like, before we break up, to discuss this question of extinction from a Gaian perspective.

Varela   May I add a brief point before we break up, one that

245

touches on this problem of extinction, John, and that is something that I was thinking about as the conversation between Wes and Jim was going on? This goes back, Jim, to your point about Gaian memory: mountains as opposed to DNA. I say as opposed to DNA because, in fact, this I think reveals the nature of distributive properties. You see, when you take a cell — suppose you take it with a scissors and snip it in two — we all know that then you don't have two cells, for if you snip the chromosomes in half, the whole thing doesn't work. In that sense, DNA is more like the idea of classical computers where you have some elements stored: there is something in storage that is stable from one generation to the other, and this allows the whole thing to work. Now, on the other hand, a distributive system is interesting because you can snip it right in the middle and it still works. Take the brain, for example: I can have whole chunks of my brain taken out and still function, still do pretty much the same thing. So my question to people is: What would happen, given some of the data that you yourselves have presented, if we snip the Earth in two? Would we have two Gaias? In the sense that I am asking the question, I don't know, but the snipping would reveal the nature of a distributive memory. If you needed to include all the mountains, the Andes and the Himalayas, in order to make the system work, then that would tell us something. This becomes a scientific question in the following sense, and this goes back to Wes's point: What would be the minimal necessary snippet that you would have to have to still keep Gaia? If you have a meteorite striking the Earth and destroying whatever percentage of life, as seems to have happened, what would it have to destroy for Gaia to stop?

Lovelock You need most of what we've got. Otherwise, we might see Gaia in places like the moon. We need most of what we've got.

Varela But you yourself have said, and this gets to John's point about the extinction of species from a Gaian perspective, that the Cretaceous extinction wiped out most of life.

Lovelock There's no question but that planetesimals have knocked off up to 90 percent of all life on this planet. And yet life bounced back. Yes, you can do without a lot of it, and it will come back, but as far as the planet goes, you cannot get rid of much of the matter of the planet without being in big trouble.

Varela   That being the case, it seems to me that Gaia is more like the brain than DNA; it's distributive.

Lovelock   [Shakes his head skeptically in silence.]

Thompson   I guess this is a difference between your languages. If you slice the Earth in half, you will have half an Earth, but perhaps not half a Gaia. Perhaps, in much the same way, you can slice a human body in two, and have half a body but not half a soul. Perhaps when the whole as the sum of its parts produces an emergent property we can say that the whole is halvable but the emergent property is not.

Varela   That's precisely my point. My language was a metaphorical way of getting to the point about the differences in the nature of a distributive learning mechanism. If Gaia has a learning system, then it's got to be distributive.

Thompson   Well, as the one charged with serving as *il capo* for this session, I like this artistic and appropriately Italian operatic structure of *Aria da Capo* that brings us back to this problem with which we opened the session. I guess we have come back to this issue of the contribution of connectionist cognitive science to Gaian biology because that is the actual intellectual horizon of our time. So what better place to end than on this horizon?

Notes

1. See Francisco Varela, *Principles of Biological Autonomy* (New York: Elsevier North Holland, 1979).

2. See Lynn Margulis, "A Review of Genetic and Evolutionary Consequences of Symbiosis," *Experimental Parasitology*, Vol. 39 (1976): 277-349.

3. See Marvin Minsky, *The Society of Mind* (New York: Simon & Schuster, 1985).

4. See Varela, "Laying down a Path in Walking," in *Gaia: A Way of Knowing* (Great Barrington, MA: Lindisfarne Press, 1987).

5. See Francisco Varela and Evan Thompson, *Worlds Without Ground: Cognitive Science and Human Experience* (forthcoming).

6. See Humberto Maturana and Francisco Varela, *The Tree of Knowledge: The Biological Roots of Human Understanding* (Boston: New Science Library, 1987).

CONCLUSION

WILLIAM IRWIN THOMPSON

Politics Becoming a Planet

In 1977 Gregory Bateson lived at Lindisfarne in Southampton, New York, as our Scholar-in-Residence. He was at work on his last book, *Mind and Nature,* and to help advance this project I suggested to Bateson that we hold one of those small conferences of which he was so fond and that we should invite the young Chilean neurophysiologist Francisco Varela to enable him to think out loud with gifted colleagues about the process of "mind in nature." Happily, Varela accepted our invitation, and, in fact, so took to Lindisfarne that he became the next Scholar-in-Residence in 1978 and '79. I was pleased because I thought I could begin to see developing a Lindisfarne school of thought in biology and ecology, one quite different from that of the academic establishment, and I hoped, rather naively as it was to turn out in Reagan's America, that this approach might speak to the heart of the ecological and political challenges of the eighties.

Francisco Varela was a good forty years younger than Bateson and his generation seemed to be taking the ideas of "self-organization from noise" several steps further in the new field of cognitive science than had the founders of cybernetics in the famous Macy Conferences in which Bateson had taken part.[1] What would happen, I wondered as I watched Bateson and Varela interact, if we brought together Gregory Bateson and Heinz von Foerster of the founding era of the Macy Conferences with the Santiago School of Cognitive Biology of Maturana and Varela, and the new vision of planetary self-organization expressed in the Gaia Hypothesis of

Lovelock and Margulis? Unfortunately, Gregory Bateson became too ill to attend the Lindisfarne Fellows Conference of 1980 and sent us what became his farewell address on audio tape.[2] We were all deeply moved and touched as we listened to the cassette; three weeks later, on July 1, 1980, Gregory died. To honor his memory and his contributions to our Lindisfarne Fellowship, we held a memorial meeting in the same room the following year in which Heinz von Foerster, Henri Atlan, Humberto Maturana, Heinz and Elaine Pagels, Francisco Varela, James Lovelock, and Lynn Margulis joined with the Lindisfarne Fellows to try to take the planetary ecology of mind one step further in Gregory's honor.

From the perspective of the sociology of knowledge, it is interesting to reflect that in the same week that we were meeting at the Zen Center in Marin County, Francisco Varela, Henri Atlan, and Jean Pierre Dupuy were also taking part in a conference at Stanford University organized by Professor René Girard. Here were two quite different cultural historians organizing conferences in cognitive science, and both were using highly individualistic approaches to the study of myth and science as the bridge between "the two cultures" of the sciences and the humanities. The two orientations to myth expressed in lectures in New York and Palo Alto in the seventies, the approach of Girard's *The Scapegoat* and the approach of *The Time Falling Bodies Take to Light,* could not be more different. In the former "the lie that is myth" is seen as a ritual mystification of murder and is interpreted as part of the ghastly heritage of the pagan, pre-Christian world, but in the latter myth is seen as a highly developed astronomical language of an initiatic elite for whom a cosmological description is transformed into a performance of the very reality the myth seeks to describe. "The Origin of Geometry," for René Girard's disciple Michel Serres, is in sacrifice, but as is too often the case with European thinkers such as Serres, Girard, and Heidegger, their concept of origin begins merely with the Greeks, and they ignore the complex astronomical cosmologies of the megalithic cultures that have been rather differently explicated by Alexander Thom and Keith Critchlow.[3]

The bifurcation between the academic establishment and the alternative movement, say between Lindisfarne and Stanford, has not narrowed in the last ten years, and it is fair to say that Girard's anthropology has become the intellectual currency and medium of exchange among the various disciplines of the Parisian school, from the economics of Jacques Attali and Jean Pierre Dupuy to the literary criticism of Andrew McKenna and Paisley Livingston.[4] In the decade since Gregory Bateson's death, "sacrifice" has become the shibboleth for the academy and "Gaia" has become the archetypal symbol for the alternative movement. So these two small conferences in northern California that took place in June of 1981 seem to have streamed into two different cultural watersheds. The ecological crises of the nineties, however, would appear to be demonstrating a greater global relevance of the anthropology of Gregory Bateson than that of René Girard, so my step in the ecology of mind from Bateson to Lovelock may yet prove to be more of a leap across the threatening chasm than a stumble into the dark.

The new sciences of planetary dynamics, so articulately presented to us in the work of James Lovelock and Lynn Margulis, have provided us with new ways of understanding the power of life to shape the Earth, but what has magnified the historical impact of this work is that it comes at a time when our mathematical imagination is also being transformed by the phase-portraits of chaos dynamics. When one tries to imagine the atmosphere in the narratives of Lovelock, or the planetary bioplasm of bacteria in the narratives of Margulis, one cannot generate an appropriate image if one still holds to the modernist science of Galileo and Newton in which linear equations and linear sequences of causal impacts describe a billiard ball world that is a vast container for colliding discreet objects controlled by absolutistic scientific laws. The mechanization of the world picture succeeded in its time because there was a synchronous emergence of new sciences and a new mathematical imagination in which the movement of money, planets, or canonballs could be schematically figured. When a new science, such as Lovelock's geophysiology, is added to a new mathematical imagination of the world, you don't simply get a new paradigm, you get a new culture.

If we look back over cultural history with 20-20 hindsight, we can observe that major civilizational transformations are emergent states that involve a fascinating system of lattices of feedback and

251

networks of mutually causal agents structured between systems of communication and exchange, such as coinage and the alphabet, the appearance of new forms of world narratives in literature and mathematics, and a new polity, a new form of human social organization. The relationship between writing and the origins of urban civilization is well-known and was popularized by V. Gordon Childe. The relationship between the rise of Greek representational democracy and the use of the alphabet was described by the Toronto cultural historians, Innis and McLuhan. And the rise of capitalism and the emergence of the modern world system was the great work of Fernand Braudel. When one stops to reflect that the literature of modernism is also about the movement from rags to riches, then one can appreciate the intimate relationships that exist between mathematics and literature as examples of world narrative that structure a particular epoch's mythopoetic sense of reality. I have elsewhere suggested that the development of Western civilization can be seen as a movement through four mathematical-literary mentalities: the Arithmetic, the Geometrical, the Dynamical, and the Morphological. The Arithmetic mentality ruled from ancient Uruk to classical Athens; the Geometrical mentality ruled from ancient Athens to the Italian Renaissance; the Dynamical mentality, the mentality of modernism, ruled from the time of Galileo to 1900; and then the intuitions of Poincaré and Lipanounov set the stage for a new mathematical imagination, the Morphological mentality.[5] This contemporary Morphological mentality, developed by such mathematicians as Thom and Smale, is one in which the geometry of behavior of global systems, expressed in phase-portraits, begins to capture our imagination, but unlike earlier descriptive systems, arithmetically or algebraically expressed, these systems are open, creatively unpredictable, and chaotically complex. It is within this new historical mentality, and not the modernist mentality of Harvey, Newton, or Darwin, that the Gaian evolutionary theory has to be appreciated, and this appreciation requires not simply training and data collection, but imagination.

Imagination is the phase-space of perception. Each of the senses provides one dimension of meaning, but the dynamic that integrates the meanings and brings forth a coherent world is the faculty of the imagination. The mystics are probably right when they claim that there are more dimensions than meet the eye, but what brings forth a world is the human body as a field of metaphoric extension of the known into the unknown.[6] The universe is mind-bogglingly full of multiple possibilities, with billions of impulses per square micron, so what we attend to tells us in what particular cognitive world we choose to embody our knowing. What enables us to integrate sound and light, bit and gestalt, data and divination is the imagination, and its ability to stabilize a world derives from a set of infantile, preverbal geometries of behavior we have come to cognize as the way things happen. If we have a culturally inappropriate geometry in our minds for the thing that is happening before us, we will form our social life into problems that seem to cry out for pressing solutions. If we have an unconscious anxiety of losing our basic sense of self, we will hold onto things and flatten out the complex geometries of behavior to show lines connecting everything to everything. This is the condition of the paranoid who collapses polycentric behaviors that can be marvelously self-organizing through noise into a tightly controlled centralized system that is the work of his favored conspiracy. Since the paranoid has trouble holding onto a sense of self amid noise, he relates everything to his constructed self with its *idée fixe* and projects a geometry of behavior, a phase-portrait, onto the world that is wholly inappropriate for the novel historic dynamic that is in front of him. The difficulty of our disorienting time of cultural transition is that we are all paranoids in a way, for we are struggling to hold onto a sense of self in the world precisely at a time when all traditional human cultures are coming apart, probably because they are not truly viable in the situation in which our electronic technologies seem to be expressing self-organization through noise on their own and are bringing forth a new world we do not yet know how to interpret, much less live in.

Scientists involved in the new fields of complex system dynamics, meteorology, and geochemistry do not seem to have as much difficulty with Gaian evolutionary theory as do traditional population biologists, whose imaginations are still so heavily in debt to Darwin and the general nineteenth-century industrial mentality. These esteemed figures of British authority still serve as professorial voices for countless nature films on television in which they describe, with hushed tones in the wild, how the organism must fight to survive. Our imaginations do seem to be held captive by this Darwinian past, and we persist in a nineteenth-century mode of either/or thinking in which the little organism is constrained by the large environment to "adapt or die." We also persist in the equally nineteenth-century habit of thinking of this environment in terms of that dubious abstraction, "matter." We see this abstraction as the only thing that is real, and we see its vast cosmic power coming from the nature of "things." The universe is a container filled with material objects held in place by the laws of physics, and life is an accident contained by evolution's remorseless hold of adaptation. Although we have been told innumerable times that there is more empty space than matter in the atom and the universe, and that, like a flute that requires its geometry of holes and core of emptiness to perform its vibratory music, the universe is much more like a composition of music than it is a conglomerate of matter, yet we persist in thinking in terms of "the hard facts" that are needed for the hard sciences. It doesn't seem to matter what the softies say when they speak to us about the illusion of matter, be these softies mystics, artists, or physicists, for the rulers of states and academic disciplines insist that they know better, that the large governs the little, and that we softies are few and they are many, so we had better "adapt or die."

What we believe we can indeed bring about, for such is the power of the imagination, and so, in many ways, this Darwinian condition still does describe life camouflaged in the ivy halls of our universities and exposed in the homeless streets of our cities. But the appearance of innumerable smaller cultural institutes and programs, such as Lindisfarne, does seem to indicate that there is a new culture abroad in which the little institute can challenge the dominant imagination of the large institution. And these new narratives in mathematics, science, and literature indicate that part of our civilization has already passed over into a new world.

The little institute and the large institution, of course, should not be seen as yet another either/or dyadic set in which the little is right and the large is wrong, for if we have learned anything from the insights of the narratives of symbiosis in the biology of Lynn Margulis, it is that the little and the large require one another. The little stumble upon innovations; the large reproduce those innovations in a stable system, stable, that is, only for a longer period of time. So the photosynthesizing cyanobacterium is little, but the numbers of these atmospherically transformative cyanobacteria become large. As one considers Margulis's truly visionary theory of the role of spirochetes in building the connectionist architecture of evolution in the mitotic spindle, the spermatic flagellum, and the neural axon, one begins to appreciate that her vision of symbiosis and evolution has political implications as profound for our era of global electronic restructuring as Darwin's vision of competition had for the era of industrial development.

As one begins to hear a new language in cognitive biology one begins to wonder if the re-cognizing of biology could lead to a new recognition of Life. The old language of the population biologists and the sociobiologists was atomistic and hard, but this new language speaks of "connectionism," of neural nets, distributive lattices, and a metadynamic in which the global behavior of a system shows learning and emergent properties and new cognitive domains.[7] If I imagine myself to be an object in a container, then I will invest my identity in containers, be they cars, houses, banks, or nation-states, and I will see most relationships which touch my boundaries as threatening infringements on that identity. If, on the other hand, I see myself as a process, a cloud in the sky or an algaeal mat in the sea, then other clouds or waves that share the dynamic of my emergence will not be seen to threaten me. This may seem to be an excessively Buddhist or Taoist way to look at life for Westerners with their habitual egos invested in discrete genes, cares, and private property, but one of the effects of the planetization of the esoteric that brought these Eastern philosophies into the technological culture of the West has been to provide us with other models of consciousness right at the time when we were making the shift from industrial to informational society.

That we are still having difficulty in making a shift of consciousness away from an industrial mentality is obvious in our ozone holes and greenhouse effects. Because we think in terms of containers, we think there is an outside to which we can throw things "away." We see objects, not relationships, as holding value, and so

255

public space is irrelevant. Some people, claiming to be our political "leaders," will disparage any attention to the public space as Liberalism, or "the dirty L-word." Such a Republican political philosophy is, of course, inappropriate to the ecological conditions of the nineties, and although the Democratic Party in the U.S.A. is brain-dead, individual liberals are beginning to realize that they cannot form a political philosophy for the nineties out of the remains of the industrial mentality of the Depression. The nineties is the period in which we shall have to shift from economics to ecology as the governing science of the modern world. Just as the "Chicago School" provided the orientation for Thatcher, Kohl, Reagan, and Bush in the eighties, I think the "Gaian School" can provide us in the nineties, not with a new ideology, but with a new understanding for complex dynamical systems in which opposed ideologies must co-exist to structure an ecology of consciousness.

This shift from economics to ecology as the governing science of the modern world, I think, will also be accompanied by a shift from American behavioral science to planetary cultural history as the required course for future political scientists. Precisely because we are entering a new culture, we need to have some understanding of what culture is all about. American popular culture is certainly "a strange attractor," and it can be highly instructive of the shape of things to come, but American behavioral science cannot, for it is at once too behavioristic and too American. Ecologies with people in them are not mechanistic ecosystems; they are cultural ecologies, and the values of the organisms have much to say about the way in which trees grow and water flows. To deal with the insoluble problems of people in Northern Ireland, Beirut, Palestine, or Azerbaijan, we will have to stop looking at people as problems to be solved in finding the correct system of quantification or the right econometric model. We shall have to immerse ourselves in cultural history, and this means not simply gathering statistics in samples, but understanding the heart of the culture in its language, myth, religion, and art. As we begin to appreciate the complex membrane dynamics of cultural ecologies, we shall begin to move from the concept of the state as a container or a piece of turf to the idea of the noetic polity.[8] This shift in focus requires an act of imagination more than research and data-gathering;

it involves a movement away from regarding post industrial society as a collection of atomistic individuals competing to insert dollars in the bank and genes in females and articles in academic journals to a vision of symbiotic process in which groups constellate cognitive domains that encourage us to wonder about "the pattern that connects" the bank to the ecology, the university to the universe.[9]

If we are open to wonder and if our imagination is not simply a store of images from the past, then the new science of planetary dynamics is providing us with new imagery and perceptions with which to re-envision the nature of life on Earth. Our planet is not a hunk of rock with a slime coating of life in a hostile, dark, Newtonian space. The organism is not soft passive clay clamped into place by an industrial iron mold of adaptive constraint. Both the planet and the organism, the macrocosm and the microcosm, are not contained things, but constructive processes. They are flows of time: rivers directed by the banks they sculpt to bring forth an evolutionary landscape. In a re-imagination of the old mechanistic world picture, the Gaian biologists are looking at the origins of our planetary atmosphere above us in the air, the origins of cellular life below us in the sea, and the origins of the neural networks within the brain, and beginning to tell us that the old world view of objects in containing space, or organisms in constraining niches, simply won't tell us what we need to know about where we are now in time and space.

A planet, a brain, and a cell cannot be fully described as objects in Euclidian space, be they continents in a biosphere or genes within a molecule: rather, they have to be re-envisioned as dynamic processes emanating their own phase-space. "Gaia," "Mind," and "Life" are the emergent domains for the dynamics for Earth, brain, and cell. If you have already effected this transformation of mentality, you have already taken one step out of the era of the warring politics of the industrial nation-states and moved that much closer to the biospheric politics of a planetary culture.

You can tell when folks have not effected this transformation of imagination for they will seek to solve all political problems through destructive force and enforced re-containment. Whether it is the case of a Stalinist in the Soviet Union, a member of an extreme right death squad in El Salvador, or a member of the

Aryan Nation in the U.S.A., the response of the terrified is always terrifying. Imagination is, therefore, no idle pastime, but the generation of ideas that can calm the terror by re-explaining the world. It is the imagination which presents us with a world view that holds out some hope for granting humanity a more graceful transition from one world to another. If you feel that you are living in a time of disintegration, your activities will be fearful and violent; if you feel that you are living in a time of re-integration and evolutionary emergence, your activities will be more open and filled with hope and wonder. Gaian planetary science thus holds out an entire storehouse of images and insights for the emergence of a Gaian planetary culture.

If you have looked over the shoulder of Lynn Margulis to think about symbiosis and cell evolution, then you can appreciate the notion that endosymbionts share a constructive process and not simply a containing space.[10] Their space in the cell is a state-space, or phase-space, and the multiple dimensions of the phenomenon tell us that it is the dynamic that is critical, and not simply the space. The organ of this dynamic is a membrane, a chemical language, and not a wall. If you take this vision of symbiosis and cell evolution to heart, then you can re-imagine the Middle East and all of Europe, as the Palestinians, Lithuanians, Basques, and Armeni-ans take on a new dynamic in a new phase-space. The little requires the large, but sometimes this means that as things become smaller, the old large is no longer large enough. If you are a chloroplast, you require light; if you are a Lithuanian, you require not the large of the Soviet Union, but the larger envelopment of European civilization. If Lithuania were to follow Finland, then the little could end up leading the large as Russia began to discover that its true cultural ecology is Europe. The Stalinist reaction, of course, would be to see the loss of Lithuania as a strategic threat to its nineteenth-century conception of space, and so it would seek to maintain the containment of a military space through violent suppression.

Margulis has argued that some organelles were once ingested by the large cell in the hope of consuming them as food; but they proved indigestible, held on to their own DNA, and proved themselves to be as tough as they were tiny. Then, because they could produce energy or oxygen, the large and sluggish cell found that the organelles were worth more as architecture than as food, so the eukaryotic cell went on its way, bumping into some novel evolutionary transformations without really intending to. Clearly, this problem of the little and the large is not simply a metaphor, but a way of perceiving the architecture of the world; it is certainly the essential political problem of this moment, and concepts of "territorial sovereignty" from the past will not help us to resolve what are more complex metabolic processes of identity for cultural organelles within a global, electronic, noetic polity.

If in the lingering politics of the nationalism of the nineteenth century you see endosymbionts as a threat to your "territory," the container in which you hold your identity, then you will play out another nineteenth-century cowboy and Indians game in which you will use the army to conquer the savages and then build reservations to contain the defeated. Here we can consider the cases of the Palestinians in Israel or the Blacks in South Africa.

One can also appreciate the educational impact of Gaian dynamics on our imagination of the world if we look at the global problem of cocaine smuggling in a new way. The internationalist world view sees the drug traffic as "noise" in the transmissions of the world economy, a noise that needs to be filtered out of the channels of world trade through effective police action. Since both the U.S.A. and the U.S.S.R. have invested so heavily in military power, they have to find a new post-Cold War role for their expensive defense forces. At the winter summit in Malta, Gorbachev and Bush alluded to the uses of "a fire brigade" for ethnic conflagrations. Gorbachev was looking ahead to his problems in Azerbaijan, and Bush was preparing for his invasion of Panama and his use of the American Navy as a planetary coast guard on patrol off Colombian shores; both were signaling to one another their desires to deflect their armies away from U.S.-Soviet conflict toward police actions closer to home. The world view of planetary culture, however, is one that is more instructed by the insights of ecologies of mind and unconscious polities, and considers this noise of the drug economy as information. Just as a shadow is descriptive of a form, so is a shadow economy descriptive of an economic system. The Latin American cocaine economy, then, rather than being marginal is a profound signal of historical transition and transformation.

The cocaine traffic is a signal of the collapse of the postwar doctrine of economic "development." Since 1945 the U.S.A. has engineered a system of international development that has devalued traditional cultures and tried to replace them with industrial or even postindustrial service economies. So the forests are cleared of trees to produce the cattle ranches necessary to supply the McDonald's stands in the U.S.A. with cheap hamburgers. But there is absolutely no moral difference between turning a rain forest into a fast-food hamburger and turning a coca leaf into cocaine. Since recent studies suggest that the antibiotics and growth hormones given to cattle in feedlots are carcinogenic, that the styrofoam packaging of fast food is contributing to the ozone hole, and that the burning of the forests is contributing to the greenhouse effect, one could say that the assault on the biosphere and this threat to the human race is an even greater menace to society than the criminality of the cocaine traffic.

Now, there is no question that the homicide rates in North American cities such as New York, Detroit, Los Angeles, and Washington, can be directly related to the drug economy and the wars between drug lords, so the evil of this situation is clear and straightforward. But the Republican-Democrat approach is to pontificate about the horrors of this drug traffic and seek to stop it in a "Miami Vice" game that only energizes both cops and robbers to sustain the game and not to eliminate the economy. Those who profit from the interdiction are the police-military powers who receive funding, and the criminals whose commodity is sustained in an unconscious system of price supports. Yuppie materialism plays both sides of the game, for cocaine sustains the frenetic trading, junk-bonding, and corporate raiding of the managerial class, but the drug also sustains the shadow economy and cash flow of the structurally unemployed. The banks that receive the laundered money recirculate the funds as loans to the Latin countries so that Latin American indebtedness becomes a new kind of national junk-bond which allows the banks to effect a leveraged buy-out of the nation-state with a subsequent breakup and selling off of its resources. The only protection a Latin country has against this hostile takeover is the shadow economy of drugs which returns hard currency to itself and allows it to buy up American resources and real estate. By reinvesting the laundered funds in the U.S.A., the Latin Americans, much like the Japanese who buy U.S. Treasury bonds, are purchasing United States "nation-state futures" instead of specific commodities or unharvested crops. Indebtedness is, therefore, like pollution, an unconscious polity, a form of replacement of representation by participation in the global game. In the future, when it is to be hoped we are more enlightened about global systems dynamics, these unconscious polities and shadow economies will be understood as the phase-spaces of noetic polities.[11]

As a dynamic of indebtedness the shadow economy is an endosymbiotic process inseparable from the metabolic processes of the light economy. The Latin Americans are saying, in effect: "Why should we strip our resources so that you can build Trump Towers and bank skyscrapers in Manhattan? What difference is there between the eighties style of business in 'the light economy' of Donald Trump and 'the shadow economy' of Noriega?" Since the Latin American drug traffic provides a massive transfer of hard currency, it is, much like OPEC in the seventies, a vast pool of dollars in Latin hands that allows them to buy back their own land and turn the tables on us by buying up American properties. Small wonder, then, that Noriega was not so easy to uproot, for his battalions of "Dignidad" were deeply rooted in the folk soil of Latino versus Gringo. In our hemisphere, the Latin Americans know that we would never invade Canada in the ways we have invaded Mexico, Guatemala, Grenada, and Panama, so Latin Americans experience our Anglo-Saxon sense of abstract, conceptual justice as simply a racist mystification and an ethnocentric failure to understand the nature of values in a different culture.

If you can appreciate how Latin Americans feel themselves to be the Palestinians of Gringo imperialism, from the days of the indentured servitude of the United Fruit Company to the days of the invasions of Mexico, Guatemala, and Panama, you will not be surprised that Noriega's followers did think in terms of "Dignidad" and were willing to die for their identity. In terms of Dodd's distinction between "shame cultures" and "guilt cultures," we need to realize that shame cultures think in terms of imagery; guilt cultures think in terms of concepts and abstractions of law. Latin, Islamic, and Asian cultures are more shame cultures than guilt cultures, and if Israeli, American, and Soviet polities attempt to maintain their own abstractions with force, then we shall not have a planetary cultural ecology in which difference generates values in transaction across a living membrane, we will have a planetary Beirut. Our ability to move from the endangered species we have become to a new biological level of planetary life now depends upon our ability to understand the new language of planetary biology and cultural ecologies.

If we look at the close structural coupling of the evolution of plants in diverse cultures, down to the microcosmic ecologies of the neuroreceptors that bond with these substances, then we will understand that plants and humans have so co-evolved together that the concept of "addiction" is as culturally dependent as the concept of "illegal." The shadow-side to our fabulously sensitive nervous system is that it is extremely open to learning, and it learns to bond tightly with coffee, tea, chocolate, tobacco, Coca Cola, Diet Pepsi, alcohol, Valium, even junk food dyes and additives. Throughout history various societies have set up cultural ecologies in which a particular plant, be it the Soma of Indra, the corn of Quetzalcoatl, or the tea of Boddhi Dharma, served as a ritual plant that could make humans conscious of the membrane between culture and nature. The legendary eyelids of Boddhi Dharma are themselves a thin membrane between sleeping and wakefulness, ignorance and enlightenment, and when they fell to the ground to spring up again as the leaves of tea, they expressed the homology of one membrane and the other.

The devic level that bonds heaven and Earth, however, has always been shadowed by a demonic level that binds Earth and hell, so addiction is not a simple problem that can be eliminated by a simple interdiction. In fact, the social interdiction can increase the slope in the basin of attraction. What is required is a much more complex cultural response of compassion and constraint: one similar to the legislative response that eliminated the shadow economy of Prohibition and the spiritual response that inspired the founding of Alcoholics Anonymous.[12]

Such a systemic perception would sensitize us to understand light and shadow in the circulation of money and plants in the global economy. When the Colombian ambassador recently asked Congress to shift from our unconscious, shadow-economy price supports for cocaine to conscious social price supports for coffee, he was expressing a more ethnological perspective on Colombian plants and the neuroreceptors of North Americans, but we found it too difficult to look at the problem systemically, for that would require losing some of our illusions and would not give rise to the television dramas in which a President becomes popular with a show of force as he sends in the military to protect our state of unconsciousness.

In a Gaian understanding of planetary dynamics, we can begin to use a new language for understanding the dynamics of cultural ecologies within a biosphere. We can begin to understand that shadow economies are descriptions of the metabolic forms of light economies, and that Noriega and Bush are linked by more history than the record of their conversations through the C.I.A. The imperial president and the C.I.A. client anticommunist dictator are endosymbionts that have been living off one another for some time.

The conventional wisdom of the Left sees this situation as a perfect indictment of late capitalism and an argument for its replacement with international socialism. But the trouble with this teeter-totter game between ideologies of Right and Left is that the movement of thought is bolted to the same industrial ground and goes nowhere. The poisoning of air, water, and soil is even worse in the socialist countries of Eastern Europe than in the capitalist countries of Western Europe. The transition from an ideological to an ecological mode of consciousness requires that we move to another level of awareness beyond Left and Right, and for this level the Gaia theory can be highly instructive for it shows how oppositions, such as ocean and continent, can still be constitutive of the whole in global dynamic behavior.

Just as the old mechanistic philosophy of science interacted with industrial capitalism to give us the social world of nation-states, factories, and schools with their paper books and paper money, so now is this new world of cognitive biology interacting with the electronic world of Artificial Intelligence, investment banking, video arts, and pop music. In the age of public lending libraries and mass education, a writer, such as Charles Dickens, could become a public figure and a popular star of the lecture circuit; but now in the shift from mass education to mass entertainment, celebrities become the new currency of social exchange. The celebrity, be he or she rock star or president, is paid to be famous so that the wise and the powerful are free to work in peace while the powerless feel affirmed as loyal subjects of the majestic electronic realm. On CNN, Entertainment News is reported along with the events of the day in politics and economics, for in an electronic society, entertainment is both. What a celebrity celebrates is fantasy participation in the noetic polity, and this is more emotionally meaningful to the ex-citizen than mental representation in a literate republic. To be sure, this condition of electropeasantry and intellectual voluntary servitude to fantasy is repellent to intellectuals from the days of literary civilization, but we have to face the truth about ourselves, that our works do not touch the minds and hearts of people in a media society, for their attention spans have shortened and reading is no longer for them a constructive social process. My hope is that this loss of culture will be temporary, like the loss of oral culture that preceded the rise of literature in classical Athens, and that a future electronic mode of participation in a musical polity will free the electropeasantry from their bondage to television. To endure another American presidential election like the last one, however, would turn that hope into despair.

Transitions have never been graceful and easy in history, and ours is no exception. From electronic money and electronic music and entertainment, a new planetary distributive lattice is coming into place: like a vast coral reef that is the large end-product of little living processes.In all of these evolutionary processes of what Francois Jacob calls tinkering and Francisco Varela calls "natural drift,"[13] there is no Natural Selection making choices on who is best adapted to the environment that is itself but the crystalline record of the past; and there is no Rockefeller dynasty organizing the world through a Trilateral Conspiracy. But there is indeed fractal complexity, self-organization from noise, and novel and emergent domains that synchronously and unpredictably interact.

Individuals in such a system do not know what they are doing, and they certainly are not in control. The cyanobacteria did not decide to create an oxygen-bearing atmosphere anymore than we decided to create an ozone hole or a greenhouse effect. We surrounded industrial products that we wished to mass produce with a new post industrial envelopment of advertising information, and this envelopment of advertising encouraged us to be ashamed of taking the streetcar to work or smelling sweaty in public, so we withdrew into cars and a deodorized and air-conditioned state of rugged individualism and privatism, and this has generated its opposite as we are forced to confront our new smelly public space, the polluted biosphere in which we live our common life.

The process of cultural evolution is, of course, not completely negative, for doom is often the way in which an old society expresses its inability to imagine a novel emergent one. Our planetary unconscious electronic *umwelt* of advertising is driving us to create a conscious electronic *umwelt* of Artificial Intelligence in which technology and ecology are restructured within biospheres. These biospheres, in which electronics and microbiology are crossed, are as full of evolutionary potential as the neolithic villages of ten thousand years ago. They are not containers, genetic banks, but vessels, or in the language of John Todd, alembics for a new alchemy. Without the insights of Gaian scientists such as Todd, Lovelock, Margulis, and Varela, this shift from postindustrial civilization to planetary culture will not be possible.

In any shift from the old to the new, the new is uninferable from the old. You cannot infer life by looking at the prebiotic sea, and you cannot infer agricultural society by looking at a few women deciding to gather some wild grasses on the hillsides of the Zagros Mountains some ten thousand years ago. And so now you cannot infer the global dynamics of planetary culture by looking at the ground of industrial nation-states or the greed of junk-bond brokers and investment bankers. Business people make money the way cyanobacteria make oxygen; it's just how they respond to the historical stream they find themselves moving in. You can be sure that most businessmen are not thinking about the cultural drift from a national, industrial polity to a planetary noetic polity in which identities are based more on music than matter, on a language that is sung more than spoken.

One can begin to understand now why every little nation-state wants to have its last chance, because we are indeed at the stage of the last chance to be a nation-state; and so the Basques and the Quebecois, the Lithuanians and the Hopi no longer feel at home inside the manifest destinies of national Spain, Canada, Russia, or America. In the giantism that is always characteristic of vanishing forms, from dinosaurs to totem poles or sailing ships, the gigantic nation-state with its identity based upon turf is on its way out, for in the noetic polities of the twenty-first century identity is based upon a performance of the self in the music that is all about us.

The noetic polity is a phase-space in which the dynamics express themselves through more than the three dimensions of extensive location. Thus people living in the same noetic polity may be separated by conventional, Euclidian space. If one fails to effect the transformation of one's mathematical imagination, and is culturally unable to take one's identity from multidimensional dynamics, then one could implode into a condition of paranoid terror and terrorism. This collapse will involve a situation not of planetary culture, but cultural entropy in which there is a tribal war of each against each: Armenians against Azerbaijanis, Palestinians against Israelis, Bulgarians against Turks, Rumanians against Hungarians, Jura Separatists against the Bernese, and Basques against Castillians. All these cultures are becoming "hot," because in the release of heat in the phase change from civilization to planetization, traditional human cultures probably have no future except as art. The people who seem to understand this instinctively are the Blacks, and that is why, from Black Jazz to rap songs and graffiti, the Blacks have been such prophetic leaders in the emergence of noetic polities. Since the Afro-Americans were the first people to be ripped out of their traditional culture, it is not surprising that they have been able to take the lead in prefiguring the emergence of chaos dynamics and musical polities in the elaboration of Jazz. Top and Pop, music and math, aerospace sophistication and street smarts are the parallel processors for this transformation, for in the chaos dynamics of this complex, planetary culture, no white-shirted NASA bureaucracy of technocrats

266

would be able to bring forth the shift from matter to music as the ground of economic value and social identity.

To lead the world away from the dangerous situation of cultural entropy, the simultaneous collapse of all traditional human cultures, North Americans must once again express the global leadership they showed in 1945. As popular art is only part of the planetary ecology of mind, we need to continue our development of aerospace technologies. At the geopolitical level, we North Americans must respond quickly and imaginatively to the emergence of Eastern Europe by rescuing our former enemy the Soviet Union. We should on one hand insist on developing the Helsinki process for human rights, and on the other accept Gorbachev's offer of a joint Soviet-American space program so that a planetary scientific economy can lift our horizons and sustain our participation in a planetary culture. But at the same time, we have to pass out of our old imperial politics of the Monroe Doctrine and Manifest Destiny to realize that the days of Teddy or Franklin Roosevelt are gone forever. Just as the Soviets will have to come to new terms of symbiosis with the Baltic or Central Asian peoples, so we North Americans will have to begin to listen with new ears to what the Polynesians, the Latin Americans, the Quebecois, or the Hopi Nation have been trying to tell us. We are going to have to come to a new understanding of the little and the large and only a deeper understanding of the planet as the large can give us the insights we need to appreciate the critical, enzymatic life of the little.

If the new is uninferable from the old, it is imaginable, and that is why imaginative writers and artists can teach us some things that the political scientists alone cannot. Republican politicians and businessmen think that capitalism triumphed over communism because it is God's way. But it is not the ideology of capitalism that has won out over the ideology of communism, but rather that the center and periphery structures of empire, American or Russian, are unable to hold territorial identities in the chaos dynamics of a planetary flow of electronic information. Postindustrial capitalism, in shifting from British industrial centralism to electronic polycentralism in Massachusetts, California, and Japan, became much more expressive of dynamical states of

267

"self-organization from noise." Both the centralizing empire and the industrial nation-state are dissolving; the endosymbiotics for the planetary cell are not the territorial state but the organelles that produce identity, the cultural biome. The industrial mentality that would seek to level a Rumanian village to replace it with an agri-industrial complex, or to drain a continental aquifer to replace a genetically diverse prairie with a pesticized mono-crop of Kansan wheat is being everywhere challenged by the revolts of culture and nature.

H.G. Wells said that the future is a race between catastrophe and education; the nineties is the last lap of the race. If we persist in thinking in the old mentality, if we think that a discrete gene contains a discrete trait, that a nation contains a sovereign identity, and that a planet is a container with life-support-systems, then we will manipulate genes, nations, and biospheres to engineer our own well-deserved extinction. If, on the other hand, we understand that the complete ecology of the enzymes in the cytoplasm as well as the morphological dynamics of the folding of the DNA strand bring about inheritance, we will ourselves experience a different flow through time in which we continue to generate descendants. If you have a Gaian imagination of planetary dynamics, you will understand that endosymbionts share in metabolic processes, and you will invest your identity in that constructive process of planetary life, rather than in the container called the nation-state. And so the Russians or Palestinians will become constitutive of your identity, not as the shadow, the hated enemy you need to support your military economy, but the symbiotic partner in the cultural ecology of your biome; in moving to save them, we save us.

To understand the political relationships between the greenhouse effect and the revolutions in Eastern Europe, one has to have a different vision of the dynamics of cultures and ecologies. The enforced imposition of old ideologies will only lead to continual explosions of violence in cycles of suppression from the center and terrorism from the periphery. What is called for is not an analysis of international relations by a panel of academic experts, but a re-imagination of the world. In this task there are no experts and we are all needed, for while the powerful meet in their chambers, some teenager out on the streets may just prove to us that wisdom is available for a song.

Notes

1. See *Cybernetics-Circular Causal and Feedback Mechanisms in Biological and Social Systems* (New York: Josiah Macy, Jr. Foundation), 5 volumes.

2. See Gregory Bateson, "Men are Grass: Metaphor and the World of Mental Process," *Gaia: A Way of Knowing*, ed. W. I. Thompson (Great Barrington, MA: Lindisfarne Press, 1987).

3. See Michel Serres, "Origin de la geometrie," *Le Passage du Nord -Ouest* (Paris: Les editions de minuit, 1980), 165-74; and W. I. Thompson, *The Time Falling Bodies Take to Light: Mythology, Sexuality, and the Origin of Culture* (New York: St. Martin's Press, 1981), 264-67.

4. See *Understanding Origin* ed. Francisco Varela (Stanford: Stanford University Press, 1989). For an application of René Girard's ideas of violence and sacrifice to the sphere of economics and contemporary affairs, see Jacques Attali's *Lignes d'horizon* (Paris: Fayard, 1990). Note that in this extension, Attali thinks of the world space in terms of Euclidian geometry, of centers and peripheries, and shows no imaginative appreciation of the political implications of new mathematical topologies in reconstructing the imaginative space of the world. Consequently, he sees a linear shift of the center of the world from New York to Tokyo, and makes a linear extrapolation of the day's news into scenarios of the future. This was the same mistake made by economists in the TOPEC crisis of the seventies, when they extrapolated the amount of dollars in Arab hands and predicted that by the nineties all the dollars in the world would be under Arab control.

5. See W. I. Thompson, "The Four Cultural Ecologies of the West," *Pacific Shift* (San Francisco: Sierra Club Books, 1986); also "Toward a Cultural History of Consciousness," *Imaginary Landscape: Making Worlds of Myth and Science* (New York: St. Martin's Press, 1989).

6. See Mark Johnson, *The Body in the Mind: The Bodily Basis of Meaning, Imagination, and Reason* (Chicago: University of Chicago Press, 1987).

7. See Humberto Maturana and Francisco Varela, *The Tree of Knowledge: The Biological Roots of Human Understanding,* (Boston: New Science Library, 1987); also Francisco Varela and Evan Thompson, *Worlds Without Ground: Cognitive Science and Embodied Experience,* (forthcoming).

8. See W. I. Thompson, "Gaia and the Politics of Life: A Program for the Nineties," *Gaia* op. cit., 167-214. For a discussion of cultural ecologies, see also the author's "The Four Cultural Ecologies of the West," op. cit.

9. See Gregory Bateson, *Mind and Nature* (New York: Dutton, 1979), 8.

10. See Lynn Margulis, *Symbiosis and Cell Evolution* (San Francisco: Freeman, 1981).

11. This concept of unconscious polity is a development of Gregory Bateson's idea of "conscious purpose" from his essay "Effects of Conscious Purpose on Human Adaptation," in *Steps to an Ecology of Mind* (New York: Ballantine, 1972), 440-48.

12. See Gregory Bateson's discussion of Alcoholics Anonymous in "The Cybernetics of Self," *Steps to an Ecology of Mind* ibid., 309-37.

13. See Maturana and Varela, op. cit., 101.

NOTES ON CONTRIBUTORS

GIANLUCA BOCCHI is an editor and translator. He edits *Oikos*, a quarterly review of the ecology of ideas, published in Bergamo, Italy.

MAURO CERUTI is Professor of Philosophy at the University of Palermo and Director of the Dipartimento di epistemologia e scienza cognitive at the Centro Luigi Bazzuchi in Perugia. He is the author of *La danza che crea: evoluzione e cognizione nell' epistemologia genetica*.

RICARDO GUERRERO is Professor of Microbiology at the Autonomous University of Barcelona and author of numerous scientific papers on bacteriology and the origins of life.

WES JACKSON is a botanist and geneticist; he is the founder of the Land Institute in Salina, Kansas, and author of *New Roots for Agriculture* and *Altars of Unhewn Stone: Nature and Technology*.

JAMES LOVELOCK is an atmospheric chemist, inventor, and Fellow of the Royal Society in England. He is the initiator of the Gaia theory and author of *Gaia: A New Look at Life on Earth* and *The Ages of Gaia*. He lives in Devon, England.

LYNN MARGULIS is Distinguished University Professor of Biology at the University of Massachusetts at Amherst. She is the co-developer of the Gaia theory and the author of the now classic work, *Symbiosis and Cell Evolution*.

SUSAN OYAMA is Professor of Psychology at the John Jay College in the City University of New York. She is the author of *The Ontogeny of Information.*

EVAN THOMPSON is Visiting Scholar in the Department of Philosophy at the University of California at Berkeley. With Francisco Varela he is co-author of *Worlds Without Ground: Cognitive Science and Embodied Experience.*

WILLIAM IRWIN THOMPSON is the founder and Director of the Lindisfarne Association in New York and author of *Imaginary Landscape: Making Worlds of Myth and Science.* He lives in Zurich and New York.

FRANCISCO VARELA is a member of the Centre National de recherches Scientifiques in Paris and is Professor at the Institut de Neurosciences at the University of Paris and Professor of Philosophy at the Ecole Polytechnique. He is author of *Principles of Biological Autonomy.*

JOHN TODD is a biologist, the inventor of the Bioshelter, and one of the founders of the New Alchemy Institute and Ocean Arks in Falmouth, Massachusetts, and is now the Director of the Water Resources Center in Woods Hole. He is the co-author of *Tomorrow is Our Permanent Address* and *Bioshelters, Ocean Arks, City Farming.*

NANCY JACK TODD is co-founder of the New Alchemy Institute in Falmouth, Massachusetts, editor of the ecological journal *Annals of Earth,* and co-author with John Todd of *Tomorrow is our Permanent Address* and *Bioshelters, Ocean Arks, City Farming.*

ARTHUR ZAJONC is Associate Professor of Physics at Amherst College in Massachusetts. He is the author of numerous papers on quantum optics as well as papers on Goethe's theory of color.